Advancing Maths for AQA
PURE MATHS 4

Sam Boardman, Tony Clough and David Evans

Series editors
Sam Boardman   Ted Graham
Keith Parramore   Roger Williamson

Heinemann Educational Publishers
a division of Heinemann Publishers (Oxford) Ltd,
Halley Court, Jordan Hill, Oxford OX2 8EJ

OXFORD MELBOURNE AUCKLAND JOHANNESBURG IBADAN
BLANTYRE GABORONE PORTSMOUTH NH (USA) CHICAGO

Text © Sam Boardman, Tony Clough and David Evans 2002
Complete work © Heinemann Educational Publishers 2002

All rights reserved. No part of this publication may be reproduced, stored in a
retrieval system, or transmitted in any form or by any means, electronic,
mechanical, photocopying, recording or otherwise without either the prior
written permission of the publisher or a licence permitting restricted copying
in the United Kingdom issued by the Copyright Licensing Agency Ltd,
90 Tottenham Road, London W1P 9HE

First published in 2002

05   04   03   02
10   9   8   7   6   5   4   3   2   1

ISBN 0 435 51303 6

Typeset and illustrated by Tech-Set Limited, Gateshead, Tyne & Wear

Printed and bound by Scotprint in the UK

Acknowledgements
The publishers' and authors' thanks are due to the AQA for the permission to
reproduce questions from past examination papers.

The answers have been provided by the authors and are not the responsibility
of the examining board.

About this book

This book is one in a series of textbooks designed to provide you with exceptional preparation for AQA's new Advanced GCE Specification B. The series authors are all senior members of the examining team and have prepared the textbooks specifically to support you in studying this course.

Finding your way around

The following are there to help you find your way around when you are studying and revising:

- **edge marks** (shown on the front page) – these help you to get to the right chapter quickly;
- **contents list** – this identifies the individual sections dealing with key syllabus concepts so that you can go straight to the areas that you are looking for;
- **index** – a number in bold type indicates where to find the main entry for that topic.

Key points

Key points are not only summarised at the end of each chapter but are also boxed and highlighted within the text like this:

> The expression $n!$ is read as 'n factorial' and its value is given by the product
>
> $$n \times (n - 1) \times (n - 2) \times \ldots \times 3 \times 2 \times 1.$$

Exercises and exam questions

Worked examples and carefully graded questions familiarise you with the specification and bring you up to exam standard. Each book contains:

- Worked examples and worked exam questions to show you how to tackle typical questions; Examiner's tips will also provide guidance;
- Graded exercises, gradually increasing in difficulty up to exam-level questions, which are marked by an [A];
- Test-yourself sections for each chapter so that you can check your understanding of the key aspects of that chapter and identify any sections that you should review;
- Answers to the questions are included at the end of the book.

Contents

CHAPTER 1

Factorials and binomial expansions

Learning objectives

After studying this chapter you should be able to:

■ evaluate factorial expressions

■ understand the notations $n!$ and $\begin{pmatrix} n \\ r \end{pmatrix}$

■ construct the rows of Pascal's Triangle
■ use the binomial expansion to expand $(a + b)^n$ for a positive integer n

■ use the binomial coefficients $\begin{pmatrix} n \\ r \end{pmatrix}$ to find terms in the expansion of $(a + b)^n$.

1.1 Factorial notation

Suppose you had ten different CDs and you wanted to arrange them in a rack with ten slots.

How many ways could you do it?

You have a choice of ten different CDs to put into the first position. Once this slot is filled, you have nine different ways of filling the second slot, then eight for the third slot. So altogether, the number of different ways of arranging your ten CDs is

$$10 \times 9 \times 8 \times 7 \times 6 \times 5 \times 4 \times 3 \times 2 \times 1.$$

This product is called ten factorial and is denoted by the special symbol 10!. You might wish to check that your calculator has a factorial button. You should then be able to evaluate 10! showing that its value is 3 628 800.

The factorial function grows very rapidly, so that 50! is approximately 3.04×10^{64}. Try to find the largest value of n for which your calculator can evaluate $n!$ Don't be surprised if your calculator cannot evaluate 100! for instance.

$x!$

You may find the factorial function is in a special statistics or probability menu. Find where it is on your calculator so you can use it in this chapter.

The expression $n!$ is read as 'n factorial' and its value is given by the product

$$n \times (n-1) \times (n-2) \times \ldots \times 3 \times 2 \times 1.$$

Worked example 1.1

Find the values of each of the following:

(a) $5!$, **(b)** $\dfrac{12!}{10!}$, **(c)** $\dfrac{6! \times 4!}{(3!)^2}$.

Solution

(a) $5! = 5 \times 4 \times 3 \times 2 \times 1 = 120$;

(b) $\dfrac{12!}{10!} = \dfrac{12 \times 11 \times 10 \times 9 \times 8 \times 7 \times 6 \times 5 \times 4 \times 3 \times 2 \times 1}{10 \times 9 \times 8 \times 7 \times 6 \times 5 \times 4 \times 3 \times 2 \times 1}$

$\qquad = 12 \times 11 = 132$;

With experience, you will realise without writing down the full product that all the terms from 10 down to 1 cancel out.

(c) $\dfrac{6! \times 4!}{(3!)^2} = \dfrac{(6 \times 5 \times 4 \times 3 \times 2 \times 1) \times (4 \times 3 \times 2 \times 1)}{(3 \times 2 \times 1) \times (3 \times 2 \times 1)}$

$\qquad = (6 \times 5 \times 4) \times 4$

$\qquad = 480.$

Cancel terms rather than evaluate $6!$ and $4!$ separately.

1.2 Inductive definition of factorial and 0!

Because $6! = 6 \times 5 \times 4 \times 3 \times 2 \times 1$ and $5! = 5 \times 4 \times 3 \times 2 \times 1$, it follows that

$$6! = 6 \times 5!$$

and similarly

$$10! = 10 \times 9!.$$

In other words, if you know that the value of 9! is 362 880 you can find 10! by simply multiplying the previous answer by 10. Hence $10! = 3\,628\,800$.

So that, in general, the inductive definition of factorial is given by

$$n! = n \times (n-1)!.$$

Using this definition, substituting $n = 1$, gives

$1! = 1 \times 0!$.

But since $1! = 1$, it follows that

$0! = 1.$

1.3 The notation $\begin{pmatrix} n \\ r \end{pmatrix}$

You will often need to evaluate expressions such as $\dfrac{10!}{7! \times 3!}$.

Notice that $7 + 3 = 10$.

If you have ten objects and need to select exactly seven of them, the number of ways of doing this is denoted by the symbol $\begin{pmatrix} 10 \\ 7 \end{pmatrix}$ and its value is $\dfrac{10!}{7! \times 3!} = \dfrac{10 \times 9 \times 8}{3 \times 2 \times 1} = 120.$

In general $\begin{pmatrix} n \\ r \end{pmatrix} = \dfrac{n!}{r!\,(n-r)!}$ and represents the number of ways that r different objects can be chosen from n objects.

Worked example 1.2

Find the number of different ways that six people can be chosen to go in a lift from a total of nine people who are waiting for the lift.

Solution

Number of ways is $\begin{pmatrix} 9 \\ 6 \end{pmatrix} = \dfrac{9!}{6! \times 3!} = \dfrac{9 \times 8 \times 7}{3 \times 2 \times 1} = 84.$

Notice that $\begin{pmatrix} 9 \\ 3 \end{pmatrix} = \dfrac{9!}{3! \times 6!} = \dfrac{9 \times 8 \times 7}{3 \times 2 \times 1} = 84$ also.

This is not surprising, because if you choose six people to go in the lift, it is exactly the same as if you choose three people who do **not** go in the lift.

In general $\begin{pmatrix} n \\ r \end{pmatrix} = \begin{pmatrix} n \\ n-r \end{pmatrix}.$

EXERCISE 1A

1 Find the value of:

(a) 3!,   (b) 6!,   (c) 8!,   (d) $(4!)^2$ (e) 0!.

2 Simplify each of the following:

(a) $\dfrac{5!}{3!}$,   (b) $\dfrac{7!}{4!}$,   (c) $\dfrac{14!}{13!}$,

(d) $\dfrac{19!}{18!}$,   (e) $\dfrac{8!}{5!}$,   (f) $\dfrac{4!}{0!}$.

3 Find the value of each of the following:

(a) $\dfrac{7!}{(3!)^2}$,   (b) $\dfrac{9!}{3! \times 4!}$,   (c) $\dfrac{12!}{8! \times 3!}$,

(d) $\dfrac{18!}{14! \times 2!}$,   (e) $\dfrac{20!}{17! \times 4!}$.

4 Evaluate:

(a) $\begin{pmatrix} 5 \\ 2 \end{pmatrix}$,   (b) $\begin{pmatrix} 7 \\ 4 \end{pmatrix}$,   (c) $\begin{pmatrix} 3 \\ 3 \end{pmatrix}$,   (d) $\begin{pmatrix} 4 \\ 0 \end{pmatrix}$,

(e) $\begin{pmatrix} 8 \\ 6 \end{pmatrix}$,   (f) $\begin{pmatrix} 8 \\ 2 \end{pmatrix}$,   (g) $\begin{pmatrix} 9 \\ 7 \end{pmatrix}$,   (h) $\begin{pmatrix} 25 \\ 24 \end{pmatrix}$,

(i) $\begin{pmatrix} 50 \\ 50 \end{pmatrix}$,   (j) $\begin{pmatrix} 13 \\ 3 \end{pmatrix}$,   (k) $\begin{pmatrix} 17 \\ 14 \end{pmatrix}$,   (l) $\begin{pmatrix} 100 \\ 99 \end{pmatrix}$,

(m) $\begin{pmatrix} 80 \\ 2 \end{pmatrix}$.

5 There are 20 people at a party and a taxi arrives that can hold five people. In how many different ways could the taxi be filled?

6 There are four tickets for a concert and 30 students each put their name on a piece of paper and four names are selected to get the tickets. In how many different ways could the four be chosen?

1.4 Pascal's Triangle

An expression with two terms and having the form $a + b$ is called a binomial expression and you are often required to find powers of $(a + b)$ such as $(a + b)^5$.

No doubt you can write down straight away that

$$(a + b)^2 = a^2 + 2ab + b^2.$$

Hence $(a + b)^3 = (a + b)(a^2 + 2ab + b^2)$
$$= a^2 + 2a^2b + ab^2$$
$$\qquad + a^2b + 2ab^2 + b^3$$
$$= a^3 + 3a^2b + 3ab^2 + b^3$$

> Multiply everything in the second bracket by a then multiply everything by b, and collect like terms.

In a similar way, you can expand $(a+b)^4$ to give

$$(a+b)^4 = a^4 + 4a^3b + 6a^2b^2 + 4ab^3 + b^4$$

but it is quite tedious.

An interesting pattern is produced when you expand $(a+b)^n$ for different integers n.

$$(a+b)^0 = 1$$
$$(a+b)^1 = a+b$$
$$(a+b)^2 = a^2 + 2ab + b^2$$
$$(a+b)^3 = a^3 + 3a^2b + 3ab^2 + b^3$$
$$(a+b)^4 = a^4 + 4a^3b + 6a^2b^2 + 4ab^3 + b^4$$

The triangular array of numbers forming the coefficients is called Pascal's Triangle. Each term is formed by adding together the two terms immediately above.

```
                    1
                1       1
            1       2       1
        1       3       3       1
    1       4       6       4       1
  1     5      10      10      5       1
1     6     15      20      15      6       1
```

Worked example 1.3

Write down the next two rows of Pascal's Triangle.

Solution

Since $1+6=7$, $6+15=21$, $15+20=35$, etc. and the row begins with 1 (which can be thought of as $0+1$ from the previous row), the next row of Pascal's Triangle is

$$\quad 1 \quad 7 \quad 21 \quad 35 \quad 35 \quad 21 \quad 7 \quad 1.$$

The row after that is obtained in a similar way and is

$$\quad 1 \quad 8 \quad 28 \quad 56 \quad 70 \quad 56 \quad 28 \quad 8 \quad 1.$$

Pascal's Triangle can be used to find the expansion of $(a+b)^n$ for small positive integers n.

You have already seen that

$$(a+b)^4 = a^4 + 4a^3b + 6a^2b^2 + 4ab^3 + b^4.$$

Notice that the coefficients are the numbers in the row of Pascal's Triangle that starts 1 4 ....

This can be written as

$$(a+b)^4 = \mathbf{1}a^4b^0 + \mathbf{4}a^3b^1 + \mathbf{6}a^2b^2 + \mathbf{4}a^1b^3 + \mathbf{1}a^0b^4.$$

> Also, the terms consist of a product of the form $a^p b^q$, where $p + q = 4$.

Worked example 1.4

Use Pascal's Triangle to find the expansion of $(x+y)^6$.

Solution

Since the index is 6, you need the row of Pascal's Triangle with values

$$1 \quad 6 \quad 15 \quad 20 \quad 15 \quad 6 \quad 1$$

Hence $(x+y)^6 = 1x^6y^0 + 6x^5y^1 + 15x^4y^2 + 20x^3y^3 + 15x^2y^4$
$$+ 6x^1y^5 + 1x^0y^6$$

which can be written in simplified form as

$$(x+y)^6 = x^6 + 6x^5y + 15x^4y^2 + 20x^3y^3 + 15x^2y^4 + 6xy^5 + y^6.$$

> Since $x^0 = 1$ and $y^0 = 1$, etc.

Worked example 1.5

Use Pascal's Triangle to find the expansions of:

(a) $(2+q)^4$,   **(b)** $(3x+1)^5$,   **(c)** $(1-2x)^6$.

Solution

(a) Since the index is 4, you need the row of Pascal's Triangle with values   1   4   6   4   1.

Although the first term in the bracket is 2, you treat it in the same way as in the previous example.

$$\begin{aligned}(2+q)^4 &= 1 \times 2^4 q^0 + 4 \times 2^3 q^1 + 6 \times 2^2 q^2 + 4 \times 2^1 q^3 + 1 \times 2^0 q^4 \\ &= 16q^0 + 4 \times 8q^1 + 6 \times 4q^2 + 4 \times 2q^3 + 1 \times 1q^4 \\ &= 16 + 32q + 24q^2 + 8q^3 + q^4\end{aligned}$$

> This expansion is said to be written in ascending powers of q.

(b) The power this time is 5, so you need the row of Pascal's Triangle with values   1   5   10   10   5   1.

$$\begin{aligned}(3x+1)^5 = {}&1 \times (3x)^5 \times 1^0 + 5 \times (3x)^4 \times 1^1 \\ &+ 10 \times (3x)^3 \times 1^2 + 10 \times (3x)^2 \times 1^3 \\ &+ 5 \times (3x)^1 \times 1^4 + 1 \times (3x)^0 \times 1^5\end{aligned}$$

Hence,

$$\begin{aligned}(3x+1)^5 = {}&3^5 x^5 + 5 \times 3^4 x^4 + 10 \times 3^3 x^3 + 10 \times 3^2 x^2 \\ &+ 5 \times 3x + 1\end{aligned}$$

which becomes

$$(3x+1)^5 = 243x^5 + 405x^4 + 270x^3 + 90x^2 + 15x + 1$$

> This expansion is said to be written in descending powers of x.

(c) Because the power is 6, you need to use the coefficients

$$1 \quad 6 \quad 15 \quad 20 \quad 15 \quad 6 \quad 1.$$

An added difficulty here is the minus sign and so it is best to write $(1 - 2x)^6$ as $[1 + (-2x)]^6$.

$$
\begin{aligned}
[1 + (-2x)]^6 &= 1 \times 1^6 \times (-2x)^0 + 6 \times 1^5 \times (-2x)^1 \\
&\quad + 15 \times 1^4 \times (-2x)^2 + 20 \times 1^3 \times (-2x)^3 \\
&\quad + 15 \times 1^2 \times (-2x)^4 + 6 \times 1^1 \times (-2x)^5 + 1 \times 1^0 \times (-2x)^6 \\
&= 1 + 6 \times (-2x) + 15 \times (-2)^2 x^2 + 20(-2)^3 x^3 \\
&\quad + 15 \times (-2)^4 x^4 + 6 \times (-2)^5 x^5 + (-2)^6 x^6
\end{aligned}
$$

This expansion simplifies to

$$1 - 12x + 60x^2 - 160x^3 + 240x^4 - 192x^5 + 64x^6.$$

> Notice how the signs alternate when a binomial expansion contains a minus sign.

EXERCISE 1B

1 Write down the first ten rows of Pascal's Triangle.

2 One of the rows of Pascal's Triangle begins

$$1 \quad 15 \quad 105 \quad 455 \quad 1365.$$

Find the first five terms of each of the next two rows.

3 One of the rows of Pascal's Triangle begins

$$1 \quad 20 \quad 190 \quad 1140 \quad 4845.$$

Find the first five terms of each of the next two rows.

4 Use Pascal's Triangle to find the expansions of:

(a) $(a + b)^3$,
(b) $(c + d)^5$,
(c) $(x + y)^7$,
(d) $(r + s)^8$.

5 Expand each of the following:

(a) $(1 + x)^5$,
(b) $(1 + 2y)^3$,
(c) $\left(1 + \dfrac{x}{3}\right)^6$,
(d) $\left(1 + \dfrac{p}{2}\right)^4$.

6 Obtain the expansion of:

(a) $(1 - a)^3$,
(b) $(1 - 3b)^4$,
(c) $\left(1 - \dfrac{x}{2}\right)^5$,
(d) $\left(1 - \dfrac{2x}{3}\right)^3$.

7 Find the expansion of each of the following:

(a) $(3 + p)^5$,
(b) $(5 + x)^4$,
(c) $(2 - m)^3$,
(d) $(3 - 2t)^6$.

8 Find the first four terms in increasing powers of x of:

(a) $(1-x)^5$,

(b) $(1+3x)^4$,

(c) $\left(1-\dfrac{x}{3}\right)^6$,

(d) $\left(1+\dfrac{2x}{5}\right)^5$.

9 Find the first four terms in decreasing powers of y of:

(a) $(y+2)^5$, (b) $(2y-1)^6$,

(c) $(4y+3)^4$, (d) $(3y-1)^7$.

10 Simplify each of the following:

(a) $(1+3x)^4 - (1-3x)^4$,

(b) $(3-2y)^5 + (3+2y)^5$.

11 Show that the first four rows of Pascal's Triangle can be written as

$$\binom{0}{0}$$

$$\binom{1}{0} \quad \binom{1}{1}$$

$$\binom{2}{0} \quad \binom{2}{1} \quad \binom{2}{2}$$

$$\binom{3}{0} \quad \binom{3}{1} \quad \binom{3}{2} \quad \binom{3}{3}$$

Write the next two rows of Pascal's triangle in a similar form.

1.5 Binomial coefficients

Expressions of the form $\binom{n}{r}$ are called the binomial coefficients.

Read as binomial coefficient $n\ r$.

As seen in the previous exercise, the binomial coefficients are in fact the same as the numbers that appeared in Pascal's Triangle.

When n is a small positive integer, it is a good idea to use Pascal's Triangle to expand $(a+b)^n$.

However, there is a more general expression that can be used without needing Pascal's Triangle.

The problem with using Pascal's Triangle is that if you want to know the numbers in row thirteen, you need to know the numbers in row twelve, and so on.

Imagine you are trying to expand $(a+b)^7$. This could be written out as

$$(a+b)(a+b)(a+b)(a+b)(a+b)(a+b)(a+b).$$

You know, for instance, that one of the terms is going to be a multiple of a^3b^4. You can select *a*s from some brackets and *b*s from others. Since there are seven brackets, you can choose the *b*s in $\binom{7}{4}$ ways. This term in the expansion is therefore

$$\binom{7}{4}a^3b^4.$$

You could reason equally well that you are selecting the three brackets which have the letter a in the product, but you will get the same answer since

$$\binom{7}{4} = \binom{7}{3}.$$

Another term is going to be $\binom{7}{2}a^5b^2$, and the leading term, when you select the a from each bracket, is a^7.

The full expansion of $(a+b)^7$ is

$$a^7 + \binom{7}{1}a^6b + \binom{7}{2}a^5b^2 + \binom{7}{3}a^4b^3 + \binom{7}{4}a^3b^4$$

$$+ \binom{7}{5}a^2b^5 + \binom{7}{6}ab^6 + b^7.$$

This result can now be generalised for $(a+b)^n$.

The general binomial expansion can be written as

$$(a+b)^n = a^n + \binom{n}{1}a^{n-1}b + \binom{n}{2}a^{n-2}b^2 + \dots$$

$$+ \binom{n}{r}a^{n-r}b^r + \dots + b^n$$

where n is a positive integer.

This formula appears in the formula booklet under the heading *Binomial Series*.

Worked example 1.6

Find the first four terms, in ascending powers of x, in the expansion of:

(a) $(1+3x)^{12}$,   **(b)** $(2-x)^{20}$.

In **(b)**, leave your answer in terms of powers of 2.

Solution

(a) Using the formula above, with $a=1$, $b=3x$ and $n=12$ gives

$$(1+3x)^{12} = 1^{12} + \binom{12}{1} \times 1^{11} \times (3x)$$

$$+ \binom{12}{2} \times 1^{10} \times (3x)^2 + \binom{12}{3} \times 1^9 \times (3x)^3 + \dots$$

You only need the first four terms.

Since $\begin{pmatrix} 12 \\ 1 \end{pmatrix} = \dfrac{12!}{11! \times 1!} = 12,$

$$\begin{pmatrix} 12 \\ 2 \end{pmatrix} = \frac{12!}{10! \times 2!} = \frac{12 \times 11}{2 \times 1} = 66 \quad \text{and}$$

$$\begin{pmatrix} 12 \\ 3 \end{pmatrix} = \frac{12!}{9! \times 3!} = \frac{12 \times 11 \times 10}{3 \times 2 \times 1} = 220,$$

$$(1 + 3x)^{12} = 1 + 12 \times (3x) + 66 \times 3^2 x^2$$
$$+ 220 \times 3^3 x^3 + \dots$$

Hence, the first four terms of $(1 + 3x)^{12}$ in ascending powers of x are

$$1 + 36x + 594x^2 + 5940x^3.$$

(b) This time, the values to substitute into the formula are $a = 2$, $b = -x$ and $n = 20$, so you get

$$(2 - x)^{20} = 2^{20} + \begin{pmatrix} 20 \\ 1 \end{pmatrix} \times 2^{19} \times (-x)$$

$$+ \begin{pmatrix} 20 \\ 2 \end{pmatrix} \times 2^{18} \times (-x)^2 + \begin{pmatrix} 20 \\ 3 \end{pmatrix} \times 2^{17} \times (-x)^3 + \dots$$

Since $\begin{pmatrix} 20 \\ 1 \end{pmatrix} = \dfrac{20!}{19! \times 1!} = 20,$

$$\begin{pmatrix} 20 \\ 2 \end{pmatrix} = \frac{20!}{18! \times 2!} = \frac{20 \times 19}{2 \times 1} = 190 \quad \text{and}$$

$$\begin{pmatrix} 20 \\ 3 \end{pmatrix} = \frac{20!}{17! \times 3!} = \frac{20 \times 19 \times 18}{3 \times 2 \times 1} = 1140,$$

$$(2 - x)^{20} = 2^{20} - 20 \times 2^{19} \times x + 190 \times 2^{18} \times x^2$$
$$- 1140 \times 2^{17} \times x^3 + \dots$$
$$= 2^{20} - 5 \times 2^2 \times 2^{19} \times x + 95 \times 2 \times 2^{18} \times x^2$$
$$- 285 \times 2^2 \times 2^{17} \times x^3 + \dots$$

> Notice how the terms alternate between plus and minus.

Hence, the first four terms of $(2 - x)^{20}$ in ascending powers of x are

$$2^{20} - 5 \times 2^{21}x + 95 \times 2^{19}x^2 - 285 \times 2^{19}x^3.$$

Worked example 1.7

Find the coefficient of x^{15} in the expansion of $(3 - 2x)^{18}$, leaving your answer as the product of prime numbers.

Solution

The term required is of the form $\begin{pmatrix} 18 \\ 15 \end{pmatrix} \times 3^3 \times (-2x)^{15}$.

$$\begin{pmatrix} 18 \\ 15 \end{pmatrix} = \frac{18!}{15! \times 3!} = \frac{18 \times 17 \times 16}{3 \times 2 \times 1} = 3 \times 17 \times 2^4.$$

So $\begin{pmatrix} 18 \\ 15 \end{pmatrix} \times 3^3 \times (-2x)^{15} = -3 \times 17 \times 2^4 \times 3^3 \times 2^{15}x^{15}$

Hence the coefficient of x^{15} in the expansion of $(3 - 2x)^{18}$ is

$-2^{19} \times 3^4 \times 17$

Worked examination question 1.1

Find the binomial expansion of $\left(1 + \frac{1}{2}x\right)^{16}$ in ascending powers of x up to and including the term in x^3.
Hence determine the coefficient of x^3 in the expansion of $(23 + 13x)\left(1 + \frac{1}{2}x\right)^{16}$. [A]

Solution

$\left(1 + \frac{1}{2}x\right)^{16} = 1^{16} + \begin{pmatrix} 16 \\ 1 \end{pmatrix} \times 1^{15} \times \left(\frac{1}{2}x\right) + \begin{pmatrix} 16 \\ 2 \end{pmatrix} \times 1^{14} \times \left(\frac{1}{2}x\right)^2$

$+ \begin{pmatrix} 16 \\ 3 \end{pmatrix} \times 1^{13} \times \left(\frac{1}{2}x\right)^3 + \ldots$

Since $\begin{pmatrix} 16 \\ 1 \end{pmatrix} = \frac{16!}{15! \times 1!} = 16,$

$\begin{pmatrix} 16 \\ 2 \end{pmatrix} = \frac{16!}{14! \times 2!} = \frac{16 \times 15}{2 \times 1} = 120$ and

$\begin{pmatrix} 16 \\ 3 \end{pmatrix} = \frac{16!}{13! \times 3!} = \frac{16 \times 15 \times 14}{3 \times 2 \times 1} = 560.$

Hence, $\left(1 + \frac{1}{2}x\right)^{16} = 1 + 16 \times \left(\frac{1}{2}x\right) + 120 \times \left(\frac{1}{2}x\right)^2 + 560 \times \left(\frac{1}{2}x\right)^3 + \ldots$
$= 1 + 8x + 30x^2 + 70x^3 + \ldots$

In order to find the coefficient of x^3 in the expansion of

$(23 + 13x)\left(1 + \frac{1}{2}x\right)^{16}$

it is necessary to multiply 23 by the term in x^3 from the previous expansion and to multiply $13x$ by the term in x^2 from the expansion of $\left(1 + \frac{1}{2}x\right)^{16}$.

This gives $23 \times 70x^3 + 13x \times 30x^2 = 2000x^3.$

The coefficient of x^3 is therefore 2000.

EXERCISE 1C

1 Find the first four terms in ascending powers of x for each of the following:

(a) $(1 + x)^{11}$, (b) $(1 + x)^{15}$, (c) $(1 - x)^8$,

(d) $(1 + 2x)^7$, (e) $(1 - x)^{12}$, (f) $\left(1 + \frac{1}{3}x\right)^9$,

(g) $\left(1 - \frac{1}{2}x\right)^{10}$, (h) $(2 - x)^9$.

2 Obtain the first four terms in descending powers of x for each of the following:

(a) $(x+1)^{12}$,   (b) $(x+2)^{17}$,

(c) $(x-3)^{10}$,   (d) $(2x-1)^7$.

3 For each of the following binomial expansions, find the term indicated:

(a) $(1+2x)^{15}$ term in x^4,   (b) $(1+3x)^{17}$ term in x^2,

(c) $(1-4x)^{13}$ term in x^3,   (d) $(2-x)^{14}$ term in x^{12},

(e) $\left(1+\frac{2}{3}x\right)^{12}$ term in x^4,   (f) $(3-x)^{18}$ term in x^{14}.

4 For each of the following binomial expansions, find the coefficients indicated:

(a) $(1-x)^{11}$ coefficient of x^7,

(b) $(1+2x)^{13}$ coefficient of x^4,

(c) $(2-3x)^{14}$ coefficient of x^3,

(d) $(2-x)^{15}$ coefficient of x^{11},

(e) $\left(1+\frac{1}{3}x\right)^9$ coefficient of x^4,

(f) $(5-x)^{17}$ coefficient of x^{15}.

5 Find the binomial expansion of $\left(1+\frac{1}{2}x\right)^8$ in ascending powers of x up to and including the term in x^3. Simplify the coefficients as much as possible.   [A]

6 Write down the binomial expansion of $(1+x)^7$ in ascending powers of x up to and including the term in x^3. Hence determine the value of 1.00001^7 correct to 15 decimal places.   [A]

7 Find the binomial expansion of $(1-3x)^{11}$ in ascending powers of x up to and including the term in x^3. Hence determine the coefficient of x^3 in the expansion of $(2+7x)(1-3x)^{11}$.

8 (a) Simplify $\dfrac{(2+h)^5-32}{h}$.

(b) A curve has equation $y=x^5$ and the points P and Q lie on the curve and have x-coordinates equal to 2 and $2+h$, respectively. By considering the gradient of the chord PQ and letting h tend to zero, deduce the gradient of the curve at P.

9 Find the first four terms in ascending powers of x in the expansion of:

(a) $(1+3x)^{12}(5-4x)$,   (b) $\left(1-\frac{1}{4}x\right)^{16}(2+3x)$.

10 Prove that $\dbinom{n+1}{k}=\dbinom{n}{k}+\dbinom{n}{k-1}$.

Key point summary

1 The expression $n!$ is read as 'n factorial' and its value   *p 2*
is given by the product
$n \times (n-1) \times (n-2) \times \ldots \times 3 \times 2 \times 1$.

2 $n! = n \times (n-1)!$.   *p 2*

3 $0! = 1$.   *p 3*

4 In general $\dbinom{n}{r} = \dfrac{n!}{r!\,(n-r)!}$ and represents the   *p 3*
number of ways that r different objects can be chosen
from n objects.

5 In general $\dbinom{n}{r} = \dbinom{n}{n-r}$.   *p 3*

6 The first few rows of Pascal's Triangle are   *p 5*

$$
\begin{array}{ccccccccccccc}
&&&&&& 1 \\
&&&&& 1 && 1 \\
&&&& 1 && 2 && 1 \\
&&& 1 && 3 && 3 && 1 \\
&& 1 && 4 && 6 && 4 && 1 \\
& 1 && 5 && 10 && 10 && 5 && 1 \\
1 && 6 && 15 && 20 && 15 && 6 && 1
\end{array}
$$

7 Pascal's Triangle is useful for expanding $(a+b)^n$ *p 5*
when n is a small positive integer.

8 The general binomial expansion can be written as   *p 9*

$$(a+b)^n = a^n + \binom{n}{1}a^{n-1}b + \binom{n}{2}a^{n-2}b^2 + \ldots$$

$$+ \binom{n}{r}a^{n-r}b^r + \ldots + b^n$$

where n is a positive integer.

Test yourself   What to review

1 Find the value of each of the following: *Sections 1.1 and 1.2*

   (a) $3!$,   **(b)** $0!$,   **(c)** $\dfrac{5!}{3!}$.

2   Evaluate: **(a)** $\dbinom{7}{2}$,   **(b)** $\dbinom{8}{8}$,   **(c)** $\dbinom{47}{46}$.   *Section 1.3*

Test yourself (continued)	What to review

3 One row of Pascal's Triangle begins

$$1 \quad 19 \quad 171 \quad 969 \quad \ldots$$

Find the first four terms of the next row.

Section 1.4

4 Find the expansion of $(x - w)^8$.

Section 1.4

5 Find the first four terms in ascending powers of x in the binomial expansion of $(1 - 2x)^{13}$.

Section 1.5

6 Find the coefficient of x^4 in the binomial expansion of $(2 + 3x)^{11}$.

Section 1.5

Test yourself **ANSWERS**

1 (a) 6; (b) 1; (c) 20.

2 (a) 21; (b) 1; (c) 47.

3 1 20 190 1140.

4 $x^8 - 8wx^7 + 28w^2x^6 - 56w^3x^5 + 70w^4x^4 - 56w^5x^3 + 28w^6x^2 - 8w^7x + w^8$.

5 $1 - 26x + 312x^2 - 2288x^3$.

6 3 421 440.

Division of polynomials and the remainder theorem

Learning objectives

After studying this chapter you should be able to:

- simplify rational expressions
- multiply and divide rational expressions
- add and subtract rational expressions
- divide a polynomial by a linear expression
- recall and use the remainder theorem
- split a rational expression into its partial fractions.

2.1 Rational expressions

A **rational expression** is an algebraic fraction.

Just like in ordinary fractions, the term at the top of the fraction is called the **numerator** and the term at the bottom of the fraction is called the **denominator**.

You will recall from P2 that an expression of the form $ax^n + bx^{n-1} + \ldots + px^2 + qx + r$ (where $a, b, \ldots, p, q, r$ are constants and n is a non-negative integer) is called a **polynomial** in x. The **degree** of a polynomial is given by the highest power of the variable.

An algebraic fraction in which the degree of the numerator is less than the degree of the denominator is called a **proper fraction**.

If the algebraic fraction is not a proper fraction it is called an **improper fraction**.

$\dfrac{x-7}{3(x^2-49)}$ is an example of a rational expression.
Its numerator is $x - 7$ and its denominator is $3(x^2 - 49)$.
The degree of $x - 7$ is 1 and the degree of $3(x^2 - 49)$ is 2.

$\dfrac{x-7}{3(x^2-49)}$ is a proper fraction.

2.2 Simplifying rational expressions

To simplify rational expressions
- factorise all algebraic expressions
- cancel any factors that are common to the numerator and denominator.

Worked example 2.1

Simplify $\dfrac{2x^2 - 8}{x^2 + 3x + 2}$.

Solution

$$\frac{2x^2 - 8}{x^2 + 3x + 2} = \frac{2(x^2 - 4)}{(x + 2)(x + 1)}$$

Factorised numerator and denominator.

$$= \frac{2(x + 2)(x - 2)}{(x + 2)(x + 1)}$$

Factorised fully using the difference of two squares.

$$= \frac{2(x - 2)}{(x + 1)}$$

Cancelled the common factor $(x + 2)$.

Worked example 2.2

Simplify $\dfrac{36 - 4x^2}{x^2 + x - 12}$.

Solution

$$\frac{36 - 4x^2}{x^2 + x - 12} = \frac{4(9 - x^2)}{(x - 3)(x + 4)}$$

Factorised numerator and denominator.

$$= \frac{4(3 - x)(3 + x)}{(x - 3)(x + 4)}$$

Factorised fully using the difference of two squares.

$$= \frac{-4(x - 3)(3 + x)}{(x - 3)(x + 4)}$$

$(3 - x) = -(x - 3)$.

$$= \frac{-4(3 + x)}{(x + 4)}$$

Cancelled the common factor $(x - 3)$.

EXERCISE 2A

Simplify the following rational expressions.

1 $\dfrac{2x^2 - 8x}{x^2 - 16}$

2 $\dfrac{x^2 + x - 6}{3x^2 - 12}$

3 $\dfrac{25 - x^2}{9x^2 - 49x + 20}$

4 $\dfrac{50 + 20x - 16x^2}{8x^2 - 50}$

5 $\dfrac{12x^2 - 11x - 36}{6x^2 - 19x - 36}$

6 $\dfrac{(x^2 - x - 6)(x^2 + 4x + 3)}{(x + 1)(x^2 - 9)}$

7 $\dfrac{(6x^2 + 15x)(2x^2 + x - 3)}{(2x^2 + 5x + 3)(4x^3 - 25x)}$

2

2.3 Multiplying and dividing rational expressions

To multiply rational expressions
- factorise all algebraic expressions
- write as a single fraction
- cancel any factors that are common to the numerator and denominator.

Worked example 2.3

Simplify $\dfrac{x^2 - 2x}{x^2 - 3x + 2} \times \dfrac{x^2 - 1}{x^2}$.

Solution

$$\frac{x^2 - 2x}{x^2 - 3x + 2} \times \frac{x^2 - 1}{x^2} = \frac{x(x - 2)}{(x - 2)(x - 1)} \times \frac{(x - 1)(x + 1)}{x^2}$$

Factorised numerators and denominators.

$$= \frac{x(x - 2)(x - 1)(x + 1)}{x^2(x - 2)(x - 1)}$$

Written as a single fraction.

$$= \frac{x(x + 1)}{x^2}$$

Cancelled the common factor $(x - 2)(x - 1)$.

$$= \frac{(x + 1)}{x}$$

Cancelled the common factor x.

$$= \frac{x + 1}{x}$$

You cannot cancel the xs here because x is not a common factor.

To divide by a rational expression
- change the division to a multiplication of the reciprocal
- factorise all algebraic expressions
- write as a single fraction
- cancel any factors that are common to the numerator and denominator.

To divide by $\dfrac{a}{b}$

change $\div \dfrac{a}{b}$ to $\times \dfrac{b}{a}$.

$$\frac{6}{25} \div \frac{3}{5} = \frac{6}{25} \times \frac{5}{3} = \frac{2}{5}$$

Worked example 2.4

Simplify $\dfrac{2x + 6}{4x} \div \dfrac{x^2 - 9}{x + 1}$

Solution

$$\frac{2x + 6}{4x} \div \frac{x^2 - 9}{x + 1} = \frac{2x + 6}{4x} \times \frac{x + 1}{x^2 - 9}$$

> Dividing by a fraction is same as multiplying by its reciprocal.

$$= \frac{2(x + 3)}{4x} \times \frac{x + 1}{(x + 3)(x - 3)}$$

> Factorised numerators and denominators.

$$= \frac{2(x + 3)(x + 1)}{4x(x + 3)(x - 3)}$$

> Written as a single fraction.

$$= \frac{2(x + 1)}{4x(x - 3)}$$

> Cancelled the common factor $(x + 3)$.

$$= \frac{(x + 1)}{2x(x - 3)}$$

> Cancelled the common factor 2.

EXERCISE 2B

Simplify:

1 $\dfrac{x^2 + 5x - 6}{x^2 - 1} \times \dfrac{x + 1}{2x}$

2 $\dfrac{1}{x^2 - 9} \div \dfrac{1}{x - 3}$

3 $\dfrac{x^2 + 3x + 2}{5x^2 + 10x} \times \dfrac{15x}{x^2 - 1}$

4 $\dfrac{2x + 3}{x^2 - x} \div \dfrac{4x^2 - 9}{(x - 1)^2}$

5 $\dfrac{x^2 + 5x + 6}{x^2 - 9} \times \dfrac{3 - x}{6}$

6 $\dfrac{2x + 3}{x^2 + x - 2} \div \dfrac{4x^2 + 12x + 9}{(x - 1)^2}$

2.4 Adding and subtracting rational expressions

To add/subtract rational expressions

- factorise all algebraic expressions
- write each rational expression with the same common denominator
- add/subtract to get a single rational expression
- simplify the numerator
- cancel any factors that are common to the numerator and denominator.

Worked example 2.5

Express $\dfrac{1}{x+1} - \dfrac{x-3}{x^2+3x+2}$ as a single fraction.

Solution

$$\frac{1}{x+1} - \frac{x-3}{x^2+3x+2} = \frac{1}{x+1} - \frac{x-3}{(x+1)(x+2)}$$

> Factorised the denominator.

$$= \frac{x+2}{(x+1)(x+2)} - \frac{x-3}{(x+1)(x+2)}$$

> Lowest common denominator is $(x+1)(x+2)$.

$$= \frac{x+2-(x-3)}{(x+1)(x+2)}$$

> Written as a single fraction.

$$= \frac{5}{(x+1)(x+2)}$$

> Simplified the numerator.

Worked example 2.6

Given that $x > 0$, show that $\dfrac{x}{x+4} + \dfrac{5x+4}{x^2+4x} > 1$.

Solution

$$\frac{x}{x+4} + \frac{5x+4}{x^2+4x} = \frac{x}{x+4} + \frac{5x+4}{x(x+4)}$$

> Factorised the denominator.

$$= \frac{x^2}{x(x+4)} + \frac{5x+4}{x(x+4)}$$

> Lowest common denominator is $x(x+4)$.

$$= \frac{x^2+5x+4}{x(x+4)}$$

> Written as a single fraction.

$$= \frac{(x+1)(x+4)}{x(x+4)}$$

> Simplified the numerator.

$$= \frac{x+1}{x}$$

> Cancelled the common factor $(x+4)$.

$$= 1 + \frac{1}{x}$$

Now, $x > 0 \Rightarrow \dfrac{1}{x} > 0 \Rightarrow 1 + \dfrac{1}{x} > 1 \Rightarrow \dfrac{x}{x+4} + \dfrac{5x+4}{x^2+4x} > 1$

EXERCISE 2C

1 Write each of the following as a single fraction in its simplest form:

(a) $\dfrac{1}{x-2} - \dfrac{1}{x+2}$,

(b) $\dfrac{x+1}{x^2-4} - \dfrac{5}{x+2}$,

(c) $\dfrac{3}{x+3} + \dfrac{4}{x+2}$,

(d) $\dfrac{x+1}{x^2-x-6} + \dfrac{1}{x+2}$,

(e) $\dfrac{4}{x^2-1} + \dfrac{2}{x+1}$,

(f) $\dfrac{x-20}{x^2-5x-6} - \dfrac{3}{x+1}$,

(g) $\dfrac{4}{x^2-9} - \dfrac{2}{x^2+3x}$,

(h) $\dfrac{3}{x^2-x} - \dfrac{4}{x^2-1}$.

2 Given that $x > 0$, show that $\dfrac{x}{x+2} + \dfrac{(x+1)(x+6)}{x^2+2x} > 2$.

2.5 Dividing a polynomial by a linear expression

In Worked example 2.6 we divided each term in the numerator by x to get $\dfrac{x+1}{x} = 1 + \dfrac{1}{x}$. This was an example of a linear expression being divided by a linear expression. In this section we extend this to dividing a non-linear polynomial by a linear expression. The method we use is called **algebraic long division**.

Worked example 2.7

Divide $2x^3 - 7x^2 - x + 12$ by $(x-3)$.

Solution

$$
\begin{array}{r}
2x^2 \\
x-3\overline{)2x^3 - 7x^2 - x + 12} \\
\underline{2x^3 - 6x^2 } \\
-x^2 - x + 12
\end{array}
$$

Dividing $2x^3$ by x gives $2x^2$. (We can think of this as 'what do we need to multiply x by to get $2x^3$?') Now multiply the answer ($2x^2$) by $x-3$ to give $2x^3 - 6x^2$.
We then subtract it from $2x^3 - 7x^2 - x + 12$ to get the remainder $-x^2 - x + 12$.
The process is repeated until the remainder is at least one degree less than the divisor $(x-3)$.

$$
\begin{array}{r}
2x^2 - x - 4 \\
x - 3 \overline{\smash{\big)}\, 2x^3 - 7x^2 - x + 12} \\
\underline{2x^3 - 6x^2} \\
-x^2 - x + 12 \\
\underline{-x^2 + 3x} \\
-4x + 12 \\
\underline{-4x + 12} \\
0
\end{array}
$$

> Dividing $-x^2$ by x gives $-x$. Now multiply the answer $(-x)$ by $x - 3$ to give $x^2 + 3x$. We then subtract it from $-x^2 - x + 12$ to get the remainder $-4x + 12$. The degree of $-4x + 12$ is not less than the degree of $(x - 3)$ so the process is repeated.

2

> Dividing $-4x$ by x gives -4.

so $(2x^3 - 7x^2 - x + 12) \div (x - 3) = (2x^2 - x - 4)$ remainder 0,

which can be written as

$$(2x^3 - 7x^2 - x + 12) = (x - 3)(2x^2 - x - 4).$$

> The expression we are dividing by is called the **divisor**. Here the divisor is $(x - 3)$.

This result was also obtained by using the method of equating coefficients in Worked example 2.7 in P2.

> The answer we get is called the **quotient**. Here the quotient is $(2x^2 - x - 4)$.

Since the remainder is 0 we can deduce that $(x - 3)$ is a factor of $2x^3 - 7x^2 - x + 12$.

In most cases the remainder will not be zero. However, the remainder will always be at least one degree less than the divisor.

> When a polynomial is divided by a linear expression the remainder will always be a constant and the quotient will always be one degree less than the polynomial.

Worked example 2.8

Divide $2x^3 - 3x^2 - 4x + 23$ by $(x + 2)$.

Solution

$$
\begin{array}{r}
2x^2 - 7x + 10 \\
x + 2 \overline{\smash{\big)}\, 2x^3 - 3x^2 - 4x + 23} \\
\underline{2x^3 + 4x^2} \\
-7x^2 - 4x + 23 \\
-7x^2 - 14x \\
\underline{} \\
10x + 23 \\
10x + 20 \\
\underline{} \\
3
\end{array}
$$

> $2x^3$ divided by x is $2x^2$.

> $2x^2$ multiplied by $x + 2$ gives $2x^3 + 4x^2$.

> Subtracted.

> $-7x$ multiplied by $x + 2$ gives $-7x^2 - 14x$.

> Subtracted.

> 10 multiplied by $x + 2$ gives $10x + 20$.

so $(2x^3 - 3x^2 - 4x + 23) \div (x + 2) \equiv (2x^2 - 7x + 10)$ remainder 3,

which can be written as

$$\frac{2x^3 - 3x^2 - 4x + 23}{x + 2} \equiv 2x^2 - 7x + 10 + \frac{3}{x + 2}$$

> Similar to numerical fractions,
> e.g. $23 \div 5 = 4$ remainder 3.
>
> $\dfrac{23}{5} = 4 + \dfrac{3}{5}.$

or

$$(2x^3 - 3x^2 - 4x + 23) = (x + 2)(2x^2 - 7x + 10) + 3.$$

> Polynomial $=$ divisor $\times$ quotient
> $+$ remainder

divisor   quotient   remainder

In the next example the linear divisor has a coefficient of x that is not 1. Also the polynomial has some terms in x missing.

> Before starting to use algebraic long division write the polynomial in descending powers of x and include all powers of x, inserting zero coefficients if necessary.

Worked example 2.9

Divide $1 - 3x^2 + 2x^3$ by $(2x - 1)$.

Solution

Rewrite the polynomial in descending powers of x and, since there is no term in x, write $0x$.

$$
\begin{array}{r}
x^2 - x - \dfrac{1}{2} \\
2x - 1 \overline{\smash{\big)}\ 2x^3 - 3x^2 + 0x + 1} \\
\underline{2x^3 - x^2} \\
-2x^2 + 0x + 1 \\
\underline{-2x^2 + x} \\
-x + 1 \\
\underline{-x + \dfrac{1}{2}} \\
\dfrac{1}{2}
\end{array}
$$

> $2x^3$ divided by $2x$ is x^2.

> x^2 multiplied by $2x - 1$ gives $2x^3 - x^2$.

> Subtracted.

> $-x$ multiplied by $2x - 1$ gives $-2x^2 + x$.

> Subtracted.

> $-\dfrac{1}{2}$ multiplied by $2x - 1$ gives $-x + \dfrac{1}{2}$.

So $(1 - 3x^2 + 2x^3) \div (2x - 1) \equiv \left(x^2 - x - \dfrac{1}{2}\right)$ remainder $\dfrac{1}{2}$,

which can be written as

$$\frac{1 - 3x^2 + 2x^3}{2x - 1} \equiv x^2 - x - \frac{1}{2} + \frac{\dfrac{1}{2}}{2x - 1} \equiv x^2 - x - \frac{1}{2} + \frac{1}{2(2x - 1)}$$

or

$$(1 - 3x^2 + 2x^3) \equiv (2x - 1)\left(x^2 - x - \frac{1}{2}\right) + \frac{1}{2}.$$

> Polynomial = divisor × quotient + remainder

EXERCISE 2D

1 Divide:

   (a) $x + 6$ by $x + 2$,

   (b) x^2 by $x + 1$,

   (c) $4x^3 - 5x^2 + 2x - 1$ by $x - 1$,

   (d) $2x^3 + 7x^2 - 4x + 5$ by $x - 2$,

   (e) $3x^3 - 4x^2 + 2x - 1$ by $3x - 1$,

   (f) $6x^3 + 2x^2 - 7x + 3$ by $2x - 1$,

   (g) $5x^3 - 2x^2 + 3x - 1$ by $5x + 2$,

   (h) $5x^3 - 2x^2 + 3x - 1$ by $5x - 2$,

   (i) $4x^3 - x^2 - 7x + 1$ by $2x + 1$,

   (j) $9x^3 - 1$ by $3x - 2$.

2 Find **(i)** the quotient and **(ii)** the remainder when the polynomial P(x) is divided by $(2x + 1)$:

   (a) P$(x) = 4x^2 - 3$,

   (b) P$(x) = 6x^3 - 2x + 7$,

   (c) P$(x) = 2x^4 - 1$,

   (d) P$(x) = 2x^3 + 8x^2 - 9$.

3 When the polynomial $x^3 - 4x^2 + x + k$, where k is a constant, is divided by $x - 2$ the remainder is 3. Find the value of k and the quotient.

2.6 The remainder theorem

In the previous section we noted that dividing a polynomial by a linear expression led to the identity

    Polynomial = Divisor × Quotient + Remainder.

When the divisor is a linear expression (degree 1), the remainder is a constant (degree 0) so

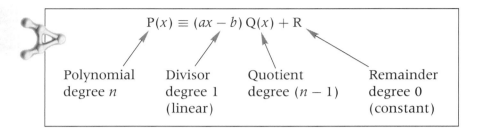

$$P(x) \equiv (ax - b)\,Q(x) + R$$

| Polynomial degree n | Divisor degree 1 (linear) | Quotient degree $(n - 1)$ | Remainder degree 0 (constant) |

Since this identity is true for all values of x, consider the case when $x = \dfrac{b}{a}$,

> Choose the value of x so that $(ax - b) = 0$.

so
$$P\left(\frac{b}{a}\right) = (b - b)\,Q\left(\frac{b}{a}\right) + R$$

$$\Rightarrow \quad P\left(\frac{b}{a}\right) = 0 + R$$

$$\Rightarrow \quad R = P\left(\frac{b}{a}\right)$$

This is called the **remainder theorem**.

If a polynomial $P(x)$ is divided by $(ax - b)$, the remainder is $P\left(\dfrac{b}{a}\right)$.

> If the remainder is 0 then $(ax - b)$ is a factor of $P(x)$ so
> $$P\left(\frac{b}{a}\right) = 0 \Leftrightarrow (ax - b) \text{ is}$$
> a factor of $P(x)$. This result is called the **factor theorem** and was established in section 2.4 of P2.

Worked example 2.10

Find the remainder when the polynomial $1 - 3x^2 + 2x^3$ is divided by $(2x - 1)$.

Solution

Let $P(x) = 1 - 3x^2 + 2x^3$.
$$P(x) = (2x - 1)\,Q(x) + R$$
$$P\left(\frac{1}{2}\right) = 0 + R$$
$$R = P\left(\frac{1}{2}\right) = 1 - 3\left(\frac{1}{2}\right)^2 + 2\left(\frac{1}{2}\right)^3 = 1 - \frac{3}{4} + \frac{1}{4} = \frac{1}{2}$$

When $1 - 3x^2 + 2x^3$ is divided by $(2x - 1)$ the remainder is $\dfrac{1}{2}$.

> See Worked example 2.9.

Worked example 2.11

When $2x^3 - 3x^2 + kx + 3$ is divided by $x + 2$ the remainder is -21.

Find the value of the constant k.

Solution

Let $P(x) = 2x^3 - 3x^2 + kx + 3$

$\quad P(x) = (x + 2)Q(x) + R$

$\quad \Rightarrow P(-2) = 0 + R$

$\quad R = P(-2) = 2(-2)^3 - 3(-2)^2 + k(-2) + 3$

$\quad \Rightarrow -21 = -16 - 12 - 2k + 3$

$\quad \Rightarrow k = -2$

Worked example 2.12

The polynomial $P(x) = ax^3 + x^2 + bx - 4$ when divided by $x - 1$ leaves a remainder of -9. Given also that $(x - 2)$ is a factor of $P(x)$ find the values of the constants a and b. Hence find the roots of the equation $P(x) = 0$.

Solution

$\quad P(x) = ax^3 + x^2 + bx - 4$

$\quad P(x) = (x - 1)Q(x) + R$

$\quad \Rightarrow P(1) = 0 + R$

$\quad R = P(1) \Rightarrow -9 = a + 1 + b - 4 \Rightarrow a + b = -6 \qquad [1]$

$(x - 2)$ is a factor of $P(x)$

$\quad \Rightarrow P(2) = 0 \Rightarrow 8a + 4 + 2b - 4 = 0 \Rightarrow 4a + b = 0 \qquad [2]$

Solving equations [1] and [2] simultaneously leads to $a = 2$, $b = -8$.

Knowing that $(x - 2)$ is a factor of $P(x) = 2x^3 + x^2 - 8x - 4$ you could find the other factor by long division.

However, with a little thought, $2x^3 + x^2 - 8x - 4$ can be factorised as follows:

$$2x^3 + x^2 - 8x - 4 = x^2(2x + 1) - 4(2x + 1)$$
$$= (2x + 1)(x^2 - 4)$$
$$= (2x + 1)(x - 2)(x + 2)$$

so $\qquad P(x) = (2x + 1)(x - 2)(x + 2)$

$\Rightarrow$ roots of $P(x) = 0$ are $x = 2, -2$ and $-\dfrac{1}{2}$.

$$\begin{array}{r} 2x^2 + 5x + 2 \\ x - 2\overline{)2x^3 + x^2 - 8x - 4} \\ \underline{2x^3 - 4x^2} \\ 5x^2 - 8x - 4 \\ \underline{5x^2 - 10x\ldots\ldots} \\ 2x - 4 \\ \underline{2x - 4} \\ 0 \end{array}$$

so $P(x) = (x - 2)(2x^2 + 5x + 2)$

$\Rightarrow P(x) = (x - 2)(2x + 1)(x + 2)$

$\Rightarrow$ roots of $P(x) = 0$ are $x = 2$,

-2 and $-\dfrac{1}{2}$.

EXERCISE 2E

1 Find the remainder when the polynomial $2x^4 + 2x^3 + 8x^2 - 5$ is divided by:

(a) $x - 1$, (b) $x + 2$, (c) $2x - 1$,

(d) $2x - 3$, (e) x.

2 Find the remainder when the polynomial P(x) is divided by the linear expression f(x):

(a) P$(x) = x^3 - 3$ f$(x) = x - \dfrac{1}{2}$,

(b) P$(x) = -x^3 + 2x^2 - 3x + 4$ f$(x) = x + 2$,

(c) P$(x) = 16x^4 - 3x^2 + 1$ f$(x) = 4x - 1$,

(d) P$(x) = 5 - 2x + x^2 - 3x^3$ f$(x) = 2 - x$,

(e) P$(x) = 3 - x^5$ f$(x) = 1 - 2x$,

(f) P$(x) = (2 + 3x)^4 + 5$ f$(x) = x - 1$.

3 The polynomial P(x) is defined by
P$(x) = x^4 + 4x^3 - 3x^2 + 20x + k$, where k is a constant.
When P(x) is divided by $x - 1$ the remainder is -17.
Show that $k = -39$.

4 When $4x^3 - kx^2 + 6x - 2$ is divided by $x + 1$ the remainder is 7. Find the value of the constant k.

5 The polynomial P$(x) = x^3 + ax^2 - x + 12$ leaves a remainder of 9 when divided by $x - 3$. Find the remainder when P(x) is divided by $x - 2$.

6 The polynomial P$(x) = x^3 + 3x^2 - 2x + k$ has a factor $x + 1$. Find the remainder when P(x) is divided by $x - 3$.

7 Given that P(x), where P$(x) = x^3 + 3x^2 + kx + 4$ and k is a constant, is such that the remainder on dividing P(x) by $(x - 1)$ is three times the remainder on dividing P(x) by $(x + 1)$, find the value of k.

8 When divided by $(2x - 1)$ the polynomial
P$(x) = 8x^3 - ax^2 + bx - 6$ leaves a remainder of 2.
When divided by $(x - 2)$ P(x) leaves a remainder of 14.

(a) Find the values of the constants a and b.

(b) Show that $(x - 1)$ is **not** a factor of P(x).

9 The polynomial P$(x) = 3x^3 - 11x^2 + 8x + k$ leaves a remainder of -18 when divided by $x + 1$.

(a) Find the value of the constants k.

(b) Show that $(3x + 1)$ is a factor of P(x).

(c) Hence find the roots of the equation P$(x) = 0$.

10 The polynomials f(x) and g(x) are defined by
f(x) = $x^3 + px^2 - x + 5$, g(x) = $x^3 - x^2 + px + 1$, where p is a
constant. When f(x) and g(x) are divided by $x - 2$, the
remainder is R in each case. Find the values of p and R. [A]

11 The polynomial P(x) = $x^3 - 4x^2 + 2x + k$ has ($x - 2$) as a
factor.

  (a) Find the value of the constant k.

  (b) Calculate the remainder when P(x) is divided by
($x + 3$).

  (c) Find the exact values of the roots of the equation
P(x) = 0. [A]

2.7 Partial fractions

In section 2.4 you were shown how to add and subtract rational
expressions to produce a single fraction. Sometimes it is more
useful to split a single fraction into the sums or differences of
other rational expressions. This process is called **writing a
rational expression in terms of its partial fractions**.

$$\frac{2}{2x + 1} - \frac{1}{x + 2}$$

$$\equiv \frac{3}{(2x + 1)(x + 2)}$$

Reversing the process we would
say 'Express $\dfrac{3}{(2x + 1)(x + 2)}$ in

partial fractions'.

Only proper fractions can be expressed in terms of
partial fractions. If the given rational expression is
improper you must first carry out a long division to
obtain a proper fraction.

There are three types of rational expressions for which you may
be expected to find the corresponding partial fractions.

A proper fraction which has up to three linear factors in
the denominator,

$$\frac{p(x)}{(x - a)(x - b)(x - c)}, \text{ has three partial fractions of}$$

the form $\dfrac{A}{(x - a)} + \dfrac{B}{(x - b)} + \dfrac{C}{(x - c)}.$

A proper fraction which has a repeated linear factor in
the denominator,

$$\frac{q(x)}{(x - a)^3}, \text{ has partial fractions of the form}$$

$$\frac{A}{(x - a)} + \frac{B}{(x - a)^2} + \frac{C}{(x - a)^3}.$$

In each case A, B and C are
constants which need to be
determined.

> A proper fraction which has a linear factor and a quadratic factor in the denominator,
>
> $\dfrac{q(x)}{(x-k)(ax^2+bx+c)}$, has partial fractions of the
>
> form $\dfrac{A}{(x-k)} + \dfrac{Bx+C}{(ax^2+bx+c)}$.

Worked example 2.13

Express $\dfrac{x+4}{(x+1)(x-2)}$ in partial fractions.

Solution

$\dfrac{x+4}{(x+1)(x-2)} \equiv \dfrac{A}{x+1} + \dfrac{B}{x-2}$, where A and B are constants.

| *Only linear factors in the denominator.*

$\dfrac{x+4}{(x+1)(x-2)} \equiv \dfrac{A(x-2)+B(x+1)}{(x+1)(x-2)}$

| *Writing both sides with the same denominators.*

Since the denominators are the same we can equate the numerators.

$$x+4 \equiv A(x-2)+B(x+1)$$

Let $x = 2 \Rightarrow 6 = 3B \Rightarrow B = 2$
Let $x = -1 \Rightarrow 3 = -3A \Rightarrow A = -1$

So $\dfrac{x+4}{(x+1)(x-2)} = \dfrac{-1}{x+1} + \dfrac{2}{x-2}$.

In past examination questions partial fractions have often been asked for in the first part and the result is then required to, for example, evaluate an integral.

Because of this it is well worthwhile spending time checking your values for the constants. In the above example this could be done by comparing coefficients of x: $\Rightarrow 1 = A + B$.
Since $1 = -1 + 2$, you can be confident that the values are correct to use in the next part of the question.

In some questions you will be told the form of the partial fractions. The next worked example is such a question.

> *When the denominator has only linear factors the **cover up** method can be used to find A and B. For example, the denominator for B is $x - 2$. The value of x for this to be zero is 2. **Cover up** the $(x - 2)$ factor in the denominator of*
>
> $\dfrac{x+4}{(x+1)(x-2)}$ *and evaluate*
>
> $\dfrac{x+4}{(x+1)}$ *when $x = 2$ to find B.*
>
> *This gives $B = \dfrac{6}{3}$. Similarly*
>
> $A = \dfrac{3}{-3}$.

> *You will be shown how to evaluate integrals using partial fractions in chapter 9.*

Worked example 2.14

Express $\dfrac{1}{x^2(x-1)}$ in the form $\dfrac{A}{x} + \dfrac{B}{x^2} + \dfrac{C}{x-1}$, and state the values of the constants A, B and C.

> *Note the denominator has a repeated linear factor, x, and a single linear factor $x - 1$, hence the form of the three partial fractions.*

Solution

$$\frac{1}{x^2(x-1)} \equiv \frac{A}{x} + \frac{B}{x^2} + \frac{C}{x-1}$$

$$\frac{1}{x^2(x-1)} \equiv \frac{Ax(x-1) + B(x-1) + Cx^2}{x^2(x-1)}$$

Since the denominators are the same we can equate the numerators.

$$1 \equiv Ax(x-1) + B(x-1) + Cx^2$$

Let $x = 1 \Rightarrow 1 = C \Rightarrow C = 1$

Let $x = 0 \Rightarrow 1 = -B \Rightarrow B = -1$

Equate coefficients of $x^2 \Rightarrow 0 = A + C \Rightarrow A = -1$

So $\dfrac{1}{x^2(x-1)} \equiv \dfrac{-1}{x} + \dfrac{-1}{x^2} + \dfrac{1}{x-1}$.

> Writing both sides with the same denominators. Be careful with repeated factors. A **common error** is to write the numerator as $Ax^2(x-1) + Bx(x-1) + Cx^3$.

> To check you must use a method that involves all the constants:
> Let $x = 2$
> $\Rightarrow 1 = 2A + B + 4C$
> $1 = -2 - 1 + 4$;
> this is true.

The next worked example considers the case when the denominator of the given rational expression is not factorised. It also looks at the case when a quadratic expression occurs in the denominator.

Worked example 2.15

Express $\dfrac{x^3 - 2}{x^4 - 1}$ as a sum of three partial fractions.

> Note the denominator is not factorised.

Solution

The first step is to fully factorise the denominator:

$$x^4 - 1 = (x^2 + 1)(x^2 - 1) = (x^2 + 1)(x + 1)(x - 1)$$

$$\frac{x^3 - 2}{x^4 - 1} \equiv \frac{x^3 - 2}{(x^2 + 1)(x + 1)(x - 1)} \equiv \frac{Ax + B}{x^2 + 1} + \frac{C}{x + 1} + \frac{D}{x - 1}$$

> The denominator has a single quadratic factor and two single linear factors.

$$\frac{x^3 - 2}{(x^2 + 1)(x + 1)(x - 1)}$$

$$\equiv \frac{(Ax + B)(x + 1)(x - 1) + C(x^2 + 1)(x - 1) + D(x^2 + 1)(x + 1)}{(x^2 + 1)(x + 1)(x - 1)}$$

Since the denominators are the same we can equate the numerators.

$$x^3 - 2 \equiv (Ax + B)(x + 1)(x - 1) + C(x^2 + 1)(x - 1) + D(x^2 + 1)(x + 1)$$

Let $x = 1 \Rightarrow -1 = 4D \Rightarrow D = \dfrac{-1}{4}$

Let $x = -1 \Rightarrow -3 = -4C \Rightarrow C = \dfrac{3}{4}$

Let $x = 0 \Rightarrow -2 = -B - C + D \Rightarrow B = 1$

Equate coefficients of $x^3 \Rightarrow 1 = A + C + D \Rightarrow A = \dfrac{1}{2}$

> Check: Let $x = 2$:
> $6 = 6A + 3B + 5C + 15D$
> $6 = 3 + 3 + 3.75 - 3.75$ which
> is true.

So $\dfrac{x^3 - 2}{x^4 - 1} = \dfrac{\frac{1}{2}x + 1}{x^2 + 1} + \dfrac{\frac{3}{4}}{x + 1} + \dfrac{-\frac{1}{4}}{x - 1}$

which can be written as

$$\dfrac{x^3 - 2}{x^4 - 1} \equiv \dfrac{1}{4}\left(\dfrac{2x + 4}{x^2 + 1} + \dfrac{3}{x + 1} - \dfrac{1}{x - 1}\right).$$

The next Worked example looks at a rational expression that is improper. As we have stated earlier, before starting to form partial fractions the rational expression must be written as a proper fraction. The method of algebraic long division is extended to division by non-linear expressions to cope with this case.

Worked example 2.16

Express $\dfrac{x^2 - x + 1}{(x - 2)(x + 1)}$ in partial fractions.

> Since the degrees of the numerator and denominator are the same, both 2, the fraction is improper so we need to divide out.

Solution

The first step involves a long division

$$
\begin{array}{r}
1 \\
x^2 - x - 2 \overline{)\,x^2 - x + 1} \\
\underline{x^2 - x - 2} \\
3
\end{array}
$$

$$\dfrac{x^2 - x + 1}{(x - 2)(x + 1)} \equiv 1 + \dfrac{3}{x^2 - x - 2} \equiv 1 + \dfrac{3}{(x - 2)(x + 1)}$$

Consider $\dfrac{3}{(x - 2)(x + 1)} \equiv \dfrac{A}{x - 2} + \dfrac{B}{x + 1}$

$\Rightarrow 3 = A(x + 1) + B(x - 2)$

Let $x = 2 \Rightarrow A = 1$

Let $x = -1 \Rightarrow B = -1$

So $\dfrac{x^2 - x + 1}{(x - 2)(x + 1)} \equiv 1 + \dfrac{1}{x - 2} + \dfrac{-1}{x + 1}$

or $\dfrac{x^2 - x + 1}{(x - 2)(x + 1)} \equiv 1 + \dfrac{1}{x - 2} - \dfrac{1}{x + 1}.$

EXERCISE 2F

1 Express $\dfrac{x - 1}{(x + 2)(x + 1)}$ in the form $\dfrac{A}{x + 2} + \dfrac{B}{x + 1}$, and state the values of the constants A and B.

2 Express $\dfrac{3x + 7}{(x - 2)(x - 1)}$ in the form $\dfrac{A}{x - 2} + \dfrac{B}{x - 1}$, and state the values of the constants A and B.

3 Express $\dfrac{x}{(1-x)(2+x)}$ in the form $\dfrac{A}{1-x}+\dfrac{B}{2+x}$, and state the values of the constants A and B.

4 Express $\dfrac{4}{x^2-4}$ in the form $\dfrac{A}{x+2}+\dfrac{B}{x-2}$, and state the values of the constants A and B.

5 Express $\dfrac{2}{(x-1)^2(x+1)}$ in the form $\dfrac{A}{(x-1)^2}+\dfrac{B}{x-1}+\dfrac{C}{x+1}$ and state the values of the constants A, B and C.

6 Express $\dfrac{x-2}{(x-1)(x^2+2)}$ in the form $\dfrac{A}{x-1}+\dfrac{Bx+C}{x^2+2}$, and state the values of the constants A, B and C.

7 Express $\dfrac{3x}{(x+2)(x+1)}$ in partial fractions.

8 Express $\dfrac{3x-5}{x^2-1}$ in partial fractions.

9 Express $\dfrac{x^2+1}{x(x+1)^2}$ in partial fractions.

10 Express $\dfrac{3x^2+2x}{(x^2+3)(x+2)}$ in partial fractions.

11 Express $\dfrac{x^2}{4-x^2}$ in partial fractions.

12 Express $\dfrac{3x}{(x+2)(x+1)^2}$ in partial fractions.

13 Express $\dfrac{x^2-2x-3}{(x+2)(x^2+1)}$ in partial fractions.

14 Express $\dfrac{x+4}{(x+3)(x+2)(x+1)}$ in partial fractions.

Key point summary

1 To simplify rational expressions   *p 15*
  - factorise all algebraic expressions
  - cancel any factors that are common to the numerator and denominator.

2 To multiply rational expressions   *p 17*
- factorise all algebraic expressions
- write as a single fraction
- cancel any factors that are common to the numerator and denominator.

3 To divide by a rational expression   *p 17*
- change the division to a multiplication of the reciprocal
- factorise all algebraic expressions
- write as a single fraction
- cancel any factors that are common to the numerator and denominator.

4 To add/subtract rational expressions   *p 18*
- factorise all algebraic expressions
- write each rational expression with the same common denominator
- add/subtract to get a single rational expression
- simplify the numerator
- cancel any factors that are common to the numerator and denominator.

5 Polynomial = divisor × quotient + remainder   *p 21*

6 When a polynomial is divided by a linear expression the remainder will always be a constant and the quotient will always be one degree less than the polynomial.   *p 21*

7 Before starting to use algebraic long division write the polynomial in descending powers of x and include all powers of x, inserting zero coefficients if necessary.   *p 22*

8 **The remainder theorem:**   *p 24*
If a polynomial P(x) is divided by ($ax - b$), the remainder is $P\left(\dfrac{b}{a}\right)$.

9 Only proper fractions can be expressed in terms of partial fractions. If the given rational expression is improper you must first carry out a long division to obtain a proper fraction.   *p 27*

10 A proper fraction which has up to three linear factors in the denominator, $\dfrac{p(x)}{(x-a)(x-b)(x-c)}$, has three partial fractions of the form   *p 27*
$$\frac{A}{(x-a)} + \frac{B}{(x-b)} + \frac{C}{(x-c)}.$$

11 A proper fraction which has a repeated linear factor   *p 27*

in the denominator, $\dfrac{q(x)}{(x-a)^3}$, has partial fractions

of the form $\dfrac{A}{(x-a)} + \dfrac{B}{(x-a)^2} + \dfrac{C}{(x-a)^3}$.

12 A proper fraction which has a linear factor and a   *p 28*
quadratic factor in the denominator,

$\dfrac{q(x)}{(x-k)(ax^2+bx+c)}$, has partial fractions of the

form $\dfrac{A}{(x-k)} + \dfrac{Bx+C}{(ax^2+bx+c)}$.

Test yourself	What to review
1 Simplify $\dfrac{18x - 2x^3}{x^2 + 2x - 15}$.	*Section 2.2*
2 Simplify $\left(\dfrac{2x^2 + x - 1}{x^2 - 1} \times \dfrac{2x^2 - 5x + 3}{2x^2 - 7x + 3}\right) \div \left(\dfrac{6x^2 + x - 2}{3x^2 - 7x - 6}\right)$.	*Section 2.3*
3 Express $\dfrac{4}{x+5} + \dfrac{1}{x-2} - \dfrac{7}{x^2 + 3x - 10}$ in its simplest form.	*Section 2.4*
4 Find **(a)** the quotient and **(b)** the remainder when the polynomial $6 + x - 9x^3$ is divided by $(3x + 5)$.	*Section 2.5*
5 The polynomial $x^3 + ax^2 + bx + c$ leaves the remainders 2, 2 and 6 when divided by $(x + 1)$, x and $(x - 1)$ respectively. Find the values of the constants a, b and c.	*Section 2.6*
6 Express $\dfrac{18x - 10x^2}{(1-x)^2(3-x)}$ as the sum of three partial fractions.	*Section 2.7*

Test yourself ANSWERS

6 $\dfrac{4}{(1-x)^2} - \dfrac{1}{(1-x)} - \dfrac{9}{(3-x)}$.

5 $a = 2$, $b = 1$, $c = 2$.

4 **(a)** $-3x^2 + 5x - 8$;   **(b)** 46.

3 $\dfrac{5}{x+5}$.

2 $\dfrac{2x-3}{2x-1}$.

1 $\dfrac{-2x(x+3)}{x+5}$.

CHAPTER 3

Additional formulae in trigonometry

Learning objectives

After studying this chapter you should be able to:

■ work with the inverse trigonometric functions $\sin^{-1}$, $\cos^{-1}$ and $\tan^{-1}$ and be able to draw their graphs over appropriate restricted domains
■ use the compound angle identities in trigonometry to prove other identities and to solve equations
■ use the double angle identities in trigonometry to prove other identities and to solve equations
■ differentiate $\sin x$ and $\cos x$ from first principles.

3.1 Inverse trigonometric functions

In section 5.11 of P1 you read that in order for an inverse function f^{-1} to exist, the function f must be one–one. The sine function, defined over the domain of real numbers, is clearly a many–one function as can be seen from its graph.

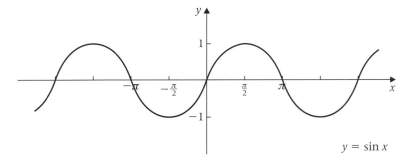

$$y = \sin x$$

So, at first sight, it would seem that the sine function has no inverse. To overcome this problem the domain of the sine function is restricted so that it becomes a one–one function but still takes all real values in the range $-1 \leqslant \sin x \leqslant 1$. You can do this by restricting the domain to $-\dfrac{\pi}{2} \leqslant x \leqslant \dfrac{\pi}{2}$, where x is in radians.

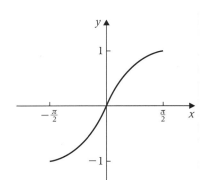

The inverse function of $\sin x$, $-\dfrac{\pi}{2} \leqslant x \leqslant \dfrac{\pi}{2}$, is written as $\sin^{-1} x$.

From the general definition of an inverse function you can deduce that $y = \sin^{-1} x \Leftrightarrow \sin y = x$ and $-\dfrac{\pi}{2} \leqslant y \leqslant \dfrac{\pi}{2}$.

$\sin^{-1}x$ has domain $-1 \leqslant x \leqslant 1$ and range $-\dfrac{\pi}{2} \leqslant \sin^{-1}x \leqslant \dfrac{\pi}{2}$.

The graph of $y = \sin^{-1}x$, $-1 \leqslant x \leqslant 1$ is obtained by reflecting the graph of $y = \sin x$, $-\dfrac{\pi}{2} \leqslant x \leqslant \dfrac{\pi}{2}$, in the line $y = x$.

Warning: $\sin^{-1}x \neq \dfrac{1}{\sin x}$.

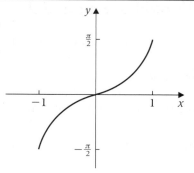

Worked example 3.1

Find the exact values of:

(a) $\sin^{-1}\dfrac{1}{2}$,

(b) $\cos\left(\sin^{-1}\dfrac{1}{3}\right)$.

Solution

(a) $\sin^{-1}\dfrac{1}{2} = \dfrac{\pi}{6}$

since $\sin\dfrac{\pi}{6} = \dfrac{1}{2}$ and $\dfrac{\pi}{6}$ lies between $-\dfrac{\pi}{2}$ and $\dfrac{\pi}{2}$.

(b) Let $\alpha = \sin^{-1}\dfrac{1}{3} \Rightarrow \sin\alpha = \dfrac{1}{3}$.

Using the identity $\cos^2\alpha + \sin^2\alpha = 1$, you have $\cos^2\alpha = \dfrac{8}{9}$.

Since α has to lie between $-\dfrac{\pi}{2}$ and $\dfrac{\pi}{2}$ you can deduce that $\cos\alpha$ is positive.

$\Rightarrow \cos\left(\sin^{-1}\dfrac{1}{3}\right) = \cos\alpha = \sqrt{\dfrac{8}{9}} = \dfrac{2\sqrt{2}}{3}$.

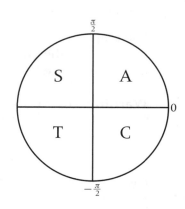

Although the following direct results are true

$\sin^{-1}(\sin x) = x$ for $-\dfrac{\pi}{2} \leqslant x \leqslant \dfrac{\pi}{2}$,

$\sin(\sin^{-1}x) = x$ for $-1 \leqslant x \leqslant 1$.

Composite functions and inverse functions are considered in P1 chapter 5.

you must be careful when x lies outside the given inequalities. The next worked example shows you how to deal with such a case.

Worked example 3.2

Find the exact value of $\sin^{-1}\left(\sin\dfrac{4\pi}{3}\right)$.

Solution

Since $\dfrac{4\pi}{3}$ does not lie between $-\dfrac{\pi}{2}$ and $\dfrac{\pi}{2}$ you cannot use the

direct result. Instead you evaluate $\sin\dfrac{4\pi}{3} = -\sin\dfrac{\pi}{3} = -\dfrac{\sqrt{3}}{2}$.

Let $\alpha = \sin^{-1}\left(\sin\dfrac{4\pi}{3}\right) = \sin^{-1}\left(-\dfrac{\sqrt{3}}{2}\right) \Rightarrow \sin\alpha = -\dfrac{\sqrt{3}}{2}$.

The value of α which satisfies $\sin\alpha = -\dfrac{\sqrt{3}}{2}$ and lies between

$-\dfrac{\pi}{2}$ and $\dfrac{\pi}{2}$ is $-\dfrac{\pi}{3}$

$\Rightarrow \sin^{-1}\left(\sin\dfrac{4\pi}{3}\right) = -\dfrac{\pi}{3}$.

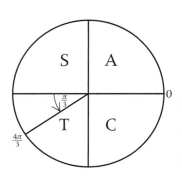

The inverse functions of $\cos x$ and $\tan x$ are dealt with in a similar way.

The restricted domain for $\cos x$ is not the same as that used for $\sin x$.

The inverse function of $\cos x$, $0 \leqslant x \leqslant \pi$, is written as $\cos^{-1} x$.

$y = \cos^{-1} x \Leftrightarrow \cos y = x$ and $0 \leqslant y \leqslant \pi$.

> Restricting the domain of $\cos x$
> to $-\dfrac{\pi}{2} \leqslant x \leqslant \dfrac{\pi}{2}$ would not give
> the negative values in the range
> 0 to -1.

$\cos^{-1} x$ has domain $-1 \leqslant x \leqslant 1$
and range $0 \leqslant \cos^{-1} x \leqslant \pi$.

The graph of $y = \cos^{-1} x$, $-1 \leqslant x \leqslant 1$ is obtained
by reflecting the graph of $y = \cos x$, $0 \leqslant x \leqslant \pi$,
in the line $y = x$.

Warning: $\cos^{-1} x \neq \dfrac{1}{\cos x}$.

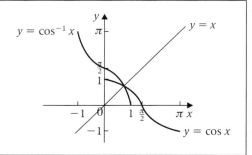

$\cos^{-1}(\cos x) = x$ for $0 \leqslant x \leqslant \pi$,
$\cos(\cos^{-1} x) = x$ for $-1 \leqslant x \leqslant 1$.

The tangent function can be made one–one by restricting its
domain to $-\dfrac{\pi}{2} < x < \dfrac{\pi}{2}$.

The inverse function of $\tan x$, $-\dfrac{\pi}{2} < x < \dfrac{\pi}{2}$, is written as $\tan^{-1} x$.

$y = \tan^{-1} x \Leftrightarrow \tan y = x$ and $-\dfrac{\pi}{2} < y < \dfrac{\pi}{2}$.

$\tan^{-1}x$ has domain all real numbers and range $-\dfrac{\pi}{2} < \tan^{-1}x < \dfrac{\pi}{2}$.

The graph of $y = \tan^{-1}x$, is obtained by reflecting the graph of $y = \tan x$, $-\dfrac{\pi}{2} < x < \dfrac{\pi}{2}$, in the line $y = x$.

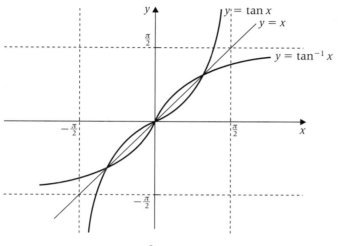

Warning: $\tan^{-1}x \neq \dfrac{1}{\tan x}$.

The lines $x = -\dfrac{\pi}{2}$ and $x = \dfrac{\pi}{2}$ are vertical asymptotes of the graph of tan. When reflected in the line $y = x$ they become horizontal. The lines $y = -\dfrac{\pi}{2}$ and $y = \dfrac{\pi}{2}$ are horizontal asymptotes of the graph of $\tan^{-1}$.

You will study asymptotes in more detail in P5.

Worked example 3.3

By considering the graphs of $y = 0.5x$ and $y = \cos^{-1}x$ determine the number of real roots of the equation $2\cos^{-1}x = x$.

Solution

The equation $2\cos^{-1}x = x$ can be rearranged into the form $\cos^{-1}x = 0.5x$.

The number of real roots of the equation correspond to the number of times the graphs $y = \cos^{-1}x$ and $y = 0.5x$ intersect.

The graphs intersect in just one point so the equation $2\cos^{-1}x = x$ has only one real root.

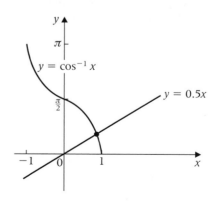

EXERCISE 3A

1 Find the exact values of:

(a) $\cos^{-1}\dfrac{1}{2}$,

(b) $\cos(\cos^{-1}0)$,

(c) $\cos^{-1}\left(\cos\dfrac{2\pi}{3}\right)$,

(d) $\cos^{-1}\left(\cos\dfrac{4\pi}{3}\right)$,

(e) $\cos^{-1}\left(\sin\dfrac{2\pi}{3}\right)$,

(f) $\cos^{-1}\left(\sin\dfrac{4\pi}{3}\right)$.

2 Find the exact values of:

(a) $\tan^{-1}\dfrac{1}{\sqrt{3}}$,

(b) $\tan[\tan^{-1}(-1)]$,

(c) $\tan^{-1}\left(\tan\dfrac{3\pi}{4}\right)$,

(d) $\tan\left(\cos^{-1}\dfrac{1}{2}\right)$,

(e) $\tan\left(\cos^{-1}\dfrac{1}{3}\right)$,

(f) $\sin\left(\tan^{-1}\dfrac{1}{2}\right)$.

3 You are given that $\mathrm{h}(x) = \sin^{-1}x + \cos^{-1}x - 3\tan^{-1}x$. Find the value of:

(a) $\mathrm{h}(1)$,

(b) $\mathrm{h}(-1)$.

4 Determine the number of real roots of the equation $2\sin^{-1}x = x$.

5 Show that the equation $\tan^{-1}x = kx$, where k is a constant, has only one real root when $k < 0$ and state its value.

6 For very large positive values of the constant k, state the number of real roots of the equation $k\tan^{-1}x = x$.

3.2 Compound angle identities

In P2 you were shown how to find the exact values of trigonometric functions of some special angles. This table summarises the results.

Angle θ in degrees	Angle θ in radians	$\sin\theta$	$\cos\theta$	$\tan\theta$
0	0	0	1	0
30	$\dfrac{\pi}{6}$	$\dfrac{1}{2}$	$\dfrac{\sqrt{3}}{2}$	$\dfrac{1}{\sqrt{3}}$
45	$\dfrac{\pi}{4}$	$\dfrac{1}{\sqrt{2}}$	$\dfrac{1}{\sqrt{2}}$	1
60	$\dfrac{\pi}{3}$	$\dfrac{\sqrt{3}}{2}$	$\dfrac{1}{2}$	$\sqrt{3}$
90	$\dfrac{\pi}{2}$	1	0	∞
180	π	0	-1	0

In this section you will be shown how to obtain identities for trigonometric expressions of compound angles similar to $\sin (A + B)$.

A common error is to assume that $\sin (A + B) = \sin A + \sin B$. You can easily disprove this result by finding a counter example.

$$\sin (30° + 60°) = \sin 90° = 1$$

$$\sin 30° + \sin 60° = \frac{1}{2} + \frac{\sqrt{3}}{2} \neq 1$$

so $\sin (A + B) \neq \sin A + \sin B$.

Consider a line of length 1 unit. Initially the line is in the position OB, where O is the origin. The line OB makes an angle β with the positive x-axis so the coordinates of B are $(\cos \beta, \sin \beta)$. Rotate the line about O through an angle $(\alpha - \beta)$ so the line OA makes an angle α with the positive x-axis and the coordinates of A are $(\cos \alpha, \sin \alpha)$.

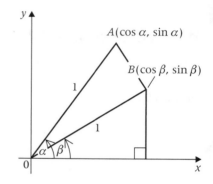

Using the formula for the distance between two points you get
$$AB^2 = (\cos \alpha - \cos \beta)^2 + (\sin \alpha - \sin \beta)^2.$$

Using the cosine rule for triangle OAB you get
$$AB^2 = 1^2 + 1^2 - 2(1)(1) \cos (\alpha - \beta).$$
$$\Rightarrow (\cos \alpha - \cos \beta)^2 + (\sin \alpha - \sin \beta)^2 = 2 - 2 \cos (\alpha - \beta)$$
$$\Rightarrow \cos^2 \alpha + \cos^2 \beta - 2 \cos \alpha \cos \beta + \sin^2 \alpha + \sin^2 \beta - 2 \sin \alpha \sin \beta = 2 - 2 \cos (\alpha + \beta)$$
$$\Rightarrow 2 - 2 \cos \alpha \cos \beta - 2 \sin \alpha \sin \beta = 2 - 2 \cos (\alpha - \beta)$$
$$\Rightarrow \cos (\alpha - \beta) = \cos \alpha \cos \beta + \sin \alpha \sin \beta. \qquad [1]$$

> Used $\cos^2 x + \sin^2 x = 1$.

Let $\alpha = A$ and $\beta = -B$ in [1] leads to
$$\cos (A + B) = \cos A \cos B - \sin A \sin B.$$

> Used $\cos (-\theta) = \cos \theta$ and $\sin (-\theta) = -\sin \theta$.

Let $\alpha = \frac{\pi}{2} - A$ and $\beta = B$ in [1] gives
$$\cos \left[\frac{\pi}{2} - (A + B) \right] = \cos \left(\frac{\pi}{2} - A \right) \cos B + \sin \left(\frac{\pi}{2} - A \right) \sin B,$$

which leads to
$$\sin (A + B) = \sin A \cos B + \cos A \sin B.$$

> Used $\cos \left(\frac{\pi}{2} - \theta \right) = \sin \theta$ and $\sin \left(\frac{\pi}{2} - \theta \right) = \cos \theta$.

Replacing B by $-B$ leads to
$$\sin (A - B) = \sin A \cos B - \cos A \sin B.$$

Writing $\tan (A + B) = \dfrac{\sin (A + B)}{\cos (A + B)}$ and using the previous identities you can show that, provided $(A + B) \neq \left(k + \frac{1}{2} \right) \pi,$

$$\tan (A + B) = \frac{\tan A + \tan B}{1 - \tan A \tan B}.$$

Replacing B by $-B$ leads to
$$\tan (A - B) = \frac{\tan A - \tan B}{1 + \tan A \tan B}.$$

You now have the six compound angle identities which can be summarised as

$$\sin(A \pm B) = \sin A \cos B \pm \cos A \sin B$$
$$\cos(A \pm B) = \cos A \cos B \mp \sin A \sin B$$
$$\tan(A \pm B) = \frac{\tan A \pm \tan B}{1 \mp \tan A \tan B}, \quad \left[A \pm B \neq \left(k + \frac{1}{2}\right)\pi\right]$$

> These identities are given in this form in the formulae booklet which you will have in your examination. You must ensure that you understand the signs in the identities.

Worked example 3.4

Show that $\tan 15° = 2 - \sqrt{3}$.

Solution

$$\tan 15° = \tan(60° - 45°) = \frac{\tan 60° - \tan 45°}{1 + \tan 60° \tan 45°}$$

$$= \frac{\sqrt{3} - 1}{1 + \sqrt{3}(1)} = \frac{\left(\sqrt{3} - 1\right)^2}{\left(\sqrt{3} - 1\right)\left(1 + \sqrt{3}\right)} = \frac{3 - 2\sqrt{3} + 1}{3 - 1} = 2 - \sqrt{3}$$

Worked example 3.5

Prove the identity $\dfrac{\sin(A - B)}{\cos A \cos B} \equiv \tan A - \tan B$.

> As mentioned in earlier books, the symbol $\equiv$, meaning *identically equal to*, should be used for identities. However, it is often replaced by an *equals* sign.

Solution

$$\frac{\sin(A - B)}{\cos A \cos B} \equiv \frac{\sin A \cos B - \cos A \sin B}{\cos A \cos B}$$

$$\equiv \frac{\sin A \cos B}{\cos A \cos B} - \frac{\cos A \sin B}{\cos A \cos B}$$

$$\equiv \frac{\sin A}{\cos A} - \frac{\sin B}{\cos B} \equiv \tan A - \tan B$$

Worked example 3.6

Find, in terms of π, all values of x in the interval $0 \leqslant x \leqslant 2\pi$ for which $\sin x = \cos\left(x + \dfrac{\pi}{6}\right)$.

Solution

$$\sin x = \cos\left(x + \frac{\pi}{6}\right)$$

$$\Rightarrow \sin x = \cos x \cos \frac{\pi}{6} - \sin x \sin \frac{\pi}{6}$$

$$\Rightarrow \sin x = \cos x \left(\frac{\sqrt{3}}{2} \right) - \sin x \left(\frac{1}{2} \right)$$

$$\Rightarrow \frac{3}{2} \sin x = \left(\frac{\sqrt{3}}{2} \right) \cos x$$

$$\Rightarrow 3 \sin x = \sqrt{3} \cos x$$

Divide both sides of the equation by $3 \cos x$.

$$\Rightarrow \frac{\sin x}{\cos x} = \frac{\sqrt{3}}{3} \Rightarrow \tan x = \frac{1}{\sqrt{3}}$$

$\tan x$ is positive in the first and third quadrants and

$\tan^{-1} \left(\dfrac{1}{\sqrt{3}} \right) = \dfrac{\pi}{6}$ so solutions of $\tan x = \dfrac{1}{\sqrt{3}}$ in the interval

$0 \leqslant x \leqslant 2\pi$ are $\dfrac{\pi}{6}$ and $\pi + \dfrac{\pi}{6}$.

The solutions of $\sin x = \cos \left(x + \dfrac{\pi}{6} \right)$ in the interval $0 \leqslant x \leqslant 2\pi$

are $\dfrac{\pi}{6}$ and $\dfrac{7\pi}{6}$.

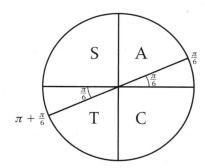

Worked example 3.7

By writing $\dfrac{1}{2} \cos x - \dfrac{\sqrt{3}}{2} \sin x$ as a single cosine, describe the

transformation that maps the graph of $y = \cos x$ onto the graph

of $y = \dfrac{1}{2} \cos x - \dfrac{\sqrt{3}}{2} \sin x$.

Solution

$$\frac{1}{2} \cos x - \frac{\sqrt{3}}{2} \sin x \equiv \cos x \cos \frac{\pi}{3} - \sin x \sin \frac{\pi}{3}$$

$$\equiv \cos \left(x + \frac{\pi}{3} \right)$$

$$\frac{1}{2} = \cos \frac{\pi}{3}, \quad \frac{\sqrt{3}}{2} = \sin \frac{\pi}{3}.$$

so you need the transformation that maps the graph of $y = \cos x$

onto the graph of $y = \cos \left(x + \dfrac{\pi}{3} \right)$.

The required transformation is the translation $\begin{bmatrix} -\dfrac{\pi}{3} \\ 0 \end{bmatrix}$.

Sketching graphs of curves with equations of the form $y = a \cos x + b \sin x$ will be considered for general cases in P5.

EXERCISE 3B

1 Show that $\tan 75° = 2 + \sqrt{3}$.

2 Show that $\sin 15° = \dfrac{\sqrt{6} - \sqrt{2}}{4}$.

3 Show that $\cos 15° = \dfrac{\sqrt{6} + \sqrt{2}}{4}$.

4 Write the following as $\sin k°$, where k is a constant to be determined:

(a) $\sin 40° \cos 20° + \cos 40° \sin 20°$,

(b) $\sin 40° \cos 20° - \cos 40° \sin 20°$,

(c) $\cos 40° \cos 30° + \sin 40° \sin 30°$,

(d) $\cos 40° \cos 30° - \sin 40° \sin 30°$.

5 Prove the identity $\dfrac{\sin (A + B)}{\cos A \cos B} \equiv \tan A + \tan B$.

6 Prove the identity $\sin (x + y) - \sin (x - y) \equiv 2 \cos x \sin y$.

7 Prove the identity $\tan (x + 45°) \equiv \dfrac{1 + \tan x}{1 - \tan x}$.

8 Given that $\tan (x - y) = k$ and $\tan x = 1$, express $\tan y$ in terms of k.

9 Solve the equation $\cos x \sin \dfrac{\pi}{3} + \sin x \cos \dfrac{\pi}{3} = \dfrac{1}{4}$, for $0 \leqslant x \leqslant 2\pi$.

10 The angles x and y are acute and x is greater than y. Given that $\cos x \cos y = \dfrac{1}{4}$ and $\sin x \sin y = \dfrac{1}{4}$, find the values of $\cos (x + y)$ and $\cos (x - y)$ and hence, or otherwise, find the values of x and y.

11 Prove that $\cos \left(x + \dfrac{4\pi}{3} \right) + \cos \left(x + \dfrac{2\pi}{3} \right) + \cos x \equiv 0$.

12 Find, in terms of π, all values of x in the interval $0 \leqslant x \leqslant 2\pi$ for which $2 \left[\cos \left(x + \dfrac{\pi}{3} \right) - \cos \left(x - \dfrac{\pi}{3} \right) \right] = 3$.

13 By writing $\dfrac{1}{2} \cos x + \dfrac{\sqrt{3}}{2} \sin x$ as a single cosine, describe the transformation that maps the graph of $y = \cos x$ onto the graph of $y = \dfrac{1}{2} \cos x + \dfrac{\sqrt{3}}{2} \sin x$.

14 Describe the transformation that maps the graph of $y = \sin x$ onto the graph of $y = \dfrac{1}{2} \sin x - \dfrac{\sqrt{3}}{2} \cos x$.

3.3 Double angle identities

In P1 and P2 you solved equations of the form $\cos ax = k$. In this section you will learn how to solve other equations including those of the form $\cos 2ax = \sin ax$ and $\sin 2ax = \cos ax$.

Using the identities in section 3.2 and replacing B by A you can show that

$$\sin 2A = 2 \sin A \cos A,$$

$$\cos 2A = \cos^2 A - \sin^2 A, \text{ or, using } \cos^2 A + \sin^2 A = 1,$$

$$\cos 2A = 2 \cos^2 A - 1,$$

$$\cos 2A = 1 - 2 \sin^2 A$$

$$\tan 2A = \frac{2 \tan A}{1 - \tan^2 A}$$

> These identities will **NOT** be given in the examination formulae booklet.

3

Worked example 3.8

Show that $\sin 3x = 3 \sin x - 4 \sin^3 x$.

Solution

$$\begin{aligned}
\sin 3x = \sin(2x + x) &= \sin 2x \cos x + \cos 2x \sin x \\
&= (2 \sin x \cos x) \cos x + (1 - 2 \sin^2 x) \sin x \\
&= 2 \sin x \cos^2 x + \sin x - 2 \sin^3 x \\
&= 2 \sin x (1 - \sin^2 x) + \sin x - 2 \sin^3 x \\
\Rightarrow \sin 3x &= 3 \sin x - 4 \sin^3 x
\end{aligned}$$

> Need expression in terms of $\sin x$ only so use the form $1 - 2 \sin^2 x$ for $\cos 2x$.

> Used $\cos^2 x + \sin^2 x = 1$.

Worked example 3.9

Prove the identity $\dfrac{1}{\cos A + \sin A} + \dfrac{1}{\cos A - \sin A} = \dfrac{\tan 2A}{\sin A}$.

Solution

$$\frac{1}{\cos A + \sin A} + \frac{1}{\cos A - \sin A} = \frac{\cos A - \sin A + \cos A + \sin A}{(\cos A + \sin A)(\cos A - \sin A)}$$

$$= \frac{2 \cos A}{\cos^2 A - \sin^2 A} = \frac{2 \cos A}{\cos 2A}$$

$$= \frac{2 \cos A \sin 2A}{\cos 2A \sin 2A}$$

> Need to get $\tan 2A = \dfrac{\sin 2A}{\cos 2A}$ so multiply numerator and denominator by $\sin 2A$.

$$\frac{1}{\cos A + \sin A} + \frac{1}{\cos A - \sin A} = \frac{2 \cos A \tan 2A}{\sin 2A}$$

$$= \frac{2 \cos A \tan 2A}{2 \sin A \cos A}$$

> $\sin 2A = 2 \sin A \cos A$

$$= \frac{\tan 2A}{\sin A}.$$

> Cancel $2 \cos A$.

Worked example 3.10

Solve the equation $\sin 2x = \cos x$, for $0 \leqslant x < 360°$.

> The given equation involves angles $2x$ and x. Make the angles the same if possible.

Solution

$\sin 2x = \cos x$
$\Rightarrow 2 \sin x \cos x = \cos x$
$\Rightarrow \cos x(2 \sin x - 1) = 0$
$\Rightarrow \cos x = 0 \text{ or } \sin x = \dfrac{1}{2}$

> Do **not** cancel the $\cos x$ terms.

$\cos x = 0 \Rightarrow x = 90°, 270°; \quad \sin x = \dfrac{1}{2} \Rightarrow x = 30°, 150°$

The relevant solutions of $\sin 2x = \cos x$, are $30°, 90°, 150°\ 270°$.

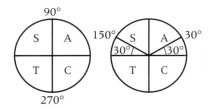

Worked example 3.11

Solve the equation $\cos 2\theta = 2 \cos \theta$ for $-\pi \leqslant \theta < \pi$.

> The given equation involves angles 2θ and θ. Make the angles the same by using the double angle formulae.

Solution

$\cos 2\theta = 2 \cos \theta$
$\Rightarrow 2 \cos^2 \theta - 1 = 2 \cos \theta$
$\Rightarrow 2 \cos^2 \theta - 2 \cos \theta - 1 = 0$

So, $\cos \theta = \dfrac{2 \pm \sqrt{(4 + 8)}}{4} = \dfrac{2 \pm \sqrt{12}}{4} = 1.366\,025 \text{ or } -0.366\,025.$

> $\cos 2\theta$ has three possible forms. Choose the form which only involves the remaining term, $\cos \theta$.

> Rearrange into a quadratic equation in $\cos \theta$ and solve using the formula.

The greatest value of a cosine is 1 so you reject $\cos \theta = 1.366\,025$ and all solutions will come from $\cos \theta = -0.366\,025$.
Cosine is negative in the second and third quadrants and $\cos^{-1}(0.366\,025) = 1.195$ rads
so, the only solutions of $\cos 2\theta = 2 \cos \theta$ in the interval $-\pi \leqslant \theta < \pi$ are $\theta = \pi - 1.195$ and $-\pi + 1.195$

To three significant figures, $\theta = \pm 1.95$ radians.

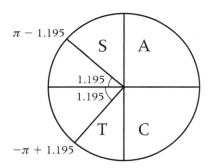

EXERCISE 3C

1 Prove the identity $\cos 3x \equiv 4 \cos^3 x - 3 \cos x$.

2 Prove the identity $\dfrac{\sin 2x}{1 + \cos 2x} \equiv \tan x$.

3 Solve the equation $2 \sin 2x = \sin x$, for $0° \leqslant x < 360°$.

4 Solve the equation $3 \sin 2\theta = \cos \theta$, for $0 \leqslant \theta < 2\pi$.

5 Solve the equation $\cos \theta + \cos 2\theta = 0$, for $0 \leqslant \theta \leqslant 2\pi$.

6 Prove the identity $\dfrac{1 - \cos 2A}{1 + \cos 2A} \equiv \tan^2 A$.

7 Prove the identity $(\sin A + \cos A)^2 - 1 \equiv \sin 2A$.

8 Prove the identity $\sqrt{\dfrac{1 + \sin 2A}{1 - \sin 2A}} \equiv \tan\left(A + \dfrac{\pi}{4}\right)$.

9 Solve the equation $\cos 2\theta + 5 \sin \theta = 3$, for $-\pi \leqslant \theta \leqslant \pi$.

10 Solve the equation $\tan 2\theta = 3 \tan \theta$, for $0 \leqslant \theta \leqslant 2\pi$.

11 Solve the equation $2 \cos^2 x = 2 \sin x \cos x + 1$, for $0° \leqslant x < 360°$.

12 Solve the equation $2 \sin 2x = \tan x$, for $0° \leqslant x < 360°$.

13 Express $\dfrac{\sin 2x}{1 - 2 \cos 2x}$ in terms of $\tan x$.

14 Prove the identity $\dfrac{1 + \sin 2A - \cos 2A}{1 + \sin 2A + \cos 2A} \equiv \tan A$. Hence find the exact value of $\tan 22.5°$.

15 Solve the equation $\cos 2\theta - 5 \cos \theta = 2$, for $-\pi \leqslant \theta \leqslant \pi$.

16 Given that $\cos 2A = \tan^2 x$, show that $\cos 2x = \tan^2 A$.

17 (a) Show that $\cos 2x - 3 \cos x - 1 \equiv (2 \cos x + 1)(\cos x - 2)$.

   (b) Given that $0° \leqslant x < 180°$, solve the equation
   $\cos 2x - 3 \cos x - 1 = 0$.   [A]

18 (a) Use the expansion of $\tan(A + B)$ to show that
   $\tan 3x = \dfrac{3 \tan x - \tan^3 x}{1 - 3 \tan^2 x}$.

   (b) Use the result of **(a)** to find all solutions in the interval
   $0 < x < \pi$ of the equation
   $3 \tan x - \tan^3 x = 1 - 3 \tan^2 x$.   [A]

19 Solve the equation $2 \sin \theta \cos 2\theta + \sin 2\theta = 0$, for $0 \leqslant \theta \leqslant 2\pi$.
                                                                  [A]

3.4 Differentiation of sin x and cos x

In previous modules you have been differentiating expressions of the form x^n, $\ln x$ and e^x. In this section you will be shown how to differentiate $\sin x$ and $\cos x$, where x is in radians.

You will recall, from section 6.6 in P1, that when differentiating functions from first principles you use the following result:

$$\text{if } y = f(x) \text{ then } \frac{dy}{dx} = \lim_{h \to 0}\left\{\frac{f(x + h) - f(x)}{h}\right\}.$$

In this section you will also need two other results which you met in the P2 module; they are $\sin x \approx x$ and $\cos x \approx 1 - \dfrac{1}{2}x^2$ for small x, where x is in radians.

Differentiation of sin x from first principles

Let $f(x) = \sin x$, where x is in radians, then $f(x + h) = \sin(x + h)$.

$$\frac{dy}{dx} = \lim_{h \to 0} \left\{ \frac{f(x + h) - f(x)}{h} \right\}$$

$$\frac{dy}{dx} = \lim_{h \to 0} \left\{ \frac{\sin(x + h) - \sin x}{h} \right\}$$

$$= \lim_{h \to 0} \left\{ \frac{\sin x \cos h + \cos x \sin h - \sin x}{h} \right\}$$

Used $\sin(A + B) = \sin A \cos B + \cos A \sin B$.

$$= \lim_{h \to 0} \left\{ \frac{\sin x \left(1 - \frac{1}{2} h^2 \right) + \cos x (h) - \sin x}{h} \right\}$$

Since h is small and in radians
$\cos h \approx 1 - \frac{1}{2} h^2$ and $\sin h \approx h$.

$$= \lim_{h \to 0} \left\{ \frac{\cos x (h) - \frac{1}{2} h^2 \sin x}{h} \right\}$$

$$= \lim_{h \to 0} \left\{ \cos x - \frac{1}{2} h \sin x \right\} = \cos x - 0$$

$$\Rightarrow \frac{dy}{dx} = \cos x$$

 For x in radians, $\dfrac{d(\sin x)}{dx} = \cos x$.

Differentiation of cos x from first principles

Let $f(x) = \cos x$, where x is in radians,
then $f(x + h) = \cos(x + h)$.

$$\frac{dy}{dx} = \lim_{h \to 0} \left\{ \frac{f(x + h) - f(x)}{h} \right\}$$

$$\frac{dy}{dx} = \lim_{h \to 0} \left\{ \frac{\cos(x + h) - \cos x}{h} \right\}$$

$$= \lim_{h \to 0} \left\{ \frac{\cos x \cos h - \sin x \sin h - \cos x}{h} \right\}$$

Used $\cos(A + B) = \cos A \cos B + \sin A \sin B$.

$$= \lim_{h \to 0} \left\{ \frac{\cos x \left(1 - \frac{1}{2} h^2 \right) - \sin x (h) - \cos x}{h} \right\}$$

Since h is small and in radians
$\cos h \approx 1 - \frac{1}{2} h^2$ and $\sin h \approx h$.

$$= \lim_{h \to 0} \left\{ \frac{- \sin x (h) - \frac{1}{2} h^2 \cos x}{h} \right\}$$

$$= \lim_{h \to 0}\left\{-\sin x - \frac{1}{2}h\cos x\right\} = -\sin x - 0$$

$$\Rightarrow \frac{\mathrm{d}y}{\mathrm{d}x} = -\sin x$$

For x in radians, $\dfrac{\mathrm{d}(\cos x)}{\mathrm{d}x} = -\sin x.$

Unless told otherwise you may assume that when asked to differentiate trigonometric functions the variable will be in radians.

3

These results for the derivatives of $\sin x$ and $\cos x$ must be remembered. They will not be given in the examination formulae booklet.

Worked example 3.12

Find $\mathrm{f}'(0)$ for the function $\mathrm{f}(x) = 3\sin x + 4\cos x - 7x.$

Solution

$\mathrm{f}(x) = 3\sin x + 4\cos x - 7x$

Differentiating with respect to x
gives $\mathrm{f}'(x) = 3\cos x - 4\sin x - 7,$

so $\mathrm{f}'(0) = 3\cos 0 - 4\sin 0 - 7$

$\qquad\qquad = 3(1) - 4(0) - 7$

$\Rightarrow \qquad \mathrm{f}'(0) = -4$

Worked example 3.13

The curve $y = 3\sin x + \sqrt{3}\cos x$ has domain $0 \leqslant x \leqslant 2\pi.$
Find the coordinates of the stationary points of the curve.

Solution

$y = 3\sin x + \sqrt{3}\cos x$

$\dfrac{\mathrm{d}y}{\mathrm{d}x} = 3\cos x - \sqrt{3}\sin x$

For a stationary point,

$\dfrac{\mathrm{d}y}{\mathrm{d}x} = 0 \Rightarrow 3\cos x - \sqrt{3}\sin x = 0$

$\qquad\qquad \Rightarrow \sqrt{3}\sin x = 3\cos x.$

Dividing both sides by $\sqrt{3}\cos x$

gives $\dfrac{\sin x}{\cos x} = \dfrac{3}{\sqrt{3}}$

$\Rightarrow \tan x = \sqrt{3} \Rightarrow x = \dfrac{\pi}{3}$ or $\pi + \dfrac{\pi}{3}$

When $x = \dfrac{\pi}{3}$,

$y = 3 \sin \dfrac{\pi}{3} + \sqrt{3} \cos \dfrac{\pi}{3} = 3 \dfrac{\sqrt{3}}{2} + \sqrt{3} \dfrac{1}{2} = 2\sqrt{3}.$

When $x = \dfrac{4\pi}{3}$,

$y = 3 \sin \dfrac{4\pi}{3} + \sqrt{3} \cos \dfrac{4\pi}{3} = 3\left(-\dfrac{\sqrt{3}}{2}\right) + \sqrt{3}\left(-\dfrac{1}{2}\right) = -2\sqrt{3}.$

The curve has two stationary points,

$\left(\dfrac{\pi}{3}, 2\sqrt{3}\right)$ and $\left(\dfrac{4\pi}{3}, -2\sqrt{3}\right)$.

EXERCISE 3D

1 Differentiate each of the following with respect to x:

    (a) $y = 4 - 3 \cos x$,   **(b)** $y = 2x + 3 \sin x$,

    (c) $y = 4 \sin x - 3 \cos x$,   **(d)** $y = \dfrac{\sin x}{2} - \dfrac{1}{x^2} + 2.$

2 Find $f'\left(\dfrac{\pi}{2}\right)$ for each of the following functions:

    (a) $f(x) = 3 \sin x - 4 \cos x + 7x$,

    (b) $f(x) = 6 \sin x + 5x + 1$,

    (c) $f(x) = 5 \sin x + 4 \cos x$,

    (d) $f(x) = 7 - 6 \cos x + x$.

3 For small x, in radians, $\tan x \approx x$. Use this result, and also the expansion of $\tan(A + B)$, to differentiate from first principles to show that the derivative of $\tan x$ is $1 + \tan^2 x$.

4 The curve $y = \sin x - \sqrt{3} \cos x$ has domain $0 \leqslant x \leqslant 2\pi$. Find the coordinates of the stationary points of the curve.

5 The curve $y = \sin x - \cos x$ has domain $-\pi \leqslant x \leqslant \pi$. Find the coordinates of the stationary points of the curve.

6 The curve $y = 1 - 2 \cos x$ has domain $0 \leqslant x \leqslant \pi$. Find the gradient of the curve at the point where the curve crosses the x-axis.

7 The curve $y = 1 - 2 \sin x$ has domain $0 \leqslant x \leqslant \pi$. Find the gradients of the curve at the points where the curve crosses the x-axis.

8 The curve $y = x - 2 \cos x$ has domain $0 \leqslant x < 2\pi$. Find the x-coordinates of the stationary points of the curve.

9 Given that $y = p \sin x + q \cos x$, where p and q are constants, show that $\dfrac{d^2 y}{dx^2} + y = 0$ for all values of p and q.

10 The curve $y = 7 - 2\cos x$ has domain $0 \leqslant x \leqslant \pi$. Find the coordinates of the points on the curve where the gradient of the curve is 1.

11 (a) Show that $\sin\left(x + \dfrac{\pi}{6}\right) = \dfrac{\sqrt{3}}{2}\sin x + \dfrac{1}{2}\cos x$.

  (b) Hence show that the derivative of $\sin\left(x + \dfrac{\pi}{6}\right)$ is

  $\cos\left(x + \dfrac{\pi}{6}\right)$.

3

Key point summary

1 $\sin^{-1}x$ has domain $-1 \leqslant x \leqslant 1$ and   *p 35*
range $-\dfrac{\pi}{2} \leqslant \sin^{-1}x \leqslant \dfrac{\pi}{2}$.
The graph of $y = \sin^{-1}x$, $-1 \leqslant x \leqslant 1$ is obtained by
reflecting the graph of $y = \sin x$, $-\dfrac{\pi}{2} \leqslant x \leqslant \dfrac{\pi}{2}$, in the
line $y = x$.

Warning: $\sin^{-1}x \neq \dfrac{1}{\sin x}$.

2 $\sin^{-1}(\sin x) = x$ for $-\dfrac{\pi}{2} \leqslant x \leqslant \dfrac{\pi}{2}$,   *p 35*
$\sin(\sin^{-1}x) = x$ for $-1 \leqslant x \leqslant 1$.

3 $\cos^{-1}x$ has domain $-1 \leqslant x \leqslant 1$ and   *p 36*
range $0 \leqslant \cos^{-1}x \leqslant \pi$.
The graph of $y = \cos^{-1}x$, $-1 \leqslant x \leqslant 1$ is obtained by
reflecting the graph of $y = \cos x$, $0 \leqslant x \leqslant \pi$, in the line
$y = x$.

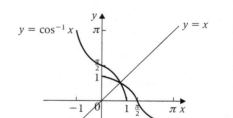

Warning: $\cos^{-1}x \neq \dfrac{1}{\cos x}$.

4 $\cos^{-1}(\cos x) = x$ for $0 \leqslant x \leqslant \pi$,   *p 36*
$\cos(\cos^{-1}x) = x$ for $-1 \leqslant x \leqslant 1$.

5 $\tan^{-1}x$ has domain all real numbers and   *p 37*

range $-\dfrac{\pi}{2} < \tan^{-1}x < \dfrac{\pi}{2}$.

The graph of $y = \tan^{-1}x$, is obtained by reflecting the

graph of $y = \tan x$, $-\dfrac{\pi}{2} < x < \dfrac{\pi}{2}$, in the line $y = x$.

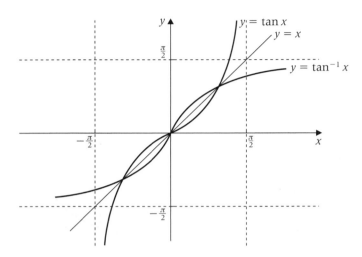

Warning: $\tan^{-1}x \neq \dfrac{1}{\tan x}$.

6 $\sin(A \pm B) = \sin A \cos B \pm \cos A \sin B$ *p 40*

$\cos(A \pm B) = \cos A \cos B \mp \sin A \sin B$

$\tan(A \pm B) = \dfrac{\tan A \pm \tan B}{1 \mp \tan A \tan B}, \ \left[A \pm B \neq \left(k + \dfrac{1}{2} \right)\pi \right]$

7 $\sin 2A = 2 \sin A \cos A,$ *p 43*

$\cos 2A = \cos^2 A - \sin^2 A,$ or, using $\cos^2 A + \sin^2 A = 1,$

$\cos 2A = 2 \cos^2 A - 1,$

$\cos 2A = 1 - 2 \sin^2 A$

$\tan 2A = \dfrac{2 \tan A}{1 - \tan^2 A}$

8 For x in radians, $\dfrac{d(\sin x)}{dx} = \cos x.$ *p 46*

9 For x in radians, $\dfrac{d(\cos x)}{dx} = -\sin x.$ *p 47*

Test yourself	**What to review**
1 Show that the equation $\cos^{-1} x = \sin^{-1} x$ has only one real root and state its exact value in surd form.	*Section 3.1*
2 Solve the equation $\cos 2x \sin 20° + \sin 2x \cos 20° = \dfrac{\sqrt{3}}{2}$, for $0° \leqslant x \leqslant 360°$.	*Section 3.2*
3 Given that $2 \sin\left(2x - \dfrac{\pi}{4}\right) = \cos\left(2x - \dfrac{\pi}{4}\right)$, show that $\tan 2x = 3$. Given that x is an acute angle, find the exact value of $\tan x$ in surd form.	*Section 3.3*
4 The function f, with domain $0 \leqslant x \leqslant \pi$, is defined by $$f(x) = \frac{1}{10}x^3 + \frac{x}{5} - 2 \cos x.$$ **(a)** Find $f'(x)$. **(b)** Show that f is an increasing function.	*Section 3.4*

3

Test yourself **ANSWERS**

4 a $f'(x) = \dfrac{3}{10}x^2 + \dfrac{1}{5} + 2 \sin x.$

3 $\tan x = \dfrac{\sqrt{10} - 1}{3}.$

2 $x = 20°, 50°, 200°, 230°.$

1 $\dfrac{\sqrt{2}}{2}.$

Coordinate geometry of lines and circles

Learning objectives

After studying this chapter you should be able to:
- calculate the angle between two lines
- calculate the distance from a point to a line
- recognise an equation of a circle and be able to find its centre and radius
- find an equation of a circle given the end-points of a diameter
- determine if a line meets a circle
- find the lengths of tangents from a point to a circle
- find the equation of the tangent at a point on a circle.

4.1 Angle between two lines

In chapter 4 of P1 you considered the gradient of a straight line and obtained conditions on the gradients for lines to be parallel and perpendicular. In this section you will be shown how to derive and use a formula for finding the angle between any two lines drawn in two-dimensional space.

> Lines with gradients m_1 and m_2
> - are parallel if $m_1 = m_2$,
> - are perpendicular if $m_1 \times m_2 = -1$.

Let θ be the angle that a line makes with the positive direction of the x-axis. Lines with a positive gradient make an acute angle, so θ is acute. Lines with a negative gradient make an obtuse angle, so θ is obtuse.

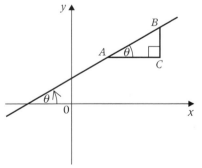

Positive gradient

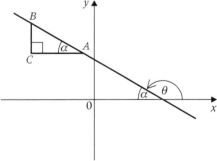

Negative gradient

When θ is acute,

gradient of line $AB = \dfrac{BC}{AC} = \tan \theta$.

When θ is obtuse,

gradient of line $AB = -\dfrac{BC}{AC} = -\tan \alpha = -\tan(180° - \theta) = \tan \theta$.

> So, in all cases, the gradient of a line is the same as $\tan \theta$, where θ is the angle between the line and the positive direction of the x-axis; $m = \tan \theta$.

The result, $m = \tan \theta$, is now used to find the formula for the angle between two lines with gradients m_1 and m_2, where $m_1 = \tan \theta_1$ and $m_2 = \tan \theta_2$.

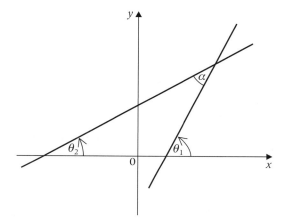

Let α be the angle between the two lines, then, by basic geometry, $\alpha = \theta_1 - \theta_2$.

$$\Rightarrow \tan \alpha = \tan(\theta_1 - \theta_2) = \frac{\tan \theta_1 - \tan \theta_2}{1 + \tan \theta_1 \tan \theta_2} = \frac{m_1 - m_2}{1 + m_1 m_2}$$

Used $\tan(A - B)$ formula in section 3.2 page 38.

If you want the acute angle between the two lines then $\tan \alpha$ will always be positive, so you use

> the acute angle between lines with gradients m_1 and m_2 is
> $$\tan^{-1}\left|\frac{m_1 - m_2}{1 + m_1 m_2}\right|.$$

This formula is given in the examination formulae booklet.

Putting $m_1 = m_2$ gives an angle $\tan^{-1}(0) = 0$, confirming the condition for the lines to be parallel.

Putting $m_1 m_2 = -1$ gives an angle $\tan^{-1}(\infty) = 90°$, confirming the condition for the lines to be perpendicular.

Worked example 4.1

Find the tangent of the acute angle between the lines $y = 3x + 7$ and $2y + 5 = 4x$.

Solution

Let m_1 be the gradient of the line $y = 3x + 7$, then $m_1 = 3$.

Rearranging $2y + 5 = 4x \Rightarrow y = 2x - 2.5$ so, if m_2 is the gradient of the line $2y + 5 = 4x$, then $m_2 = 2$.

> Line $y = mx + c$ has gradient m.

Let α be the acute angle between the two lines, then

$$\tan \alpha = \left| \frac{m_1 - m_2}{1 + m_1 m_2} \right| = \left| \frac{3 - 2}{1 + 3 \times 2} \right| = \frac{1}{7}$$

Worked example 4.2

Find the equations of the two lines through the point $(1, 6)$ which make angles of $45°$ with the line $y = 2x - 2$. Give your answers in the form $ax + by + c = 0$.

Solution

If m_1 is the gradient of the line $y = 2x - 2$, then $m_1 = 2$.

Let m_2 be the gradient of the required lines.

> Since the angle between the two lines is $45°$.

$$\Rightarrow \quad \tan 45° = \left| \frac{m_1 - m_2}{1 + m_1 m_2} \right|$$

$$\Rightarrow \quad 1 = \left| \frac{2 - m_2}{1 + 2m_2} \right|$$

$$\Rightarrow \quad \frac{2 - m_2}{1 + 2m_2} = 1 \text{ or } \frac{2 - m_2}{1 + 2m_2} = -1$$

$$\Rightarrow \quad m_2 = \frac{1}{3} \text{ or } m_2 = -3$$

Equations of lines through $(1, 6)$ are $y - 6 = m_2(x - 1)$

Required lines are $y - 6 = \frac{1}{3}(x - 1)$ and $y - 6 = -3(x - 1)$

which lead to $x - 3y + 17 = 0$ and $3x + y - 9 = 0$.

EXERCISE 4A

1 Find the acute angle, to the nearest degree, between the two lines:

   (a) $y = x$ and $y = 2x$,

   (b) $y = x$ and $y = 5 - 2x$,

   (c) $y = 2x + 1$ and $y = 3x + 2$,

   (d) $x - 2y = 5$ and $x - 3y = 9$,

   (e) $x + 2y = 5$ and $2x - 3y = 3$.

2 Find the equations of the two lines through the point $(1, 2)$ which make angles of $45°$ with the line $y = 3x - 2$. Give your answers in the form $ax + by + c = 0$.

3 Find the equations of the two lines through the point $(-1, 2)$ which make angles of $45°$ with the line $y = -3x + 2$. Give your answers in the form $ax + by + c = 0$.

4 Triangle ABC has sides with equations $AB: 3x - 4y + 3 = 0$, $BC: x + y = 3$ and $CA: 4x = 3y + 5$.

(a) Find $\tan BAC$.

(b) Show that ABC is an isosceles triangle.

4.2 Distance of a point from a line

In chapter 4 of P1 you considered the distance between two points. In this section you will be shown how to derive and use a formula for finding the perpendicular distance between a point and a line.

> The distance of a point from a line will be understood to mean the shortest distance which is the same as the perpendicular distance.

4

Consider the line with equation $ax + by + c = 0$ and any point $P(h, k)$ at a distance d from the line.

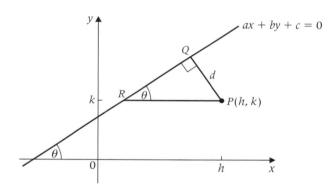

Points Q and R lie on the line $ax + by + c = 0$ such that PQ is perpendicular to the line and PR is horizontal.

The y-coordinate of R is k so the x-coordinate of R is $-\dfrac{(bk + c)}{a}$

> Since R is a point on the line $ax + by + c = 0$.

and the distance PR is $h - \left(-\dfrac{bk + c}{a}\right) = \dfrac{ah + bk + c}{a}$.

> Rearranging $ax + by + c = 0$ gives $y = -\dfrac{a}{b}x - \dfrac{c}{b}$.

The gradient of the line $ax + by + c = 0$ is $-\dfrac{a}{b}$.

Since θ is the angle that the line makes with the positive direction of the x-axis, $\tan \theta = -\dfrac{a}{b}$.

$$\Rightarrow \frac{\sin^2 \theta}{\cos^2 \theta} = \frac{a^2}{b^2} \Rightarrow \sin^2 \theta = \frac{a^2}{b^2}\cos^2 \theta$$

> Used $\tan \theta = \dfrac{\sin \theta}{\cos \theta}$.

$$\Rightarrow b^2 \sin^2 \theta = a^2(1 - \sin^2 \theta) \Rightarrow \sin^2 \theta = \frac{a^2}{a^2 + b^2}.$$

> Used $\cos^2 \theta = 1 - \sin^2 \theta$.

Now $\quad \dfrac{d}{PR} = \sin\theta \Rightarrow d^2 = \dfrac{a^2}{a^2 + b^2} \times \dfrac{(ah + bk + c)^2}{a^2}$

$\Rightarrow \quad d = \dfrac{|ah + bk + c|}{\sqrt{a^2 + b^2}}$

> Since distance is always positive, use the modulus sign.

The perpendicular distance from (h, k) to $ax + by + c = 0$ is $\dfrac{|ah + bk + c|}{\sqrt{a^2 + b^2}}$.

> This formula is given in the examination formulae booklet.

Before applying this formula you must write the equation of the line in the form $ax + by + c = 0$.

> Note: if (h, k) lies on the line then $ah + bk + c = 0$ which gives $d = 0$ as you would expect.

Worked example 4.3

Find the shortest distance between the parallel lines $4x + 3y - 6 = 0$ and $4x + 3y - 12 = 0$.

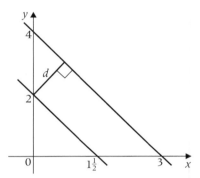

Solution

Since $4(0) + 3(2) - 6 = 0$, point $(0, 2)$ lies on the line $4x + 3y - 6 = 0$.

> You could have chosen any other point on the line.

The shortest distance between the two parallel lines is the perpendicular distance from the point $(0, 2)$ to the line $4x + 3y - 12 = 0$.

$\Rightarrow \text{distance} = \dfrac{|4(0) + 3(2) - 12|}{\sqrt{4^2 + 3^2}} = \dfrac{6}{5}$

Worked example 4.4

The perpendicular distance from the point $(1, k)$ to the line $6x + 9 = 8y$ is 5.5. Find the possible values of k.

Solution

$6x + 9 = 8y \Rightarrow 6x - 8y + 9 = 0$.

> Rearrange into form $ax + by + c = 0$

Distance from $(1, k)$ to $6x - 8y + 9 = 0$ is

$\dfrac{|6(1) - 8(k) + 9|}{\sqrt{6^2 + (-8)^2}} = \dfrac{|15 - 8k|}{10}$

$$\Rightarrow \qquad \frac{|15 - 8k|}{10} = 5.5 \Rightarrow |15 - 8k| = 55$$

$$15 - 8k = 55 \text{ or } 15 - 8k = -55$$

$$k = -5 \text{ or } k = \frac{35}{4}.$$

EXERCISE 4B

1 Find the lengths of the perpendiculars from the origin to the straight lines:

    (a) $4x - 3y + 10 = 0$,   **(b)** $12x + 5y + 39 = 0$,

    (c) $2x + 3y + 6 = 0$,   **(d)** $3x = 8 - 4y$.

2 Find the shortest distances from the point $(2, 3)$ to the straight lines:

    (a) $4x - 3y + 7 = 0$,   **(b)** $12x + 5y = 26$.

3 Find the shortest distance from the point $(2, 1)$ to the line $y = 4x + 5$.

4 Show that the origin and the point $(2, 3)$ are equidistant from the line $x + 4y = 7$.

5 The points $(1, 2)$ and $(-3, k)$ are equidistant from the line $3x - 4y = 3$. Find the possible values of the constant k.

6 Two sides of a square have equations $4x + 3y - 9 = 0$ and $4x + 3y - 29 = 0$. Calculate the area of the square.

7 The lines PQ, QR and RP have equations $x + y = 0$, $3y = x + 6$ and $y = 2x - 3$, respectively. Find the perpendicular distance from R to PQ.

8 Find the perpendicular distance from the origin to the line joining $(4, 0)$ to the point of intersection of $13x - 4y = 8$ with the y-axis.

9 The equations of the sides of a triangle ABC are AB: $y + 2x = 4$, AC: $11y + 2x = 74$, BC: $3y = 4x + 2$.

    (a) Show, by finding the angles of the triangle, that the triangle is isosceles.

    (b) Show that A is the point $(-1.5, 7)$.

    (c) Find the distance of A from BC.

    (d) Given that C is the point $(4, 6)$, find, in surd form, the shortest distance from C to AB.

10 Show that, for all values of α, the distance from the origin to the line $x \cos \alpha + y \sin \alpha = p$ is p.

By considering a sketch which interprets α and p, or otherwise, show that the foot of the perpendicular from the origin to the line $x \cos \alpha + y \sin \alpha = p$ is $(p \cos \alpha, p \sin \alpha)$.

4.3 The cartesian equation of a circle

In your GCSE course a circle was defined to be the locus of points which are at a constant distance from a fixed point. The constant distance is the radius and the fixed point is the centre of the circle. In this section you will derive, recognise and use the equation of a circle in cartesian coordinates.

Consider a circle of radius r and centre $C(a, b)$.

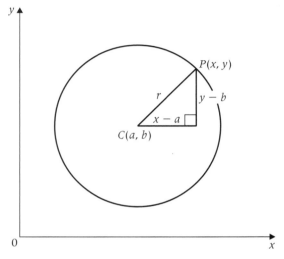

Let $P(x, y)$ be any point on the circle then $CP = r$

$\Rightarrow \quad CP^2 = r^2.$

But $CP^2 = (x - a)^2 + (y - b)^2$
$\Rightarrow (x - a)^2 + (y - b)^2 = r^2.$

> The equation of a circle with centre (a, b) and radius r is
> $(x - a)^2 + (y - b)^2 = r^2.$

This equation is **NOT** given in the examination formulae booklet.

Worked example 4.5

Find an equation of the circle with centre the origin and radius $\sqrt{2}$.

Solution

The centre is $(0, 0)$.
The equation of the circle is $(x - 0)^2 + (y - 0)^2 = (\sqrt{2})^2$, which can be written as $x^2 + y^2 = 2$.

The equation $(x - a)^2 + (y - b)^2 = r^2$ can be expanded and written as $x^2 + y^2 - 2ax - 2by + a^2 + b^2 - r^2 = 0$.

Comparing this with $x^2 + y^2 + 2fx + 2gy + c = 0$, where f, g and c are constants, you have $f = -a$, $g = -b$ and $c = a^2 + b^2 - r^2$.

The final equation, when rearranged, becomes $r^2 = f^2 + g^2 - c$.

If r exists, $r^2 > 0$, so you must have constants f, g and c so that $f^2 + g^2 - c > 0$.

> $x^2 + y^2 + 2fx + 2gy + c = 0$, is the general equation of a circle provided that $f^2 + g^2 - c > 0$.
>
> The centre of the circle is $(-f, -g)$ and the radius is $\sqrt{f^2 + g^2 - c}$.

Note: The equation is of degree 2 and the coefficients of x^2 and y^2 are equal. Also there are no xy terms.

The next worked example shows you how to find the centre and radius of a circle using the method of completing the square.

Worked example 4.6

Determine the coordinates of the centre and the radius of the circle with equation $2x^2 + 2y^2 - 8x + 4y - 15 = 0$.

Solution

Dividing throughout $2x^2 + 2y^2 - 8x + 4y - 15 = 0$ by 2 leads to

$$x^2 + y^2 - 4x + 2y - \frac{15}{2} = 0$$

$$\Rightarrow x^2 - 4x + y^2 + 2y = \frac{15}{2}$$

$$\Rightarrow (x - 2)^2 + (y + 1)^2 = 4 + 1 + \frac{15}{2}$$

$$\Rightarrow (x - 2)^2 + (y + 1)^2 = \frac{25}{2}$$

Circle with centre $(2, -1)$ and radius $\sqrt{\dfrac{25}{2}} = \dfrac{5\sqrt{2}}{2}$.

Make the coefficients of x^2 and y^2 equal to 1.

Completing the square. See P1 section 7.3.

If you want to avoid this approach, and you can remember the general equation, try this example for yourself using the general equation.

One of the GCSE results, which it will be assumed you will know, is that the angle in a semicircle is a right angle. The next example shows you how it may appear.

Worked example 4.7

A right-angled triangle PQR has vertices $P(2, 14)$, $Q(-6, 2)$ and $R(12, -10)$. Find the equation of the circle which passes through the three points P, Q and R.

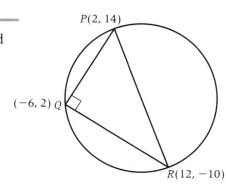

Solution

Angle $PQR = 90° \Rightarrow PQR$ is a semicircle $\Rightarrow PR$ is a diameter.

So the centre, C, of the circle is the midpoint of PR.

C is $\left(\dfrac{2+12}{2}, \dfrac{14+(-10)}{2} \right) = C(7, 2)$.

> Use this method to find the equation of a circle when the coordinates of the end-points of the diameter are known.

The radius of the circle $= QC = \sqrt{(7-(-6))^2 + (2-2)^2} = 13$.

The equation of the circle with centre $(7, 2)$ and radius 13 is
$(x-7)^2 + (y-2)^2 = 13^2$,

> Used $(x-a)^2 + (y-b)^2 = r^2$.

so the circle through the points P, Q and R has equation
$x^2 + y^2 - 14x - 4y - 116 = 0$.

> Unless told otherwise, both forms of the equation will be acceptable in the examination.

EXERCISE 4C

1 Find an equation of the circle with centre C and radius r:

   (a) $C(2, 0)$, $r = 2$,   **(b)** $C(2, 3)$, $r = 4$,

   (c) $C(2, -1)$, $r = \sqrt{3}$,   **(d)** $C(-3, -2)$, $r = 3$.

2 Determine the coordinates of the centre and the radius of the circle with equation:

   (a) $x^2 + y^2 - 2x + 4y = 0$,

   (b) $x^2 + y^2 - 6x + 4y = 3$,

   (c) $x^2 + y^2 - 12x + 4y = 10$,

   (d) $2x^2 + 2y^2 - 16x + 4y = 1$.

3 PQ is a diameter of a circle. Find an equation of the circle when:

   (a) P is $(2, 0)$, Q is $(6, 0)$,

   (b) P is $(0, 5)$, Q is $(0, -1)$,

   (c) P is $(2, 1)$, Q is $(6, 4)$,

   (d) P is $(3, 5)$, Q is $(7, -3)$,

   (e) P is $(-2, -3)$, Q is $(6, 2)$,

   (f) P is $(1, 3)$, Q is $(0, -4)$.

4 Triangle PQR has vertices $P(-2, -1)$, $Q(-7, 4)$ and $R(-1, 1)$.

   (a) Show that PR is perpendicular to QR.

   (b) Find the equation of the circle which passes through the three points P, Q and R.

5 Points A and B lie on the circle $(x-3)^2 + (y-1)^2 = 25$ such that AB is a diameter of the circle. Given that A is the point $(7, -2)$ find the coordinates of B.

6 The origin, O, and the point A lie on the circle $x^2 + y^2 - 4x + 2y = 0$. Given that OA is a diameter of the circle find the coordinates of A.

4.4 Conditions for a line to meet a circle

Clearly any line, which passes through a given point that lies inside a circle, will intersect the circle in two points no matter what the gradient of the line is. If the given point lies outside the circle the problem is less trivial. In this section you will be shown the conditions **(i)** for the line to intersect the circle, **(ii)** for the line to be a tangent to the circle and **(iii)** for the line not to meet the circle.

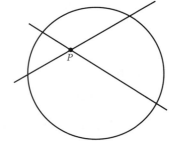

The diagram shows three lines drawn through the origin.

Line 1 does not intersect the circle;
Line 2 intersects the circle in two distinct points;
Line 3 touches the circle at a single point and is called a tangent.

In P1, sections 7.6, 7.7 and 10.3, you were shown how to find the points of intersection of graphs. When applied to a line and a circle you have the following general method:

- from the equation of the line make x (or y) the subject
- substitute into the equation of the circle to get a quadratic equation in y (or x) of the form
  $ay^2 + by + c = 0$ (or $ax^2 + bx + c = 0$)
- **(i)** if the discriminant $b^2 - 4ac < 0$, there are no real roots and the line does not intersect the circle (**Line 1** type)
  (ii) if the discriminant $b^2 - 4ac > 0$, there are two real distinct roots and the line intersects the circle at two points (**Line 2** type)
  (iii) if the discriminant $b^2 - 4ac = 0$, there is one real (repeated) root and the line touches the circle at one point, the line is a tangent to the circle (**Line 3** type)
- if asked to find the coordinates of the points of intersection, solve the quadratic equation and substitute found value(s) into the equation of the line to find the other coordinate(s).

Worked example 4.8

Show that the line $x + y + 3 = 0$ and the circle $x^2 + y^2 = 4$ do not intersect.

Solution

Rearranging the equation of the line gives $y = -x - 3$.

Substituting into $x^2 + y^2 = 4$ gives

$$x^2 + (-x - 3)^2 = 4$$
$$\Rightarrow x^2 + x^2 + 6x + 9 = 4$$
$$\Rightarrow 2x^2 + 6x + 5 = 0$$
$$\Rightarrow \text{discriminant } b^2 - 4ac = 6^2 - 4(2)(5) = -4 < 0$$

so the line does not intersect the circle.

Worked example 4.9

Show that the line $x + y + 3 = 0$ and the circle $x^2 + y^2 = 5$ intersect, and find the coordinates of the points of intersection.

Solution

Rearranging the equation of the line gives $y = -x - 3$.
Substituting into $x^2 + y^2 = 5$ gives

$$x^2 + (-x - 3)^2 = 5$$
$$\Rightarrow x^2 + x^2 + 6x + 9 = 5$$
$$\Rightarrow 2x^2 + 6x + 4 = 0$$
$$\Rightarrow \text{discriminant } b^2 - 4ac = 6^2 - 4(2)(4) = 4 > 0$$

so the line intersects the circle in two points.

Factorising the quadratic gives $2(x + 2)(x + 1) = 0$
$\Rightarrow x = -2, x = -1$.

When $x = -2$, $y = -(-2) - 3 = -1$.

When $x = -1$, $y = -(-1) - 3 = -2$.

Line $x + y + 3 = 0$ intersects the circle $x^2 + y^2 = 5$ at $(-1, -2)$ and $(-2, -1)$.

Worked example 4.10

The line $y = mx - 3$ is a tangent to the circle $x^2 + y^2 = 5$. Find the possible values of m.

Solution

Substituting $y = mx - 3$ into $x^2 + y^2 = 5$ gives

$$x^2 + (mx - 3)^2 = 5$$

$$\Rightarrow x^2 + m^2 x^2 - 6mx + 9 = 5$$

$$\Rightarrow (1 + m^2)x^2 - 6mx + 4 = 0$$

For the line to be a tangent to the circle the roots of this quadratic must be real and equal,

$$\Rightarrow b^2 - 4ac = 0$$

$$\Rightarrow 36m^2 - 4(1 + m^2)(4) = 0$$

$$\Rightarrow 20m^2 = 16$$

$$\Rightarrow m^2 = \frac{4}{5} \Rightarrow m = \pm\frac{2}{\sqrt{5}}.$$

> You may like to answer this question by finding the centre and radius of the circle and then sketching the circle and tangents through the point $(0, -3)$. Find a right-angled triangle with sides 3, $\sqrt{5}$ and calculate the third side as 2. Using $m = \tan\theta$ will then lead to the answers
>
> $$m = \pm\frac{2}{\sqrt{5}}.$$

4

EXERCISE 4D

1 Show that the line $2y + x = 5$ intersects the circle $x^2 + y^2 = 25$ and find the coordinates of the points of intersection.

2 Show that the line $2y + x = 7$ does not meet the circle $x^2 + y^2 = 9$.

3 Show that the line $y - 2x = 5$ is a tangent to the circle $x^2 + y^2 = 5$ and find the coordinates of the point of contact.

4 Show that the line $8x + y + 10 = 0$ is a tangent to the circle $x^2 + y^2 - 6x + 3y - 5 = 0$ and find the coordinates of the point of contact.

5 Show that the line $2y + x = 9$ does not meet the circle $x^2 + y^2 + 8y + 1 = 0$.

6 Show that the line $y + x = 3$ intersects the circle $x^2 + y^2 - 6x + 8y - 1 = 0$ and find the coordinates of the points of intersection.

7 The line $y = mx$ is a tangent to the circle $x^2 + y^2 - 10y + 16 = 0$

   (a) Find the two possible values of m.

   (b) The tangents meet the circle at points A and B. Find the length of AB.

4.5 The length of the tangents from a point to a circle

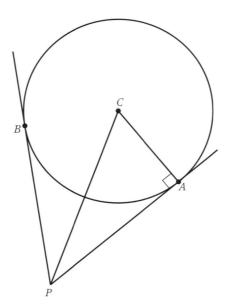

Tangents PA and PB are drawn from point P to the circle with centre C. The radius CA is perpendicular to the tangent PA.

> The radius is always perpendicular to the tangent.

To find the length of the tangent PA use Pythagoras' theorem $PA^2 = CP^2 - CA^2$.

> Tangents from a point to a circle have equal lengths.

Worked example 4.11

Find the length of the tangents from the point $P(5, 6)$ to the circle $(x - 1)^2 + (y - 2)^2 = 9$.

Solution

The circle $(x - 1)^2 + (y - 2)^2 = 9$ has centre $C(1, 2)$ and radius 3.

P is the point $(5, 6)$ so
$CP^2 = [(5 - 1)^2 + (6 - 2)^2] = 32$.

> The distance between (x_1, y_1) and (x_2, y_2) is $\sqrt{(x_2 - x_1)^2 + (y_2 - y_1)^2}$.

If A is the point of contact of one of the tangents then PA is the length of the tangent and CA is the radius.

$\quad CAP = 90°$ so $PA^2 = CP^2 - CA^2$.
$\Rightarrow PA^2 = 32 - 3^2 = 23$
$\quad\Rightarrow PA = \sqrt{23}$.

> Radius and tangent are perpendicular. Pythagoras in triangle CAP.

$\Rightarrow$ Lengths of the tangents are $\sqrt{23}$.

> Tangents from a point to circle are equal.

EXERCISE 4E

1 Find the lengths of the tangents from the point $(3, 4)$ to the circle $x^2 + y^2 = 4$.

2 Find the lengths of the tangents from the point $(5, 7)$ to the circle $x^2 + y^2 - 2x - 4y - 4 = 0$.

3 The lengths of the tangents from the point $(4, k)$ to the circle $x^2 + y^2 = 9$ are $4\sqrt{2}$. Find the possible values of the constant k.

4 Show that the tangents from the point $(3, -4)$ to the circles $x^2 + y^2 + 2x - 4y + 4 = 0$ and $x^2 + y^2 + 4x - 4y - 2 = 0$ are equal in length.

5 Show that the lengths of the tangents from the point (h, k) to the circle $x^2 + y^2 + 2fx + 2gy + c = 0$ are
$\sqrt{h^2 + k^2 + 2fh + 2gk + c}$.

4.6 The equation of the tangent at a point on a circle

The equation of a tangent at a given point on a circle can be found without using calculus. The following Worked example shows you the steps involved.

Worked example 4.12

Find the equation of the tangent at the point $P(4, -2)$ on the circle $x^2 + y^2 - 4x + 10y + 16 = 0$.

Solution

$x^2 + y^2 - 4x + 10y + 16 = 0 \Rightarrow (x - 2)^2 + (y + 5)^2 = 13$.
The centre of the circle is $C(2, -5)$.

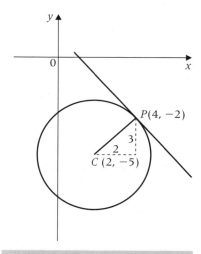

The gradient of the radius $CP = \dfrac{-2 - (-5)}{4 - 2} = \dfrac{3}{2}$,

so the gradient of the tangent at $P(4, -2)$ is $-\dfrac{2}{3}$.

> Used $m_1 \times m_2 = -1$, since the radius and tangent are perpendicular.

The equation of the tangent at $P(4, -2)$ is

$y - (-2) = -\dfrac{2}{3}(x - 4)$

> Used $y - y_1 = m(x - x_1)$.

or $3y + 2x = 2$.

The next Worked example shows you how to find the equation of a circle when you know its centre and the equation of a tangent. The method again uses the geometric fact that a radius is perpendicular to a tangent.

Worked example 4.13

The line $4x - 3y + 4 = 0$ is a tangent to a circle with centre $C(3, 2)$.

Find the equation of the circle.

Solution

The length of the perpendicular from $C(3, 2)$ to the line $4x - 3y + 4 = 0$ is the radius of the circle,

$$\Rightarrow \text{radius} = \frac{|4(3) + (-3)(2) + 4|}{\sqrt{4^2 + (-3)^2}} = 2 \,.$$

Equation of the circle is $(x - 3)^2 + (y - 2)^2 = 4$.

> The perpendicular distance from (h, k) to $ax + by + c = 0$ is
>
> $$\frac{|ah + bk + c|}{\sqrt{a^2 + b^2}} \,.$$

EXERCISE 4F

1 Find the equation of the tangent at the point $P(4, -3)$ on the circle $x^2 + y^2 = 25$.

2 The line $3x + 4y = 50$ is a tangent to a circle with centre $(0, 0)$. Find the equation of the circle.

3 Find the equation of the tangent at the point $P(6, 2)$ on the circle $x^2 + y^2 - 6x - 2y = 0$.

4 The line $3y - 4x = 30$ is a tangent to a circle with centre $(-2, -1)$. Find the equation of the circle.

5 The points A, B and C have coordinates $(6, 3)$, $(5, 8)$ and $(-2, 4)$, respectively.

   (a) Find the equation of the straight line which passes through the points A and B.

   (b) Find the equation of the circle with centre C and the line through the points A and B as a tangent.

6 **(a)** Determine the coordinates of the centre and the radius of the circle with equation $x^2 + y^2 - 6x + 8y = 0$.

   (b) Find the coordinates of the points, P and Q, where the line $x = 7$ intersects this circle.

   (c) Find the equations of the tangents to the circle at P and Q.

Worked examination question 4.1

The circle with equation $(x - 5)^2 + (y - 7)^2 = 25$ has centre C.

The point $P(2, 3)$ lies on the circle. Determine the gradient of PC and hence, or otherwise, obtain the equation of the tangent to the circle at P.

Find also the equation of the straight line which passes through the point C and the point $Q(-1, 4)$. The tangent and the line CQ intersect at R. Determine the size of angle PRC, to the nearest $0.1°$. [A]

Solution

4

C is the point $(5, 7)$.

Gradient of $PC = \dfrac{7 - 3}{5 - 2} = \dfrac{4}{3}$,

$\Rightarrow$ gradient of tangent at $P(2, 3)$ is $-\dfrac{3}{4}$.

> Used $m_1 \times m_2 = -1$, since radius and tangent are perpendicular.

The equation of the tangent to the circle at $P(2, 3)$ is

$$y - 3 = -\frac{3}{4}(x - 2).$$

> Used $y - y_1 = m(x - x_1)$.

The equation of the line through the points $C(5, 7)$ and $Q(-1, 4)$ is

$$\frac{y - 4}{7 - 4} = \frac{x - (-1)}{5 - (-1)}$$

> Used $\dfrac{y - y_1}{y_2 - y_1} = \dfrac{x - x_1}{x_2 - x_1}$.

or $y - 4 = \dfrac{1}{2}(x + 1)$.

Since angle PRC is acute,

$$\tan PRC = \left| \frac{\dfrac{1}{2} - \left(-\dfrac{3}{4}\right)}{1 + \dfrac{1}{2}\left(-\dfrac{3}{4}\right)} \right| = 2$$

> Used $\tan^{-1}\left| \dfrac{m_1 - m_2}{1 + m_1 m_2} \right|$.

$\Rightarrow$ angle $PRC = 63.4°$.

MIXED EXERCISE

1 A circle with centre C has equation $x^2 + y^2 - 6x + 4y = 7$.

(a) Determine the coordinates of C and the radius of the circle.

(b) Find the x-coordinates of the points A and B where the circle cuts the x-axis. Hence obtain the cosine of angle ABC, leaving your answer in surd form. [A]

2 The points A and P have coordinates $(7, 4)$ and $(2, 5)$, respectively, and O is the origin.

   (a) Find the equations of the two circles passing through P, one with centre O, the other with centre A.

   (b) Find the equations of the tangents at P to both circles.

   (c) Find the tangent of the acute angle between these two tangents.

   (d) Find the coordinates of the points at which the two circles intersect the line whose equation is $y = 3$.   [A]

3 A circle has its centre at the point $C(2, 1)$ and touches the line $3x + 4y - 60 = 0$.

   (a) Find:
      (i) its radius,
      (ii) its equation,
      (iii) the coordinates of its point of contact, P, with the given line.

   (b) Given that the line meets the x-axis at A, show that CA is a diameter of the circle passing through C, P and A.

   (c) For this second circle, find:
      (i) its equation,
      (ii) the equation of the tangent at P.   [A]

4 (a) Find the equation of the circle which passes through the point $P(-3, 4)$ and has its centre at the point $Q(-1, 8)$.

   (b) Find the equation of the tangent to the circle at P.

   (c) Show that the line whose equation is $y = 2x$ is a tangent to the circle and find the coordinates of its point of contact R.

   (d) Find the coordinates of the point of intersection, S, of these two tangents and show that $PQRS$ is a square.   [A]

5 (a) Find the equation of the circle, centre $(-3, 2)$ and radius 5.

   (b) Calculate the coordinates of the points P and Q, where this circle cuts the y-axis.

   (c) Calculate the acute angle between the tangents to the circle at P and Q.

   (d) Calculate the coordinates of the point of intersection, R, of the tangents at P and Q.

   (e) Calculate the length PR.   [A]

6 (a) Find the coordinates of the centre and the radius of the circle with equation $x^2 + y^2 - 12x + 6y - 20 = 0$.

   (b) The origin is the midpoint of a chord PQ of this circle. Show that the gradient of the chord PQ is 2 and find its length.

7 The circle C has equation $(x-4)^2 + (y-3)^2 = r^2$, where r is a positive constant, and L has equation $x = 10$.
Given that the circle C passes through the origin:

 (a) find the value of r,

 (b) show that L and C have no points of intersection,

 (c) find the coordinates of the points on the line L which are at a distance of 10 units from the centre of C. [A]

8 A circle C has equation $(x-3)^2 + (y+2)^2 = 9$ and a straight line L has equation $3x + 4y = 1$.

 (a) Show that the line L passes through the centre of the circle C.

 (b) Find, in surd form, the x-coordinates of the points where the circle C crosses the x-axis. [A]

9 A circle has equation $(x-7)^2 + (y-7)^2 = 100$.

 (a) Given that the circle intersects the x-axis at P and Q, find, in surd form, the coordinates of P and Q.

 (b) Given that the circle intersects the y-axis at R and S, write down, or find, the coordinates of R and S.

 (c) Hence show that the quadrilateral $PRQS$ has area 102 square units. [A]

10 (a) Solve the simultaneous equations
$$2x + y = 9,$$
$$(x-2)^2 + y^2 = 5.$$

 (b) Hence state the nature of the geometrical relationship between the line with equation $2x + y = 9$, and the circle with equation $(x-2)^2 + y^2 = 5$. [A]

Key point summary

1 The gradient of a line is the same as $\tan\theta$, where θ is   *p 53* the angle between the line and the positive direction of the x-axis; $m = \tan\theta$.

2 The acute angle between lines with gradients m_1 and   *p 53* m_2 is $\tan^{-1}\left|\dfrac{m_1 - m_2}{1 + m_1 m_2}\right|$.

3 The perpendicular distance from (h, k) to   *p 56* $ax + by + c = 0$ is $\dfrac{|ah + bk + c|}{\sqrt{a^2 + b^2}}$.

4 The equation of a circle with centre (a, b) and radius r *p 58* is $(x-a)^2 + (y-b)^2 = r^2$.

5 $x^2 + y^2 + 2fx + 2gy + c = 0$, is the general equation of *p59*
a circle provided that $f^2 + g^2 - c > 0$.
The <u>centre</u> of the circle is $(-f, -g)$ and the radius is
$\sqrt{f^2 + g^2 - c}$.

6 To determine the conditions for a line to intersect a *p61*
circle,
- from the equation of the line make x (or y) the
  subject
- substitute into the equation of the circle to get a
  quadratic equation in y (or x) of the form
  $ay^2 + by + c = 0$ (or $ax^2 + bx + c = 0$)
- **(i)** if the discriminant $b^2 - 4ac < 0$, there are
  no real roots and the line does not intersect
  the circle (**Line 1** type)
  (ii) if the discriminant $b^2 - 4ac > 0$, there are two
  real distinct roots and the line intersects the
  circle at two points (**Line 2** type)
  (iii) if the discriminant $b^2 - 4ac = 0$, there is one
  real (repeated) root and the line touches the
  circle at one point, the line is a tangent to the
  circle (**Line 3** type)
- if asked to find the coordinates of the points of
  intersection, solve the quadratic equation and
  substitute found value(s) into the equation of
  the line to find the other coordinate(s).

Test yourself	What to review
1 Find the tangent of the acute angle between the lines $4y = 3x + 8$ and $2y + 7 - 4x = 0$.	*Section 4.1*
2 The perpendicular distance from the point $(k, 2)$ to the line $6x = 13 - 8y$ is 1.5. Find the possible values of k.	*Section 4.2*
3 A right-angled triangle PQR has vertices $P(2, 0)$, $Q(4, 1)$ and $R(2, 5)$. Find the equation of the circle which passes through the three points P, Q and R.	*Section 4.3*
4 Find the possible values for the constant c so that the line $y = 2x + c$ is a tangent to the circle $x^2 + y^2 = 4$.	*Section 4.4*
5 Point C is the centre of the circle $(x - 1)^2 + (y + 2)^2 = 16$. Tangents from the point $P(7, 6)$ meet the circle at points A and B. Show that the area of the kite $PACB$ is $8\sqrt{21}$, and find its perimeter.	*Section 4.5*

Test yourself (continued)

	What to review
6 Find the equation of the tangent at the point $P(2, 4)$ on the circle $x^2 + y^2 - 10x = 0$.	*Section 4.6*

Test yourself ANSWERS

1 $\dfrac{1}{2}$.

2 $k = 2, -3$.

3 $x^2 + y^2 - 4x - 5y + 4 = 0$.

4 $c = \pm\sqrt{20}$.

5 $4(2 + \sqrt{21})$.

6 $4y - 3x = 10$.

CHAPTER 5

Secant, cosecant and cotangent

Learning objectives

After studying this chapter you should be able to:

- understand the secant, cosecant and cotangent functions
- sketch the graphs of the secant, cosecant and cotangent functions
- use the two identities relating to the squares of the secant, cosecant and cotangent functions to prove other identities and to solve equations.

5.1 Secant, cosecant and cotangent

So far you have worked with three trigonometric ratios, sine, cosine and tangent. The remaining three trigonometric ratios are secant, cosecant and cotangent. They are written as $\sec x$, $\operatorname{cosec} x$ and $\cot x$, respectively, and are defined as follows:

$$\sec x = \frac{1}{\cos x}$$

$$\operatorname{cosec} x = \frac{1}{\sin x}$$

$$\cot x = \frac{1}{\tan x} = \frac{\cos x}{\sin x}$$

Secant is the reciprocal of cosine. Do **not** write $\sec x$ as $\cos^{-1} x$, which means something entirely different as you saw in section 3.1. Similarly $\operatorname{cosec} x \neq \sin^{-1} x$ and $\cot x \neq \tan^{-1} x$.

Used $\tan x = \frac{\sin x}{\cos x}$, from P1 section 11.13.

Calculators do not have the function keys for secant, cosecant and cotangent. The next worked example shows you how to find the values of these functions.

Worked example 5.1

(a) Find the values of:
   (i) $\sec 40°$,
   (ii) $\operatorname{cosec} \dfrac{\pi}{5}$,
   (iii) $\cot 250°$.

(b) Find the exact value of $\cot \dfrac{\pi}{6}$.

Solution

(a) **(i)** $\sec 40° = \dfrac{1}{\cos 40°} = \dfrac{1}{0.766\,04\ldots} = 1.305$ (to 3 decimal places),

(ii) $\operatorname{cosec}\dfrac{\pi}{5} = \dfrac{1}{\sin\dfrac{\pi}{5}} = \dfrac{1}{\sin 0.628\,318\ldots}$

> Set your calculator in radian mode.

$$= \dfrac{1}{0.587\,785\ldots} = 1.701 \text{ (to 3 decimal places).}$$

(iii) $\cot 250° = \dfrac{1}{\tan 250°} = \dfrac{1}{2.747\,47\ldots} = 0.364$ (to 3 decimal places);

(b) $\cot\dfrac{\pi}{6} = \dfrac{1}{\tan\dfrac{\pi}{6}} = \dfrac{1}{\dfrac{1}{\sqrt{3}}} = \sqrt{3}.$

The next two worked examples show you how to solve some basic trigonometric equations involving a single secant, cosecant or cotangent function.

Worked example 5.2

Solve these equations for $0° \leqslant x < 360°$. Give your answers to one decimal place.

(a) $\sec x = 1.9,$ **(b)** $\operatorname{cosec} x = -1.25.$

Solution

(a) $\sec x = 1.9 \Rightarrow \cos x = \dfrac{1}{1.9} = 0.526\,315\ldots$

Cos x is positive so answers lie in the first and fourth quadrants. The acute angle $\cos^{-1}(0.526\,315\ldots) = 58.24°$
$x = 58.24°$ or $x = 360° - 58.24°$
To one decimal place, $x = 58.2°, 301.8°.$

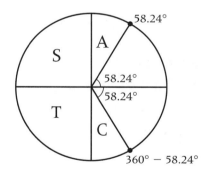

(b) $\operatorname{cosec} x = -1.25 \Rightarrow \sin x = -\dfrac{1}{1.25} = -0.8$

Sin x is negative so answers lie in the third and fourth quadrants. The acute angle, $\sin^{-1} 0.8 = 53.13°.$
$x = 180° + 53.13°$ or $x = 360° - 53.13°.$
To one decimal place, $x = 233.1°, 306.9°.$

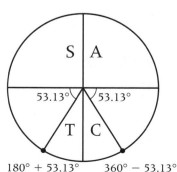

Worked example 5.3

Solve the equation $\cot 2x = -1$ for $0 \leqslant x < 2\pi.$

Solution

$\cot 2x = -1 \Rightarrow \tan 2x = -1$.

Tan $2x$ is negative so values for $2x$ lie in the second and fourth quadrants.

The acute angle, $\tan^{-1} 1 = \dfrac{\pi}{4}$.

Since $0 \leqslant x < 2\pi$, you require all values for $2x$ between 0 and 4π.

So $2x = \pi - \dfrac{\pi}{4}$ or $2\pi - \dfrac{\pi}{4}$ or $3\pi - \dfrac{\pi}{4}$ or $4\pi - \dfrac{\pi}{4}$

$\Rightarrow x = \dfrac{3\pi}{8}, \dfrac{7\pi}{8}, \dfrac{11\pi}{8}$ and $\dfrac{15\pi}{8}$.

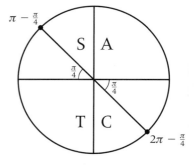

The next Worked example shows you how to use the definitions of secant, cosecant and cotangent to obtain other trigonometric identities.

Worked example 5.4

Prove the identity $\cot A \sec A \equiv \operatorname{cosec} A$.

Solution

$\cot A \sec A \equiv \dfrac{\cos A}{\sin A} \dfrac{1}{\cos A} \equiv \dfrac{1}{\sin A} \equiv \operatorname{cosec} A$

EXERCISE 5A

1 Find the values of:

   (a) $\sec 70°$,

   (b) $\operatorname{cosec} 70°$,

   (c) $\cot 20°$,

   (d) $\sec(-70°)$,

   (e) $\operatorname{cosec} 90°$,

   (f) $4 + \cot 430°$,

   (g) $\dfrac{1}{1 + \sec 60°}$,

   (h) $\dfrac{2}{6 + \cot 315°}$.

2 Find the values of:

   (a) $\sec 2$,

   (b) $\operatorname{cosec} 0.7$,

   (c) $\cot 0.5$,

   (d) $\sec(-1)$,

   (e) $\operatorname{cosec} \dfrac{\pi}{8}$,

   (f) $4 + \cot \dfrac{\pi}{8}$,

   (g) $\dfrac{1}{1 + \sec \dfrac{\pi}{10}}$,

   (h) $\dfrac{1}{6 + \cot \dfrac{\pi}{5}}$.

> The angles are measured in radians in this question.

3 Find the exact values of:

(a) $\sec 60°$,

(b) $\operatorname{cosec} 60°$,

(c) $\cot 30°$,

(d) $\sec(-180°)$,

(e) $\operatorname{cosec} 135°$,

(f) $1 + \cot 420°$,

(g) $\dfrac{1}{\sqrt{3} - \sec 30°}$,

(h) $\dfrac{2}{7 + \sqrt{3}\cot 150°}$.

4 Find the exact values of:

(a) $\operatorname{cosec}\dfrac{\pi}{4}$,

(b) $4 + \cot\dfrac{3\pi}{4}$,

(c) $\dfrac{1}{1 + \sqrt{3}\sec\dfrac{\pi}{6}}$,

(d) $\dfrac{2\sqrt{3}}{2 - \cot\dfrac{\pi}{6}}$.

5 Solve these equations for $0° \leqslant x < 360°$.
Give your answers to one decimal place.

(a) $\sec x = 1.8$,

(b) $\operatorname{cosec} x = -2.25$,

(c) $\cot x = 3$,

(d) $\sec x = -1.3$,

(e) $\operatorname{cosec} x = 3$,

(f) $\cot x = -2.4$,

(g) $4\sec 2x = -7$,

(h) $5\cot 2x = -2$.

6 Solve these equations for $0 \leqslant x \leqslant 2\pi$:

(a) $\sec x = 2$,

(b) $\operatorname{cosec} x = -2$,

(c) $\cot 2x = 1$,

(d) $\sec 5x = -1$,

(e) $\sqrt{3}\operatorname{cosec} 3x = 2$,

(f) $\cot 2x = -\sqrt{3}$,

(g) $\sec 3x = 1$,

(h) $\sqrt{12}\cot 3x = 2$.

7 Prove the following identities:

(a) $\tan A \operatorname{cosec} A \equiv \sec A$,

(b) $\sin A \cot A \equiv \cos A$,

(c) $\dfrac{\cot A}{1 + \cot A} \equiv \dfrac{1}{1 + \tan A}$,

(d) $\tan A \operatorname{cosec} A \equiv \sec A$,

(e) $\sec A - \cos A \equiv \tan A \sin A$,

(f) $\cot A - \tan A \equiv 2\cot 2A$,

(g) $\dfrac{\sin A}{1 - \cos A} \equiv \operatorname{cosec} A + \cot A$.

5

5.2 Graphs of sec *x*, cosec *x* and cot *x*

Graph of y = sec x

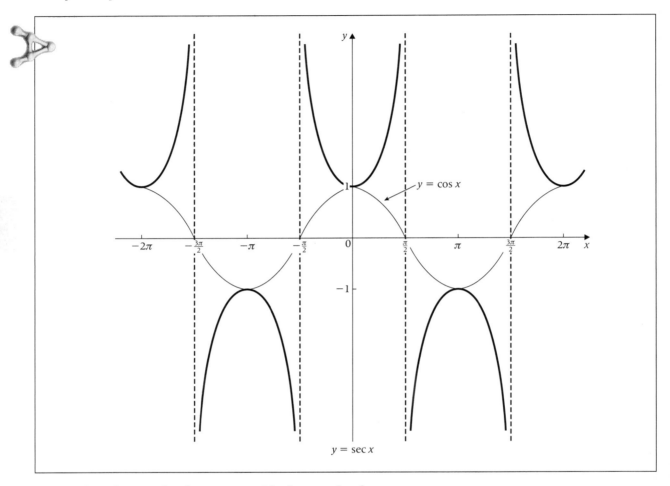

$y = \cos x$

$y = \sec x$

Comparing the graph of $y = \sec x$ with the graph of $y = \cos x$ you can see that $y = \sec x$ has maximum points where $y = \cos x$ has minimum points and has minimum points where $y = \cos x$ has maximum points.

Secant, like cosine, is a periodic function with period 2π and so the graph repeats itself every 2π radians.

The domain of $\sec x$ is all real values $\neq (2k + 1)\dfrac{\pi}{2}$ and its range is all real values **except** $-1 < y < 1$.

Graph of y = cosec x

Consider $y = \operatorname{cosec} x = \dfrac{1}{\sin x} = \dfrac{1}{\cos\left(x - \dfrac{\pi}{2}\right)}$

$\Rightarrow \operatorname{cosec} x = \sec\left(x - \dfrac{\pi}{2}\right)$

So, if $f(x) = \sec x$, then

$f\left(x - \dfrac{\pi}{2}\right) = \operatorname{cosec} x.$

So a translation of $\begin{bmatrix} \frac{\pi}{2} \\ 0 \end{bmatrix}$ transforms the graph of $y = \sec x$ into

the graph of $y = \operatorname{cosec} x$.

P1, section 12.1.

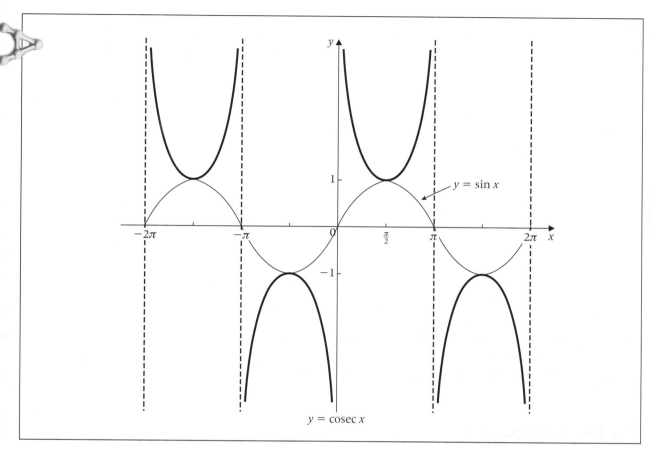

$y = \operatorname{cosec} x$

Comparing the graph of $y = \operatorname{cosec} x$ with the graph of $y = \sin x$ you can see that $y = \operatorname{cosec} x$ has maximum points where $y = \sin x$ has minimum points and has minimum points where $y = \sin x$ has maximum points.

Cosecant, like sine, is a periodic function with period 2π and so the graph repeats itself every 2π radians.

The domain of $\operatorname{cosec} x$ is all real values $\neq k\pi$ and its range is all real values **except** $-1 < y < 1$.

Graph of $y = \cot x$

Consider $y = \cot x = \dfrac{\cos x}{\sin x} = \dfrac{\sin\left(\dfrac{\pi}{2} - x\right)}{\cos\left(\dfrac{\pi}{2} - x\right)}$

$\Rightarrow \cot x = \tan\left(\dfrac{\pi}{2} - x\right) = \tan\left[2\left(\dfrac{\pi}{4}\right) - x\right]$

So, if $f(x) = \tan x$, then
$f\left[2\left(\dfrac{\pi}{4}\right) - x\right] = \cot x$.

So a reflection in the line $x = \dfrac{\pi}{4}$ transforms the graph of
$y = \tan x$ into the graph of $y = \cot x$.

P1, section 12.3.

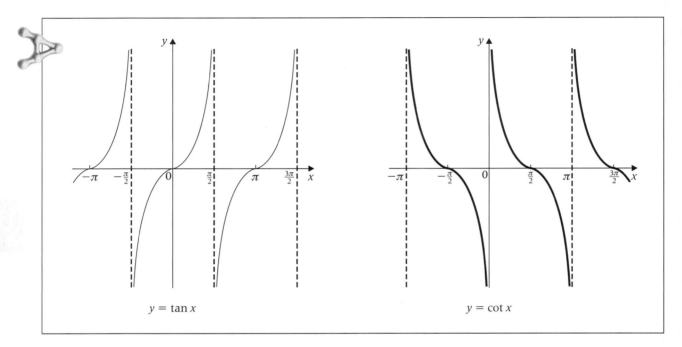

$y = \tan x$ $\qquad\qquad$ $y = \cot x$

Cotangent, like tangent, is a periodic function with period π and so the graph repeats itself every π radians.
The domain of $\cot x$ is all real values $\neq k\pi$ and its range is all real values.

Worked example 5.5

(a) Determine the transformation that maps $y = \sec x$ onto $y = \sec 2x$.

(b) State the period, in radians, of the graph $y = \sec 2x$.

(c) Sketch the graph of $y = \sec 2x$ for $0 \leqslant x \leqslant \pi$, $x \neq \dfrac{\pi}{4}, \dfrac{3\pi}{4}$.

Solution

(a) Let $f(x) = \sec x$ then $f(2x) = \sec 2x$.
The transformation that maps $y = \sec x$ onto $y = \sec 2x$ is a stretch of scale factor $\dfrac{1}{2}$ in the x-direction.

(b) The period of $y = \sec 2x$ is $\dfrac{2\pi}{2} = \pi$ radians.

(c) The graph of $y = \sec 2x$ for $0 \leqslant x \leqslant \pi$, $x \neq \dfrac{\pi}{4}$, $\dfrac{3\pi}{4}$ is

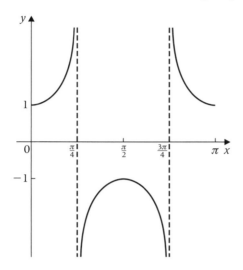

EXERCISE 5B

1 (a) Determine the transformation that maps $y = \operatorname{cosec} x$ onto $y = \operatorname{cosec} 4x$.

(b) State the period, in radians, of the graph $y = \operatorname{cosec} 4x$.

2 (a) Determine the transformation that maps $y = \cot x$ onto $y = \cot \dfrac{x}{4}$.

(b) State the period, in radians, of the graph $y = \cot \dfrac{x}{4}$.

3 Sketch the graph of $y = 1 + \sec \dfrac{x}{2}$ for $-\pi < x < \pi$.

4 (a) Sketch the graph of $y = 1 + 3 \operatorname{cosec} 2x$ for $-180° < x < 180°$, $x \neq 0°, \pm 90°$.

(b) Describe a sequence of transformations that maps the curve $y = \sec x$ onto the curve $y = 1 + 3 \operatorname{cosec} 2x$.

5.3 Identities involving the squares of secant, cosecant and cotangent

In P1, section 11.12, you used the identity $\cos^2 \theta + \sin^2 \theta \equiv 1$. In this section you will be shown two similar identities.

If you divide each term in the identity $\cos^2 \theta + \sin^2 \theta \equiv 1$ by $\cos^2 \theta$ you get

$$\frac{\cos^2 \theta}{\cos^2 \theta} + \frac{\sin^2 \theta}{\cos^2 \theta} \equiv \frac{1}{\cos^2 \theta}$$

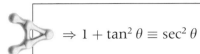

$$\Rightarrow 1 + \tan^2 \theta \equiv \sec^2 \theta$$

Similarly, if you divide each term in the identity $\cos^2 \theta + \sin^2 \theta \equiv 1$ by $\sin^2 \theta$, you get

$$\frac{\cos^2 \theta}{\sin^2 \theta} + \frac{\sin^2 \theta}{\sin^2 \theta} \equiv \frac{1}{\sin^2 \theta}$$

$$\Rightarrow \cot^2 \theta + 1 \equiv \mathrm{cosec}^2 \theta$$

These two identities, along with $\cos^2 \theta + \sin^2 \theta \equiv 1$, are frequently used to solve trigonometric equations and to prove other identities. They are not given in the examination formulae booklet so you must memorise them and know how to apply them.

Worked example 5.6

Solve the equation $\sec^2 x = 4 + 2 \tan x$, giving all solutions in the interval $0° \leqslant x < 360°$.

Solution

To solve the equation $\sec^2 x = 4 + 2 \tan x$
use the identity $\sec^2 x \equiv 1 + \tan^2 x$ to get $1 + \tan^2 x = 4 + 2 \tan x$.
$\Rightarrow \tan^2 x - 2 \tan x - 3 = 0$
$\Rightarrow (\tan x - 3)(\tan x + 1) = 0$
$\Rightarrow \tan x = 3, \tan x = -1$.

> As a starter, try to get a quadratic equation in the non-squared trigonometric term, $\tan x$ here.

When $\tan x = 3$, $\tan x$ is positive in the first and third quadrants.

The acute angle $\tan^{-1} 3 = 71.57°$, so in the required interval, $\tan x = 3 \Rightarrow x = 71.57°, 180° + 71.57°$.

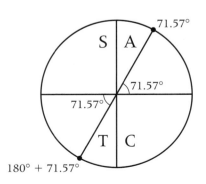

When $\tan x = -1$, $\tan x$ is negative in the second and fourth quadrants.
The acute angle $\tan^{-1} = 45°$, so in the required interval,
$\tan x = -1 \Rightarrow x = 180° - 45°, 360° - 45°$.

The solutions of the equation $\sec^2 x = 4 + 2\tan x$, in the interval $0° \leqslant x < 360°$, are $x = 71.6°, 135°, 251.6°, 315°$.

The general strategy when asked to solve trigonometric equations which involve the same angle but with a squared trigonometric function is to try to write the equation as a quadratic equation in the non-squared trigonometric function.

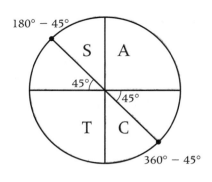

Worked example 5.7

Solve the equation $\operatorname{cosec}^2 x = 5 + 3\cot x$, giving all solutions in the interval $0 \leqslant x < 2\pi$.

Solution

To solve the equation $\operatorname{cosec}^2 x = 5 + 3\cot x$
use the identity $\operatorname{cosec}^2 x \equiv 1 + \cot^2 x$ to get
$1 + \cot^2 x = 5 + 3\cot x$
$\Rightarrow \cot^2 x - 3\cot x - 4 = 0$
$\Rightarrow (\cot x - 4)(\cot x + 1) = 0$
$\Rightarrow \cot x = 4, \cot x = -1$
$\Rightarrow \tan x = \dfrac{1}{4}, \tan x = -1$

> Try to write the equation as a quadratic equation in $\cot x$.

> Used $\tan x = \dfrac{1}{\cot x}$.

When $\tan x = \dfrac{1}{4}$, $\tan x$ is positive in the first and third quadrants.

The acute angle $\tan^{-1} \dfrac{1}{4} = 0.245$ rads, so in the required interval,

> Set calculator in radian mode.

$\tan x = \dfrac{1}{4} \Rightarrow x = 0.245$ rads, $(\pi + 0.245)$ rads.

When $\tan x = -1$, $\tan x$ is negative in the second and fourth quadrants.

The acute angle $\tan^{-1} 1 = \dfrac{\pi}{4}$ rads, so in the required interval,

$\tan x = -1 \Rightarrow x = \left(\pi - \dfrac{\pi}{4}\right)$ rads, $\left(2\pi - \dfrac{\pi}{4}\right)$ rads.

The solutions of the equation $\operatorname{cosec}^2 x = 5 + 3\cot x$, in the interval $0 \leqslant x < 2\pi$ are, in radians, $x = 0.245$, $\dfrac{3\pi}{4}$, 3.39 and $\dfrac{7\pi}{4}$.

Worked example 5.8

Prove the identity $\sec^2 A - \operatorname{cosec}^2 A \equiv (\tan A + \cot A)(\tan A - \cot A)$.

Solution

$\sec^2 A - \text{cosec}^2 A \equiv 1 + \tan^2 A - (1 + \cot^2 A)$
$\qquad\qquad\qquad\qquad \equiv \tan^2 A - \cot^2 A$
$\qquad\qquad\qquad\qquad \equiv (\tan A + \cot A)(\tan A - \cot A)$

Difference of two squares.

So $\sec^2 A - \text{cosec}^2 A \equiv (\tan A + \cot A)(\tan A - \cot A)$.

EXERCISE 5C

1 Prove the identity
$\tan^2 A - \cot^2 A \equiv (\sec A + \text{cosec} A)(\sec A - \text{cosec} A)$.

2 Prove the identity
$\cot^2 A + \sin^2 A \equiv (\text{cosec} A + \cos A)(\text{cosec} A - \cos A)$.

3 Prove the identity $\text{cosec}^2 A \cos^2 A \equiv \text{cosec}^2 A - 1$.

4 Given that $2\cos^2 x - \sin^2 x = 1$, show that $\cos^2 x = 2\sin^2 x$
and hence find the possible values of $\cot x$.

5 Given that $5\sec^2 x + 3\tan^2 x = 9$, find the possible values of
$\sin x$.

6 Prove the identity $\dfrac{(\sec A - \tan A)(\tan A + \sec A)}{\text{cosec} A - \cot A} \equiv \cot A + \text{cosec} A$.

7 Prove the identity $(\text{cosec} A + \cot A)^2 \equiv \dfrac{1 + \cos A}{1 - \cos A}$.

8 Given that $x = \sec\theta$ and $y = \tan\theta$, show that $x^2 - y^2 = 1$.

9 Eliminate θ from equations $x = \text{cosec}\,\theta$ and $y = \dfrac{1}{4}\cot\theta$.

10 Eliminate θ from equations $x = 2 + \text{cosec}\,\theta$ and $y = \dfrac{1}{4}\tan\theta$.

11 Solve the equation $\sec^2 x = 3 + \tan x$, giving all solutions in
the interval $0° \leqslant x < 360°$.

12 Solve the equation $3\sec^2 x = 5 + \tan x$, giving all solutions in
the interval $-180° \leqslant x < 180°$.

13 Solve the equation $2\,\text{cosec}^2 x = 1 + 3\cot x$, giving all
solutions in the interval $0° \leqslant x < 360°$.

14 Solve the equation $\tan^2 x = 1 - \sec x$, giving all solutions in
the interval $-180° \leqslant x < 180°$.

15 Solve the equation $\cot^2 x + \text{cosec}\,x = 11$, giving all solutions
in the interval $0° \leqslant x < 360°$.

16 Solve the equation $4\tan^2 x + 12\sec x + 1 = 0$, giving all
solutions in the interval $0° \leqslant x < 360°$.

17 Solve the equation $\cot^2 x + \text{cosec}^2 x = 7$, giving all solutions
in the interval $0 \leqslant x < 2\pi$.

18 Solve the equation $\tan^2 x + 3 = 3\sec x$, giving all solutions in the interval $0 \leqslant x < 2\pi$.

19 Solve the equation $\cot^2 x + 5\csc x = 3$, giving all solutions in the interval $0 \leqslant x < 2\pi$.

20 Solve the equation $2\csc^2 2x + \cot 2x = 3$, giving all solutions in the interval $-\pi \leqslant x < \pi$.

21 Given that $x = \sec A + \tan A$, show that $x + \dfrac{1}{x} = 2\sec A$.

22 Given that $x = \csc\theta + \cot\theta$, show that $x + \dfrac{1}{x} = 2\csc\theta$.

5.4 Use of double angle identities with the secant, cosecant and cotangent functions

In section 3.3 you used the following double angle identities:

$\sin 2A \equiv 2\sin A\cos A$,

$\cos 2A \equiv \cos^2 A - \sin^2 A$,
$\cos 2A \equiv 2\cos^2 A - 1$,
$\cos 2A \equiv 1 - 2\sin^2 A$

$\tan 2A \equiv \dfrac{2\tan A}{1 - \tan^2 A}$.

In this section you will be shown how to apply these and the results obtained in this chapter to prove other identities and to solve different types of trigonometric equations.

Worked examination question 5.1

(a) Prove the identity $\tan A + \cot A \equiv 2\csc 2A$.

(b) Find, in radians, all the solutions of the equation
$\tan x + \cot x = 8\cos 2x$, in the interval $0 \leqslant x < \pi$. [A]

Solution

(a) $\tan A + \cot A \equiv \dfrac{\sin A}{\cos A} + \dfrac{\cos A}{\sin A}$

$\equiv \dfrac{\sin^2 A + \cos^2 A}{\sin A\cos A}$

$\equiv \dfrac{1}{\sin A\cos A}$

$\equiv \dfrac{2}{2\sin A\cos A} \equiv \dfrac{2}{\sin 2A}$

$\Rightarrow \tan A + \cot A \equiv 2\csc 2A$.

> Used $\cot A = \dfrac{\cos A}{\sin A}$.

> Multiply top and bottom by 2 as $\sin 2A(= 2\sin A\cos A)$ is required in the denominator.

(b) Using the result of **(a)** you can write
$\tan x + \cot x = 8\cos 2x$ in the form

$$2\operatorname{cosec} 2x = 8\cos 2x \Rightarrow \operatorname{cosec} 2x = 4\cos 2x$$
$$\Rightarrow \operatorname{cosec} 2x = 4\cos 2x$$

$$\Rightarrow \frac{1}{\sin 2x} = 4\cos 2x$$
$$\Rightarrow 1 = 4\sin 2x \cos 2x$$
$$\Rightarrow 1 = 2(2\sin 2x \cos 2x)$$
$$\Rightarrow 1 = 2\sin 4x$$
$$\Rightarrow \sin 4x = 0.5$$
$$\Rightarrow 4x = \frac{\pi}{6}, \frac{5\pi}{6}, \frac{13\pi}{6}, \frac{17\pi}{6}$$

$$\Rightarrow x = \frac{\pi}{24}, \frac{5\pi}{24}, \frac{13\pi}{24}, \frac{17\pi}{24}.$$

> Sine is positive and $\sin^{-1}(0.5) = \dfrac{\pi}{6}$.

> Since $0 \leqslant x < \pi$ you need $0 \leqslant 4x < 4\pi$.

Worked examination question 5.2

(a) Prove the identity $\cot 2\theta + \tan \theta \equiv \operatorname{cosec} 2\theta$.

(b) Hence find the values of θ, in the interval $0° < \theta < 180°$, for which $3(\cot 2\theta + \tan \theta)^2 = 4$.   [A]

Solution

(a) $\cot 2\theta + \tan \theta = \dfrac{\cos 2\theta}{\sin 2\theta} + \dfrac{\sin \theta}{\cos \theta}$

$$= \frac{\cos 2\theta \cos \theta + \sin 2\theta \sin \theta}{\sin 2\theta \cos \theta}$$

$$= \frac{\cos (2\theta - \theta)}{\sin 2\theta \cos \theta}$$

$$= \frac{\cos \theta}{\sin 2\theta \cos \theta} = \frac{1}{\sin 2\theta}$$

$$\Rightarrow \cot 2\theta + \tan \theta \equiv \operatorname{cosec} 2\theta.$$

> Used $\cos A \cos B + \sin A \sin B \equiv \cos (A - B)$.

(b) Using the result of **(a)** you can write $3(\cot 2\theta + \tan \theta)^2 = 4$

as $3\operatorname{cosec}^2 2\theta = 4 \Rightarrow \operatorname{cosec}^2 2\theta = \dfrac{4}{3}$

$$\Rightarrow \operatorname{cosec} 2\theta = \pm \frac{2}{\sqrt{3}}$$

$$\Rightarrow \sin 2\theta = \pm \frac{\sqrt{3}}{2}$$

$$\Rightarrow 2\theta = 60°, 120°, 240°, 300°$$
$$\Rightarrow \theta = 30°, 60°, 120°, 150°.$$

> Since $0° < \theta < 180°$, you need $0° < 2\theta < 360°$.

EXERCISE 5D

1 Prove the identity $2 \sin \theta \csc 2\theta \equiv \sec \theta$.

2 Prove the identity $\dfrac{\sin 2x}{1 - \cos 2x} \equiv \cot x$.

3 Prove the identity $\csc 2A + \cot 2A \equiv \cot A$.

4 Prove the identity $\dfrac{\cot^2 \theta - 1}{\cot^2 \theta + 1} \equiv \cos 2\theta$.

5 Prove the identity $\dfrac{2 \cot \theta}{\cot^2 \theta + 1} \equiv \sin 2\theta$.

6 (a) Prove the identity $\csc 2A - \cot 2A \equiv \tan A$.

  (b) Solve the equation $4 \csc 2x - 4 \cot 2x = \sqrt{3} \sec^2 x$, for $0 < x < \pi$.

7 Solve the equation $\tan \theta = \csc 2\theta$, for $0 \leqslant \theta \leqslant 2\pi$.

8 Show that $\cot\left(x + \dfrac{\pi}{12}\right) - \tan\left(x - \dfrac{\pi}{12}\right) = \dfrac{4 \cos 2x}{1 + 2 \sin 2x}$.

5

Key point summary

1 $\sec x = \dfrac{1}{\cos x}$ $p\,72$

$\operatorname{cosec} x = \dfrac{1}{\sin x}$

$\cot x = \dfrac{1}{\tan x} = \dfrac{\cos x}{\sin x}$

2 $p\,76$

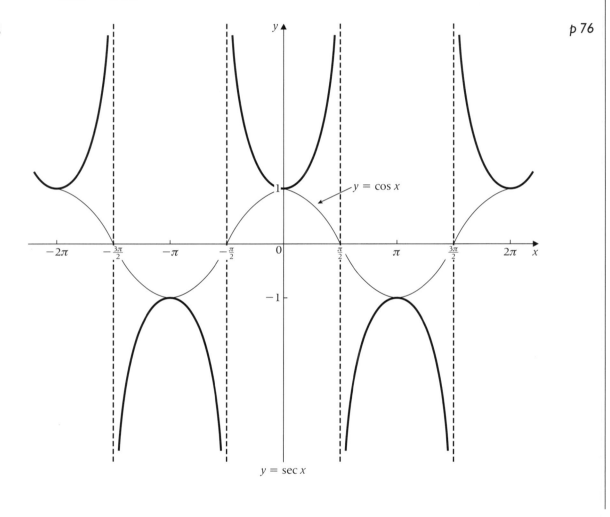

$y = \sec x$

3 ϸ 77

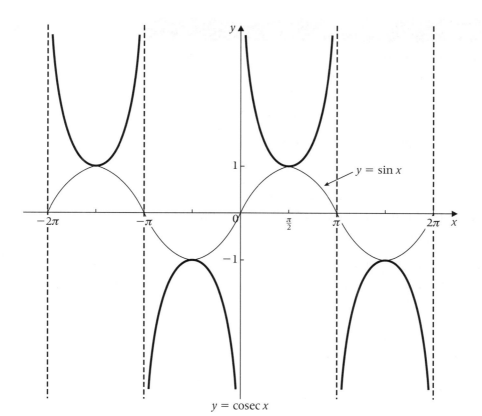

$y = \sin x$

$y = \operatorname{cosec} x$

4 ϸ 78

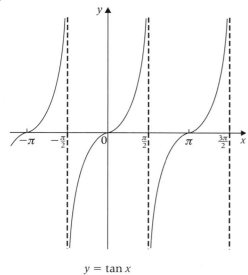

$y = \tan x$

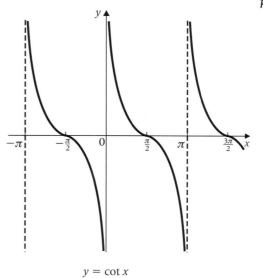

$y = \cot x$

5 $1 + \tan^2 \theta \equiv \sec^2 \theta$ ϸ 80

6 $\cot^2 \theta + 1 \equiv \operatorname{cosec}^2 \theta$ ϸ 80

Test yourself	**What to review**
1 Solve the equation $\csc(x + 30°) = 2.1$, for $0° \leqslant x < 360°$. Give your answers to 1 decimal place.	*Section 5.1*
2 By sketching the graphs of $y = \cot x$ and $y = \dfrac{x}{3}$ for $0 < x \leqslant \dfrac{\pi}{2}$, show that the equation $\cot x = \dfrac{x}{3}$ has one root and explain why this root must be in the interval $1 < x \leqslant \dfrac{\pi}{2}$.	*Section 5.2*
3 Solve the equation $3\tan^2 x + 2\sec x = 5$, giving all solutions in the interval $0 \leqslant x < 2\pi$.	*Section 5.3*
4 Prove the identity $\sec 2A - 1 \equiv \tan 2A \tan A$.	*Section 5.4*

Test yourself ANSWERS

3 $x = 0.723,\ \dfrac{2\pi}{3},\ \dfrac{4\pi}{3},\ 5.56.$

1 $x = 121.6°,\ 358.4°.$

Tangents to curves and the chain rule in differentiation

Learning objectives

After studying this chapter you should be able to:

- find the equations of tangents to curves
- differentiate composite functions using the chain rule
- solve practical problems involving rates of change using the chain rule
- use small increments in order to make approximations of the value of a function close to a value which is known.

6.1 Finding the equations of tangents to curves

As you will recall, the tangent to a curve at a point is the straight line which just touches the curve at that point.

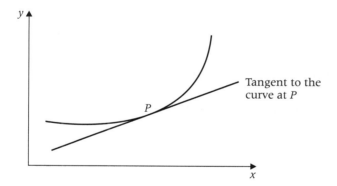

Tangent to the curve at P

You should also recall from previous work that the **gradient of the curve at P is equal to the gradient of the tangent to the curve at P**.

The aim of this section is to use some of your existing knowledge in order to find the Cartesian equation of tangents to curves.

Worked example 6.1

Find the equation of the tangent to the curve $y = 3x^2 + \dfrac{1}{x^3}$ at the point $P(1, 4)$.

Solution

Firstly, $y = 3x^2 + x^{-3}$.

Now the gradient of the curve is $\dfrac{dy}{dx} = 6x - 3x^{-4} = 6x - \dfrac{3}{x^4}$.

At P, $x = 1 \Rightarrow \dfrac{dy}{dx} = 6(1) - \dfrac{3}{(1)^4} = 6 - 3 = 3$.

This means that the **gradient of the tangent at P** must also be 3.

Now the tangent is a straight line with gradient 3 which passes through the point $P(1, 4)$.

$\Rightarrow$ the equation of the tangent at P is

> The equation of the straight line which passes through the point (x_1, y_1) and has gradient m is $y - y_1 = m(x - x_1)$.

$$y - 4 = 3(x - 1)$$
$$\Rightarrow \quad y = 3x + 1$$

This is the equation of the tangent to the curve at $(1, 4)$.

> A general method for finding the equation of the tangent to a curve at a point P can be summarised as:
>
> **(i)**   use differentiation to find the gradient of the curve at P
>
> **(ii)** substitute the gradient at P and coordinates of P into $y - y_1 = m(x - x_1)$.

Worked example 6.2

A curve is given by the equation $y = 3e^x + x + 3$.

(a) Find the equation of the tangent to the curve at the point A where $x = 0$.

(b) The tangent at A crosses the x-axis at the point B. Find the coordinates of the point B.

Solution

(a) A sketch of the curve and the tangent at A is shown below.

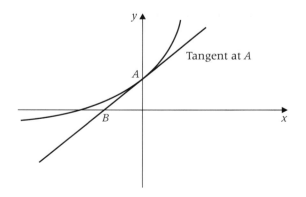

Firstly, $\dfrac{dy}{dx} = 3e^x + 1$

$\Rightarrow$ the gradient of the tangent at $A = 3e^0 + 1 = 3 + 1 = 4$
Also when $x = 0$, $y = 3e^0 + 0 + 3 = 6$.

So the tangent at A has gradient 4 and passes through the point $(0, 6)$.

$\Rightarrow$ the equation of the tangent at A is

$$y - 6 = 4(x - 0)$$
$$\Rightarrow \quad y = 4x + 6$$

This is the equation of the tangent to the curve at $A(0, 6)$.

(b) To find where the tangent crosses the x-axis you put $y = 0$ in the equation of the tangent.

$$0 = 4x + 6$$
$$\Rightarrow \quad x = -1.5$$
$$\Rightarrow B \text{ is the point } (-1.5, 0)$$

$e^0 = 1$

Worked example 6.3

A curve is defined for $x \neq 0$ by the equation $y = \dfrac{(x + 2)(x - 3)}{x^2}$.

(a) Find the equations of the tangents to the curve at the points $P(2, -1)$ and $Q(-1.5, -1)$.

(b) The tangents to the curve at P and Q meet at the point N. Find the coordinates of the point N.

Solution

The curve and the tangents at P and Q are shown in the sketch below.

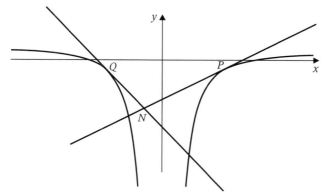

(a) Firstly, $y = \dfrac{x^2 - x - 6}{x^2} = 1 - \dfrac{1}{x} - \dfrac{6}{x^2} = 1 - x^{-1} - 6x^{-2}$

and $\dfrac{dy}{dx} = x^{-2} + 12x^{-3} = \dfrac{1}{x^2} + \dfrac{12}{x^3}$

At P, $x = 2$ and $\dfrac{dy}{dx} = \dfrac{1}{2^2} + \dfrac{12}{2^3} = \dfrac{1}{4} + \dfrac{12}{8} = \dfrac{7}{4}$

The tangent at P has gradient $\dfrac{7}{4}$ and passes through the point $(2, -1)$ and so has equation

$$y - (-1) = \frac{7}{4}(x - 2)$$

$$\Rightarrow y + 1 = \frac{7}{4}(x - 2)$$

$$\Rightarrow 4y + 4 = 7x - 14$$

$$\Rightarrow 4y = 7x - 18$$

By multiplying through by 4.

At Q, $x = -1.5$ and $\dfrac{dy}{dx} = \dfrac{1}{(1.5)^2} + \dfrac{12}{(-1.5)^3} = \dfrac{4}{9} + \dfrac{32}{9} = 4$

The tangent at Q has gradient 4 and passes through the point $(-1.5, -1)$ and so has equation

$$y - (-1) = 4(x - (-1.5))$$

$$\Rightarrow y + 1 = 4(x + 1.5)$$

$$\Rightarrow y + 1 = 4x + 6$$

$$\Rightarrow y = 4x + 5$$

(b)   You have:

the equation of the tangent at P: $4y = 7x - 18$
the equation of the tangent at Q: $y = 4x + 5$

You solve these equations simultaneously in order to find the point of intersection of the two tangents.

$$4y = 7x - 18 \qquad\qquad [1]$$

$$4y = 16x + 20 \qquad\qquad [2]$$

 $(y = 4x + 5) \times 4$

$[2] - [1]$ gives

$$0 = 9x + 38 \Rightarrow x = -\frac{38}{9}$$

$$\Rightarrow y = -\frac{107}{9}$$

N has coordinates $\left(-\dfrac{38}{9}, -\dfrac{107}{9}\right)$.

Worked example 6.4

A curve has equation $y = e^x - 2x^3$.

The tangent to the curve at the point $P(1, e - 2)$ crosses the x-axis at A and the y-axis at B.
Given that O is the origin, show that the area of triangle OAB, is

$$\frac{8}{6 - e}.$$

Solution

A sketch of the curve and the tangent at P is shown below.

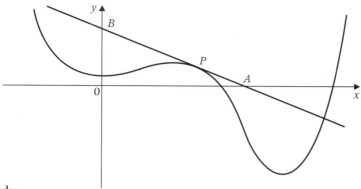

Firstly, $\dfrac{dy}{dx} = e^x - 6x^2$

At P, $x = 1 \Rightarrow \dfrac{dy}{dx} = e^1 - 6(1)^2 = e - 6$

> It is preferable to leave answers in terms of e rather than working out a decimal approximation.

$\Rightarrow$ The tangent at P has gradient $(e - 6)$ and passes through the point $(1, e - 2)$. Its equation is

$$y - (e - 2) = (e - 6)(x - 1)$$
$$\Rightarrow \quad y - e + 2 = (e - 6)x - e + 6$$
$$\Rightarrow \quad y = (e - 6)x + 4$$

To find A you put $y = 0$ in the equation of the tangent:

$$0 = (e - 6)x + 4$$
$$\Rightarrow x = \frac{-4}{e - 6} = \frac{4}{6 - e}$$

So A has coordinates $\left(\dfrac{4}{6 - e}, 0 \right)$.

To find B you put $x = 0$ in the equation of the tangent:

$$y = (e - 6)(0) + 4$$
$$\Rightarrow y = 4$$

So B has coordinates $(0, 4)$.

Area of triangle $OAB = \dfrac{1}{2} \times \text{base} \times \text{height} = \dfrac{1}{2} \times OA \times OB$

$$= \frac{1}{2} \times \frac{4}{6 - e} \times 4 = \frac{8}{6 - e} \text{ as required.}$$

Worked example 6.5

A curve has Cartesian equation $y = x^2(4x + 5)$.

(a) Find the equation of the tangent to the curve at the point $P(-1, 1)$.

(b) This tangent meets the curve again at the point Q. Find the coordinates of point Q.

Solution

A sketch of the curve and the tangent at P is shown below.

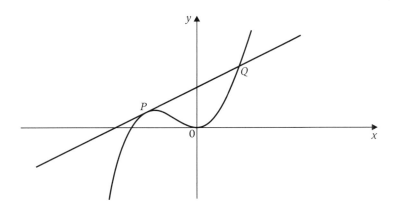

(a) $y = 4x^3 + 5x^2$

$$\Rightarrow \frac{dy}{dx} = 12x^2 + 10x$$

at P, $x = -1 \Rightarrow \dfrac{dy}{dx} = 12(-1)^2 + 10(-1) = 2$

The tangent at P has gradient 2 and passes through $(-1, 1)$ and has equation

$$y - 1 = 2(x - (-1))$$
$$\Rightarrow y - 1 = 2x + 2$$
$$\Rightarrow y = 2x + 3 \text{ is the equation of the tangent}$$

(b) The curve and the tangent meet when

$$4x^3 + 5x^2 = 2x + 3$$
$$\Rightarrow 4x^3 + 5x^2 - 2x - 3 = 0$$

In order to solve this cubic equation you need to factorise the left-hand side.

The curve and tangent meet when $x = -1$ which means that $(x + 1)$ is a factor of $f(x) = 4x^3 + 5x^2 - 2x - 3$.

> This can be achieved by searching for factors using the factor theorem, but with a little thought you may realise that one of the factors is already known to you.

You can, of course, check this using the factor theorem:

$$f(-1) = 4(-1)^3 + 5(-1)^2 - 2(-1) - 3 = -4 + 5 + 2 - 3 = 0$$

Hence, $(x + 1)$ is a factor of $f(x)$.

$$
\begin{array}{r}
4x^2 + x - 3 \\
x + 1 \overline{\smash{)}\,4x^3 + 5x^2 - 2x - 3} \\
\underline{4x^3 + 4x^2\phantom{{}- 2x - 3}} \\
x^2 - 2x\phantom{{}- 3} \\
\underline{x^2 + x\phantom{{}- 3}} \\
-3x - 3 \\
\underline{-3x - 3} \\
0
\end{array}
$$

> To find the remaining factor(s) you can use the technique of dividing polynomials from chapter 2.

So $4x^3 + 5x^2 - 2x - 3 = (x + 1)(4x^2 + x - 3)$
$= (x + 1)(x + 1)(4x - 3)$

Thus $4x^3 + 5x^2 - 2x - 3 = 0$
$\Rightarrow (x + 1)(x + 1)(4x - 3) = 0$

$\Rightarrow x = -1$ (twice) or $x = \dfrac{3}{4}$

So Q must have x-coordinate $\dfrac{3}{4} \Rightarrow y = \dfrac{9}{2}$

Q has coordinates $\left(\dfrac{3}{4}, \dfrac{9}{2}\right)$.

> Alternatively, you could have assumed the factors were $(x + 1)(ax^2 + bx + c)$ and found a, b and c by equating coefficients.

> $x = -1$ corresponds to point P. The repeated solution indicates that the line just touches the curve at this point.

EXERCISE 6A

1 Find the equation of the tangent to the curve $y = 3x^2 - 2x$ at the point $(2, 8)$.

2 Find the equation of the tangent to the curve $y = (1 - 3x)^2$ at the point P where $x = -1$.

3 Find the equation of the tangent to the curve $y = 5\sqrt{x} - 8x + 1$ at the point $(4, -21)$.

4 Find the equation of the tangent to the curve $y = \dfrac{2 - x^3}{x}$ $(x \neq 0)$ at the point where $x = -2$.

5 Show that the equation of the tangent to the curve $y = 7x^2 - 2e^x$ at the point where $x = 2$ is $y = (28 - 2e^2)x + 2e^2 - 28$.

6 Find the equation of the tangent to the curve $y = 3x - \dfrac{4}{x^2}$ which has a gradient of 4.

7 Find the equation of the tangent to the curve $y = 2e^{3x} + 4$ at the point where $x = -1$.

> $\dfrac{d}{dx}(e^{kx}) = ke^{kx}$

8 A curve has equation $y = 2\ln x + 5x$ $(x > 0)$.
   Find the equation of the tangent to this curve at the points:
   (a) P where $x = 1$,
   (b) Q where $x = \dfrac{1}{2}$. (Leave your answer in terms of $\ln 2$.)

9 A curve has equation $y = \dfrac{(x + 2)(x - 4)}{x^2}$ $(x \neq 0)$. The tangent to this curve at the point where $x = 2$ crosses the x-axis at A and the y-axis at B. Find the area of the triangle OAB, where O is the origin.

10 Find the equations of the tangents to the curve $y = (x + 1)(5 - x)$ at the points $P(-1, 0)$ and $Q(5, 0)$. The tangents at P and Q meet at the point M. Find the coordinates of the point M.

11 Find the equations of the tangents to the curve with
    equation $y = x^3 + 2x^2 - 3x$ at the points $A(-2, 6)$ and
    $B(1, 0)$. The tangents at A and B meet at the point C. Find
    the coordinates of point C.

12 A curve is given by $y = x^2 + \dfrac{1}{x}$ $(x \neq 0)$. The tangent to the
    curve at the point where $x = 1$ meets the curve again at the
    point N. Find the coordinates of the point N.

6.2 Chain rule for composite functions

Consider the expression $y = (2x - 3)^5$.
In order to differentiate with respect to x you would first have
to use the binomial expansion and then differentiate term by
term.

This is very time consuming and so fortunately there is a
much quicker and easier method that relies upon noticing
that the function is built up as a composite of two simpler
functions.

By substituting $u = 2x - 3$, you can then write y in terms of
u as

$$y = u^5.$$

Therefore,

$$\frac{dy}{du} = 5u^4 \quad \text{and} \quad \frac{du}{dx} = 2.$$

But how does this help to find $\dfrac{dy}{dx}$?

Consider the general composite function $y = gf(x)$.

Using the same notation as above,

$$u = f(x) \quad \text{and} \quad y = g(u).$$

Now making a small increase of δx in x will create a small
increase of δu in u since u is a function of x. This will, in turn,
create a small increase of δy in y since y is a function of u.

Clearly $\dfrac{\delta y}{\delta x} = \dfrac{\delta y}{\delta u} \times \dfrac{\delta u}{\delta x}$

> Since the δus cancel each other
> out on the right-hand side.

You have seen previously that

as $\delta x \to 0$, $\dfrac{\delta y}{\delta x} \to \dfrac{dy}{dx}$ and similarly $\dfrac{\delta u}{\delta x} \to \dfrac{du}{dx}$.

> Since the small increase in u was
> created by the small increase
> in x.

It should also be clear that as $\delta x \to 0$, $\delta u \to 0$.

So as $\delta x \to 0$, $\dfrac{\delta y}{\delta u} \to \dfrac{dy}{du}$ giving the result

$$\frac{dy}{dx} = \frac{dy}{du} \times \frac{du}{dx}$$

or in function notation

$$\frac{dy}{dx} = g'(u) \times f'(x), \text{ where } y = gf(x) \text{ and } u = f(x).$$

> The chain rule is an important and very useful technique.

This result is known as the **chain rule**.

Worked example 6.6

Differentiate $y = (2x - 3)^5$.

Solution

You have already seen above that you can write $u = 2x - 3$ and $y = u^5$ giving

$$\frac{du}{dx} = 2 \quad \text{and} \quad \frac{dy}{du} = 5u^4.$$

Using the chain rule gives

$$\frac{dy}{dx} = \frac{dy}{du} \times \frac{du}{dx} = 5u^4 \times 2 = 10u^4$$

but since the original function was given in terms of x and not u you should rewrite u in terms of x, so that

$$\frac{dy}{dx} = 10(2x - 3)^4.$$

Worked example 6.7

Use the chain rule to differentiate the following composite functions with respect to x.

(a) $y = (3x + 5)^2$, **(b)** $y = e^{5x}$.

Solution

(a) Here you can write

$$u = 3x + 5 \text{ and } y = u^2$$
$$\Rightarrow \frac{du}{dx} = 3 \quad \text{and} \quad \frac{dy}{du} = 2u$$

Using the chain rule gives,

$$\frac{dy}{dx} = \frac{dy}{du} \times \frac{du}{dx} = 2u \times 3 = 6u$$
$$\Rightarrow \frac{dy}{dx} = 6(3x + 5)$$

> This result can be verified using the 'old' method of expanding brackets:
> $y = (3x + 5)(3x + 5)$
> $\quad = 9x^2 + 30x + 25$
> $\Rightarrow \frac{dy}{dx} = 18x + 30 = 6(3x + 5)$

6

(b) Here you can write

$$u = 5x \text{ and } y = e^u$$

$$\Rightarrow \frac{du}{dx} = 5 \text{ and } \frac{dy}{du} = e^u$$

Using the chain rule gives,

$$\frac{dy}{dx} = \frac{dy}{du} \times \frac{du}{dx} = e^u \times 5 = 5e^u$$

$$\Rightarrow \frac{dy}{dx} = 5e^{5x}$$

> Notice that the chain rule confirms the result you met in P2:
> $$\frac{d}{dx}(e^{kx}) = ke^{kx}$$

Worked example 6.8

Differentiate the following composite functions with respect to x:

(a) $y = \sin(4x - 7)$,   **(b)** $y = 5\cos(2 - 3x)$,

(c) $y = 3\ln(x^2 + 4x - 1)$.

Solution

(a) Writing

$$u = 4x - 7 \text{ and } y = \sin u$$

$$\Rightarrow \frac{du}{dx} = 4 \quad \text{and} \quad \frac{dy}{du} = \cos u$$

The chain rule gives,

$$\frac{dy}{dx} = \frac{dy}{du} \times \frac{du}{dx} = \cos u \times 4 = 4\cos u$$

$$\Rightarrow \frac{dy}{dx} = 4\cos(4x - 7)$$

(b) You can write

$$u = 2 - 3x \quad \text{and} \quad y = 5\cos u$$

$$\Rightarrow \frac{du}{dx} = -3 \quad \text{and} \quad \frac{dy}{du} = -5\sin u$$

The chain rule gives,

$$\frac{dy}{dx} = \frac{dy}{du} \times \frac{du}{dx} = -5\sin u \times -3 = 15\sin u$$

$$\Rightarrow \frac{dy}{dx} = 15\sin(2 - 3x)$$

(c) Making the substitution

$$u = x^2 + 4x - 1 \quad \text{and} \quad y = 3\ln u$$

$$\Rightarrow \frac{du}{dx} = 2x + 4 \quad \text{and} \quad \frac{dy}{du} = \frac{3}{u}$$

The chain rule gives,

$$\frac{dy}{dx} = \frac{dy}{du} \times \frac{du}{dx} = \frac{3}{u} \times (2x + 4) = \frac{3(2x + 4)}{u}$$

$$\Rightarrow \frac{dy}{dx} = \frac{3(2x + 4)}{x^2 + 4x - 1}$$

With enough practice, it soon becomes possible to dispense with the formal approach of defining u in terms of x and then defining y in terms of u. You can simply visualise differentiating each 'layer' of the composite function and multiplying the derivatives together.

Worked example 6.9

Find $\dfrac{dy}{dx}$ for the following functions:

(a) $y = 5(2 - 6x)^3$,   **(b)** $y = 2 \sin(4x - 5)$.

Solution

(a) $\qquad y = 5(2 - 6x)^3$

$\Rightarrow \quad \dfrac{dy}{dx} = 15(2 - 6x)^2 \times -6 = -90(2 - 6x)^2$

(b) $\quad y = 2 \sin(4x - 5)$

$\Rightarrow \quad \dfrac{dy}{dx} = 2 \cos(4x - 5) \times 4 = 8 \cos(4x - 5)$

> Differentiating $5(\ \ )^3$ gives $15(\ \ )^2$ and differentiating $2 - 6x$ gives -6, then multiply the two together.

> Differentiating $2 \sin(\ \ )$ gives $2 \cos(\ \ )$ and differentiating $4x - 5$ gives 4, then multiply the two together.

6

EXERCISE 6B

1 Use the chain rule to differentiate the following composite functions with respect to x:

    (a) $y = (8x + 3)^4$ (use $u = 8x + 3$ and $y = u^4$),

    (b) $y = (3 - 4x)^6$ (use $u = 3 - 4x$ and $y = u^6$),

    (c) $y = 5(3x - 2)^{10}$ (use $u = 3x - 2$ and $y = 5u^{10}$),

    (d) $y = 7(7 - x)^8$ (use $u = 7 - x$ and $y = 7u^8$).

> In the first few questions you have been given u and $y = g(u)$, but as you gain confidence working through the exercise, you may wish to practise finding the derivative by simply visualising these.

2 Differentiate the following with respect to x:

    (a) $y = e^{5x - 2}$ (use $u = 5x - 2$ and $y = e^u$),

    (b) $y = 3 \sin(6x + 2)$ (use $u = 6x + 2$ and $y = 3 \sin u$),

    (c) $y = 2 \cos 8x$ (use $u = 8x$ and $y = 2 \cos u$),

    (d) $y = 5 \ln(9x + 1)$ (use $u = 9x + 1$ and $y = 5 \ln u$),

    (e) $y = \dfrac{1}{2x + 7}$ (use $u = 2x + 7$ and $y = u^{-1}$).

3 Find $\dfrac{dy}{dx}$ for each of these:

    (a) $y = 3 \ln(3x^2 + 3x - 1)$ ($u = 3x^2 + 3x - 1$ and $y = 3 \ln u$),

    (b) $y = \dfrac{4}{3 - 2x}$ ($u = 3 - 2x$ and $y = 4u^{-1}$),

    (c) $y = \dfrac{2}{(6x + 1)^2}$ ($u = 6x + 1$ and $y = 2u^{-2}$),

    (d) $y = \dfrac{1}{e^x + 4}$ ($u = e^x + 4$ and $y = u^{-1}$),

    (e) $y = e^{x^2}$ ($u = x^2$ and $y = e^u$).

4 Differentiate each of the following with respect to x:

(a) $y = 2(4x - 1)^6$,

(b) $y = \dfrac{(8 - 3x)^5}{15}$,

(c) $y = \dfrac{\sin(6x + 1)}{12}$,

(d) $y = 4\ln(3 - x)$,

(e) $y = 3e^{9 - 2x}$,

(f) $y = -\cos(5 - 3x)$,

(g) $y = e^{3x} + 6x^2$,

(h) $y = 6x^3 - 2\ln 3x$,

(i) $y = \dfrac{4\sin(6x - 5)}{3}$,

(j) $y = e^{4 - 3x} + \sin 5x$.

5 Find the gradient of the following curves at the specified point:

(a) $y = 3(2x - 1)^4$, where $x = 2$,

(b) $y = 4\cos 2\theta$, where $\theta = \dfrac{\pi}{4}$,

(c) $y = 4e^{3 - x}$, where $x = 2$,

(d) $y = 3\ln(x^2 + 2)$, where $x = -1$,

(e) $y = 5x^2 - (2x + 1)^3$, where $x = -2$.

6 Find the equation of the tangent to the curve given by $y = (2x - 3)^4$ at the point $P(1, 1)$.

7 A curve has equation $y = -\dfrac{2}{(2x - 1)^2} - x$.

(a) Find $\dfrac{dy}{dx}$ and hence find the coordinates of the stationary point of the curve.

(b) Find $\dfrac{d^2y}{dx^2}$ and hence determine the nature of the stationary point.

8 A curve has equation $y = (3x - 2)^3 - 5x^2$.

(a) Find $\dfrac{dy}{dx}$ and hence find the coordinates of the two stationary points of the curve.

(b) Find $\dfrac{d^2y}{dx^2}$ and hence determine the nature of each of these stationary points.

9 The value £V of a sports car can be modelled by the equation $V = Ae^{-kt}$, where t is the age of the car in years.
The car cost £32 000 when new, and after two years its value was £24 000.

(a) State the value of the constant A.

(b) Calculate the value of the constant k, giving your answer to three significant figures.

(c) Use differentiation to estimate the rate of depreciation of the car when it is exactly five years old, giving your answer to the nearest ten pounds per year. [A]

10 The depth of water at the end of a pier is H m at time t h after high tide, where

$$H = 20 + 5\cos(kt)$$

and k is a positive constant measured in radians per hour.

(a) Write down the greatest and least depths of water at the end of the pier.

(b) Sketch the graph of H against t from $t = 0$ to the time of the next high tide.

(c) The time interval between successive high tides is 11 hours and 15 minutes. Calculate the value of k, giving your answer to three significant figures.

(d) Calculate the rate of change of the depth of water exactly two hours after high tide, giving your answer in metres per hour. Interpret the sign of your answer. [A]

6.3 Extending the chain rule

You saw in section 6.2 how the chain rule can be used to differentiate composite functions.
You may have noticed that all of the composite functions considered so far have been built up of **two** simpler functions. The basic principle, however, can be extended to differentiate composite functions built up of three or more simpler functions. For example, $\sin^2(2x + 1)$, $\ln(\tan 2x)$, etc.

The chain rule can be extended for three functions to

$$\frac{dy}{dx} = \frac{dy}{dv} \times \frac{dv}{du} \times \frac{du}{dx}, \text{ if } y = \text{hgf}(x)$$

> You can imagine the dvs and dus cancelling on the right-hand side.

where $u = \text{f}(x)$, $v = \text{g}(u)$ and $y = \text{h}(v)$.

Worked example 6.10

Differentiate the following functions with respect to x:

(a) $y = \sin^3(4x + 1)$, (b) $y = \ln(\cos 3x)$.

Solution

(a) Here you can write

$$u = 4x + 1, v = \sin u \text{ and } y = v^3$$

$$\Rightarrow \frac{du}{dx} = 4, \frac{dv}{du} = \cos u \quad \text{and} \quad \frac{dy}{dv} = 3v^2$$

$$\Rightarrow \frac{dy}{dx} = \frac{dy}{dv} \times \frac{dv}{du} \times \frac{du}{dx} = 3v^2 \times \cos u \times 4 = 12v^2 \cos u$$

But you need to rewrite the expression in terms of x

$$\frac{dy}{dx} = 12 \sin^2 (4x + 1) \cos (4x + 1)$$

(b) $\dfrac{dy}{dx} = \dfrac{dy}{dv} \times \dfrac{dv}{du} \times \dfrac{du}{dx} = \dfrac{1}{\cos 3x} \times -\sin 3x \times 3$

> Again, with practice, you can visualise differentiating one 'layer' at a time.

$$= -\frac{3 \sin 3x}{\cos 3x} = -3 \tan 3x$$

EXERCISE 6C

Differentiate each of the following functions using the chain rule:

1 $y = \sin^2 5x$.

2 $y = \cos^4 9x$.

3 $y = \ln (\sin 4x)$.

4 $y = 2 \cos^5 4x$.

5 $y = (e^{2x} - 5)^3$.

6 $y = \sin \sqrt{3x + 1}$.

7 $y = (\ln \sqrt{x})^2$.

8 $y = e^{\sqrt{6x}}$.

9 $y = \cos (\ln 8x)$.

10 $y = \cos^5 \sqrt{x}$.

6.4 The reciprocal of the first derivative

You now have quite a few techniques for finding the derivative $\dfrac{dy}{dx}$ of a function. You may also occasionally find it necessary to find the derivative $\dfrac{dx}{dy}$.

Consider a small increase in x, δx, which produces a small increase in y, δy.

Now clearly $\dfrac{\delta y}{\delta x} = \dfrac{1}{\dfrac{\delta x}{\delta y}}$

and taking the limit as $\delta x \to 0$ gives

> While this result may appear obvious it cannot be taken for granted that similar results are also true. For example, the corresponding result for second (or any higher order) derivatives is **not** true.

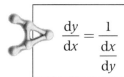

$$\frac{dy}{dx} = \frac{1}{\dfrac{dx}{dy}}$$

Since by the chain rule $\dfrac{dy}{dx} \times \dfrac{dx}{dy} = \dfrac{dy}{dy} = 1$, it also follows

immediately that $\dfrac{dy}{dx} = \dfrac{1}{\dfrac{dx}{dy}}$.

Worked example 6.11

Verify the above result in the cases where:

(a) $y = \sqrt{x}$,   **(b)** $y = \ln x$.

Solution

(a) Firstly, $y = x^{\frac{1}{2}} \Rightarrow \dfrac{dy}{dx} = \dfrac{1}{2\sqrt{x}}$

Now $y = \sqrt{x} \Rightarrow x = y^2$

which gives $\dfrac{dx}{dy} = 2y = 2\sqrt{x}.$

Using the result gives

$\dfrac{dy}{dx} = \dfrac{1}{\left(\dfrac{dx}{dy}\right)} = \dfrac{1}{2\sqrt{x}}$ as expected.

(b) Firstly, $y = \ln x \Rightarrow \dfrac{dy}{dx} = \dfrac{1}{x}$

Now $y = \ln x \Rightarrow x = e^y$

which gives $\dfrac{dx}{dy} = e^y = e^{\ln x} = x.$

Using the result gives

$\dfrac{dy}{dx} = \dfrac{1}{\left(\dfrac{dx}{dy}\right)} = \dfrac{1}{x}$ as expected.

Worked example 6.12

Find $\dfrac{dy}{dx}$ for each of the following functions and hence write down an expression for $\dfrac{dx}{dy}$.

(a) $y = 5 \ln 3x$,   **(b)** $y = (4x - 3)^3$,   **(c)** $y = \dfrac{3}{5x - 1}.$

Solution

(a) $y = 5 \ln 3x \Rightarrow \dfrac{dy}{dx} = \dfrac{5}{3x} \times 3 = \dfrac{5}{x}$

Using the above result gives

$\dfrac{dx}{dy} = \dfrac{x}{5}.$

> Notice the use of the chain rule to differentiate the composite function.

(b) $y = (4x - 3)^3 \Rightarrow \dfrac{dy}{dx} = 3(4x - 3)^2 \times 4 = 12(4x - 3)^2$

Using the above result gives

$\dfrac{dx}{dy} = \dfrac{1}{12(4x - 3)^2}.$

6

(c) $y = \dfrac{3}{5x - 1} = 3(5x - 1)^{-1}$

$$\Rightarrow \frac{dx}{dy} = -3(5x - 1)^{-2} \times 5 = -\frac{15}{(5x - 1)^2}$$

Using the above result gives

$$\frac{dx}{dy} = -\frac{(5x - 1)^2}{15}.$$

6.5 Connected rates of change

You saw in P2 how derivatives can be used to represent rates of change:

$\dfrac{dP}{dQ}$ represents the rate of change of P with respect to Q.

For example, if the volume $V\,\text{cm}^3$ of a balloon as it is being inflated is given by $V = 50\sqrt{t}$, where t is the time in seconds, then the rate at which the volume is increasing is given by

$$\frac{dV}{dt} = \frac{25}{\sqrt{t}}.$$

Notice that in this example the volume is given as a function of t and so the rate of change of volume can be found by directly differentiating V with respect to t.

However, in many practical problems involving rates of change it is not possible to differentiate directly with respect to the required variable. This is where the chain rule is particularly useful.

> The chain rule can be used to solve many practical problems involving rates of change, where there are three or more connected variables.

Worked example 6.13

The radius, $r\,\text{cm}$, of a circle is increasing at a rate of $2\,\text{cm s}^{-1}$. Find the rate at which the area, $A\,\text{cm}^2$, is increasing when the radius is $6\,\text{cm}$.

In this context 'rate' usually refers to the rate of change with respect to **time**.

Solution

It is worth writing down and interpreting the information given in the question. This may involve derivatives and any other formulae that seem relevant. In this case you will need the formula for the area of a circle.

Radius is increasing at a rate of $2\,\mathrm{cm\,s^{-1}} \Rightarrow \dfrac{dr}{dt} = 2$

> There are three variables: r, A and t. Notice that the area cannot be differentiated directly with respect to t but can be differentiated with respect to r.

The area of a circle is given by $A = \pi r^2 \Rightarrow \dfrac{dA}{dr} = 2\pi r$

You are required to find the rate of change of area , $\dfrac{dA}{dt}$.

Using the chain rule gives:

$$\frac{dA}{dt} = \frac{dA}{dr} \times \frac{dr}{dt} = 2\pi r \times 2 = 4\pi r.$$

When $r = 6\,\mathrm{cm}$, $\dfrac{dA}{dt} = 4\pi(6) = 24\pi$.

The area is increasing at a rate of $24\pi\,\mathrm{cm^2\,s^{-1}}$ ($\approx 75.40\,\mathrm{cm^2\,s^{-1}}$).

Worked example 6.14

A football is being inflated at a constant rate of $8\,\mathrm{cm^3\,s^{-1}}$. Find the rate at which the radius of the football is increasing when the volume is $\dfrac{500\pi}{3}\,\mathrm{cm^3}$, giving your answer correct to three significant figures. (You may assume that the football is spherical.)

Solution

Inflated at a constant rate of $8\,\mathrm{cm^3\,s^{-1}} \Rightarrow \dfrac{dV}{dt} = 8$

Volume of sphere is given by $V = \dfrac{4}{3}\pi r^3 \Rightarrow \dfrac{dV}{dr} = 4\pi r^2$

You are required to find rate of increase of radius , $\dfrac{dr}{dt}$.

Using the chain rule:

$$\frac{dr}{dt} = \frac{dr}{dV} \times \frac{dV}{dt} = \frac{1}{4\pi r^2} \times 8 = \frac{2}{\pi r^2}.$$

> Notice the use of the result $\dfrac{dr}{dV} = \dfrac{1}{\dfrac{dV}{dr}}$ when finding $\dfrac{dr}{dV}$.

To find the value of $\dfrac{dr}{dt}$ when the volume is $\dfrac{500\pi}{3}\,\mathrm{cm^3}$, you need to substitute the corresponding value of r:

> Since $\dfrac{dr}{dt}$ is a function of r.

$$V = \frac{4}{3}\pi r^3 \Rightarrow \frac{500\pi}{3} = \frac{4}{3}\pi r^3$$

$$\Rightarrow r^3 = \frac{500\pi}{4\pi} = 125$$

$$\Rightarrow r = \sqrt[3]{125} = 5$$

So when $r = 5$, $\dfrac{dr}{dt} = \dfrac{2}{\pi(5)^2} = \dfrac{2}{25\pi} = 0.0255$

Hence, the radius is increasing at a rate of $0.0255\,\mathrm{cm\,s^{-1}}$ (3 s.f.)

Worked example 6.15

A balloon is being blown up so that its volume is increasing at a constant rate of $10\,\text{cm}^3\,\text{s}^{-1}$. Find the rate at which the surface area of the balloon is increasing when the radius is $6\,\text{cm}$. (Assume that the balloon is spherical.)

Solution

Volume increasing at a rate of $10\,\text{cm}^3\,\text{s}^{-1} \Rightarrow \dfrac{\mathrm{d}V}{\mathrm{d}t} = 10$

Volume of a sphere is given by $V = \dfrac{4}{3}\pi r^3 \Rightarrow \dfrac{\mathrm{d}V}{\mathrm{d}r} = 4\pi r^2$

Surface area of a sphere is $A = 4\pi r^2 \Rightarrow \dfrac{\mathrm{d}A}{\mathrm{d}r} = 8\pi r$

You need to find the rate of change of surface area , $\dfrac{\mathrm{d}A}{\mathrm{d}t}$.

The chain rule gives:

Extension of the chain rule.

$$\frac{\mathrm{d}A}{\mathrm{d}t} = \frac{\mathrm{d}A}{\mathrm{d}r} \times \frac{\mathrm{d}r}{\mathrm{d}V} \times \frac{\mathrm{d}V}{\mathrm{d}t} = 8\pi r \times \frac{1}{4\pi r^2} \times 10 = \frac{20}{r}$$

$$\dfrac{1}{\dfrac{\mathrm{d}V}{\mathrm{d}r}}$$

When $r = 6\,\text{cm}$, $\dfrac{\mathrm{d}A}{\mathrm{d}t} = \dfrac{20}{6} = 3\tfrac{1}{3}$.

The surface area is increasing at a rate of $3\tfrac{1}{3}\,\text{cm}^2\,\text{s}^{-1}$.

Worked examination question 6.1

Under certain conditions, the pressure $p\,\text{N}\,\text{m}^{-2}$ and the volume $v\,\text{m}^3$ of a gas are related by the equation

$p = kv^{-\frac{4}{3}}$, where k is a constant.

(a) Given that $p = 27$ when $v = 8$, calculate the value of the constant k.

(b) **(i)** Find the value of $\dfrac{\mathrm{d}p}{\mathrm{d}v}$ when $v = 8$.

(ii) At the instant when $v = 8$, the volume of the gas is increasing at the rate of $0.04\,\text{m}^3\,\text{s}^{-1}$. Calculate the rate at which the pressure is changing, in $\text{N}\,\text{m}^{-2}\,\text{s}^{-1}$, at this instant in time, and interpret the sign in your answer.

[A]

Solution

(a) $p = kv^{-\frac{4}{3}}$

Substituting $p = 27$ and $v = 8$ gives

$$27 = k(8)^{-\frac{4}{3}} \Rightarrow 27 = k \times \frac{1}{16}$$

$$\Rightarrow k = 27 \times 16 = 432.$$

So $p = 432v^{-\frac{4}{3}}$.

(b) (i) $\dfrac{dp}{dv} = -\dfrac{4}{3} \times 432v^{-\frac{7}{3}} = -576v^{-\frac{7}{3}}$

when $v = 8$, $\dfrac{dp}{dv} = -576(8)^{-\frac{7}{3}} = -4.5$.

(ii) You are given that $\dfrac{dv}{dt} = 0.04$.

When $v = 8$, the chain rule gives

$\dfrac{dp}{dt} = \dfrac{dp}{dv} \times \dfrac{dv}{dt} = -4.5 \times 0.04 = -0.18$.

The negative sign indicates that the pressure is **decreasing** at a rate of $0.18\,\mathrm{N\,m^{-2}\,s^{-1}}$.

EXERCISE 6D

1 The radius, r cm, of a circle is increasing at the rate of $1.5\,\mathrm{cm\,s^{-1}}$. Find the rate at which the area, A cm², is increasing when the radius is 7 cm.

2 The radius of a circular oil slick is increasing at the rate of $0.8\,\mathrm{m\,min^{-1}}$. Find the rate at which the area of the oil slick is increasing when the radius is 5 m, giving your answer to three significant figures.

3 The area of a circle is increasing at a constant rate of $8\,\mathrm{cm^2\,s^{-1}}$. Find the rate at which the radius is increasing when the area is 4π cm², giving your answer to two decimal places.

4 The side, x cm, of a square is decreasing at a constant rate of $0.2\,\mathrm{cm\,s^{-1}}$. Find the rate at which the area of the square is decreasing when $x = 6$.

5 A metal cube of side x cm is heated uniformly so that the length of each side is increasing at a constant rate of $0.003\,\mathrm{cm\,s^{-1}}$ through expansion. Find the rate at which the volume of the cube is increasing when $x = 8$.

6 A ball is being inflated so that its volume is increasing at a constant rate of $12\,\mathrm{cm^3\,s^{-1}}$. Find the rate of change of the radius of the ball when the volume is 36π cm³.

7 A spherical lollipop, of radius r cm, is being sucked so that its volume is decreasing at a constant rate of $2\,\mathrm{cm^3\,min^{-1}}$. Find the rate at which the radius is decreasing when the volume of the lollipop is 10 cm³, giving your answer correct to three significant figures.

8 The surface area of a balloon as it is inflated increases at a constant rate of $20\,\mathrm{cm^2\,s^{-1}}$. Find the rate at which the volume is increasing when the radius is 3 cm.

9 The rate of change of the radius r cm, of a spherical pebble with respect to time t years is given by

$$\frac{dr}{dt} = -0.02r.$$

Using the formula for the volume of a sphere, $V = \frac{4}{3}\pi r^3$, determine the rate of change of the volume when the radius is 5 cm, giving your answer to three significant figures. State clearly the units and interpret the sign of your answer.   [A]

10 The triangle PQR is right-angled at Q, the hypotenuse $PR = 6$ cm and the variable angle QRP is θ radians, where $0 < \theta < \frac{\pi}{2}$.

  (a) Express the lengths PQ and QR in terms of θ and hence write down an expression for the area, A cm², of the triangle.

  (b) Show that $\frac{dA}{d\theta} = 18\cos 2\theta$.

  (c) Calculate the rate of change of area at the time when θ is equal to $\frac{\pi}{3}$ radians, given that θ is increasing at a rate of 0.1 rad s⁻¹. Interpret the sign of your answer.   [A]

6.6 Small increments and approximate changes

How can you make a reasonable estimate of the value of $\sqrt{26}$ without the aid of a calculator?

It is certainly going to be a little over 5 since $\sqrt{25} = 5$ but is it 5.04, 5.1, 5.2, etc.?

Rather than just guessing at the correct answer there is a more sophisticated approach, which allows you to find a reasonable estimate.

You already know that

$$\text{as } \delta x \to 0, \quad \frac{\delta y}{\delta x} \to \frac{dy}{dx}$$

Now if δx is small enough it is true to say that

$$\frac{\delta y}{\delta x} \approx \frac{dy}{dx}$$

or

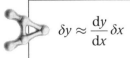

$$\delta y \approx \frac{dy}{dx}\delta x$$

This is the result which allows you to make reasonable approximations to the value of a function **close to a known value**.

It has to be close so that δx is small.

Worked example 6.16

Find an estimate for the value of $\sqrt{26}$ without using a calculator.

Solution

Let $y = \sqrt{x} = x^{\frac{1}{2}}$, so that $\dfrac{dy}{dx} = \dfrac{1}{2}x^{-\frac{1}{2}} = \dfrac{1}{2\sqrt{x}}$.

The **known value** in this case is $\sqrt{25} = 5$ and in order to approximate $\sqrt{26}$ you make a small increment of 1 in the value of x from 25 to 26 giving

$$x = 25 \text{ and } \delta x = 1$$

δx is the small increment in x.

and you can now use the above result to find the small increment, δy, in the value of the expression:

$$\delta y \approx \frac{dy}{dx}\delta x$$

$$\Rightarrow \delta y \approx \frac{1}{2\sqrt{x}}\delta x$$

$$\Rightarrow \delta y \approx \frac{1}{2\sqrt{25}}(1) = \frac{1}{10}(1) = \frac{1}{10} = 0.1$$

This is an approximation to the amount that y has increased.

$$\Rightarrow \sqrt{26} \approx 5 + 0.1$$

$$\Rightarrow \sqrt{26} \approx 5.1$$

A calculator gives 5.099 019 514 . . .

Worked example 6.17

Find an approximate value for $\sqrt[3]{1003}$.

Solution

The function here is $y = \sqrt[3]{x} = x^{\frac{1}{3}} \Rightarrow \dfrac{dy}{dx} = \dfrac{1}{3}x^{-\frac{2}{3}} = \dfrac{1}{3(\sqrt[3]{x})^2}$

The known value in this case is $\sqrt[3]{1000} = 10$ and in order to approximate $\sqrt[3]{1003}$ you make a small increment of 3 in the value of x from 1000 to 1003 giving

$$x = 1000 \text{ and } \delta x = 3$$

and you can now use the above result to find the small increment, δy, in the value of the function:

$$\delta y \approx \frac{dy}{dx}\delta x$$

$$\Rightarrow \delta y \approx \frac{1}{3(\sqrt[3]{x})^2}\delta x$$

$$\Rightarrow \delta y \approx \frac{1}{3(\sqrt[3]{1000})^2}(3) = \frac{1}{300}(3) = \frac{1}{100} = 0.01$$

$$\Rightarrow \sqrt[3]{1003} \approx 10 + 0.01$$

$$\Rightarrow \sqrt[3]{1003} \approx 10.01$$

A calculator gives
10.009 990 2 . . .

Worked example 6.18

Find the approximate value of $e^{-0.01}$, without using a calculator.

Solution

The expression here is $y = e^x \Rightarrow \dfrac{dy}{dx} = e^x$

The known value in this case is $e^0 = 1$.

The difference here is that x **decreases** and in order to approximate $e^{-0.01}$ you make a small decrease of 0.01 in the value of x from 0 to -0.01 giving

$$x = 0 \text{ and } \delta x = -0.01$$

and $\delta y \approx \dfrac{dy}{dx}\delta x$

$$\Rightarrow \delta y \approx e^x \delta x$$

$$\Rightarrow \delta y \approx e^0(-0.01) = 1(-0.01) = -0.01$$

$$\Rightarrow e^{-0.01} \approx 1 - 0.01$$

$$\Rightarrow e^{-0.01} \approx 0.99$$

A calculator gives
0.990 049 833 . . .

Worked example 6.19

A metal cube has side 4 cm. The cube is heated uniformly so that each side increases by 0.1 cm due to expansion. Find the approximate increase in the volume, V cm³ of the cube.

Solution

Let the cube have side of length x so that

$$V = x^3 \Rightarrow \frac{dV}{dx} = 3x^2$$

The approximate increase in the volume, δV, is given by

$$\delta V \approx \frac{dV}{dx}\delta x$$

$$\Rightarrow \delta V \approx 3x^2\delta x$$

$$\Rightarrow \delta V \approx 3(4)^2(0.1) = 4.8$$

So the approximate increase in volume is 4.8 cm³.

EXERCISE 6E

1 Use the fact that $\ln 1 = 0$ to find an approximation for $\ln 1.01$.

2 Assuming that $e^0 = 1$, use calculus to obtain approximations for:

(a) $e^{0.1}$, (b) $e^{-0.1}$.

3 Find approximations to the following, without using a calculator:

(a) $\sqrt{1.1}$, (b) $\sqrt{5}$, (c) $\sqrt{99}$, (d) $\sqrt{2499}$.

4 Use the fact that $\sqrt[5]{1} = 1$ with small increments to make estimates for:

(a) $\sqrt[5]{1.1}$, (b) $\sqrt[5]{0.9}$.

5 A square measures 10 cm by 10 cm. Find the approximate increase in the area of the square if each side increases by 0.1 cm.

6 A sphere has a radius of 7 cm. Find an approximate value for the increase in surface area if the radius increases to 7.02 cm.

7 A sphere has a radius of 12 cm. Find an estimate for the decrease in volume of the sphere if the radius decreases to 11.95 cm.

6

Key point summary

1 To find the equation of the tangent to a curve at a   *p 90*
   point P
   (i)   use differentiation to find the gradient of the curve at P;
   (ii) substitute the gradient and coordinates of P into
         $$y - y_1 = m(x - x_1).$$

2 The chain rule can be used to differentiate composite   *p 97*
   functions. The chain rule is
   $$\frac{dy}{dx} = \frac{dy}{du} \times \frac{du}{dx} \text{ or in function notation}$$
   $$\frac{dy}{dx} = g'(u) \times f'(x) \text{ where } y = gf(x) \text{ and } u = f(x).$$

3 The chain rule can be extended to   *p 101*
   $$\frac{dy}{dx} = \frac{dy}{dv} \times \frac{dv}{du} \times \frac{du}{dx}.$$

4 $\dfrac{dy}{dx} = \dfrac{1}{\dfrac{dx}{dy}}$ *p 102*

5 The chain rule can be used to solve many practical   *p 104*
problems involving rates of change, where there are
three or more connected variables.

For example, $\dfrac{dV}{dt} = \dfrac{dV}{dx} \times \dfrac{dx}{dt}$.

6 The formula involving small increments   *p 108*

$$\delta y \approx \dfrac{dy}{dx} \delta x$$

can be used to calculate approximate changes.

Test yourself	**What to review**
1 Find the equation of the tangent to the curve $y = \sqrt{x} + 2x$ at the point $P(4, 10)$.	*Section 6.1*
2 Differentiate the following functions with respect to x: **(a)** $y = 5(3x - 2)^4$, **(b)** $y = 4 \sin 7x$, **(c)** $y = 4e^{3x-2} + 3x^3$.	*Section 6.2*
3 Find $\dfrac{dy}{dx}$ for these functions: **(a)** $y = \sin^4 2x$, **(b)** $y = \ln(\cos 4x)$.	*Section 6.3*
4 Find $\dfrac{dy}{dx}$ for these functions and hence write down an expression for $\dfrac{dx}{dy}$: **(a)** $y = 3(5 - 2x)^5$, **(b)** $y = \dfrac{1}{3x - 5}$.	*Section 6.4*
5 The volume of a spherical soap bubble is increasing at a constant rate of $9 \, \text{cm}^3 \, \text{s}^{-1}$. Find the rate at which the surface area of the bubble is increasing when the radius is $4 \, \text{cm}$.	*Section 6.5*
6 A cube of ice has side $20 \, \text{cm}$. Find an approximation for the decrease in surface area when each side decreases by $0.5 \, \text{cm}$.	*Section 6.6*

Test yourself ANSWERS

6 $120 \, \text{cm}^2$.

5 $4.5 \, \text{cm}^2 \, \text{s}^{-1}$.

4 **(a)** $\dfrac{dy}{dx} = -30(5 - 2x)^4$;   **(b)** $\dfrac{dy}{dx} = -\dfrac{3}{(3x - 5)^2}$.

3 **(a)** $8 \sin^3 2x \cos 2x$;   **(b)** $-\dfrac{4 \sin 4x}{\cos 4x}$ or $-4 \tan 4x$.

2 **(a)** $60(3x - 2)^3$;   **(b)** $28 \cos 7x$;   **(c)** $12e^{3x-2} + 9x^2$.

1 $4y = 9x + 4$.

Differentiation using product rule and quotient rule

Learning objectives

After studying this chapter you should be able to:
- differentiate using the product rule
- differentiate using the quotient rule
- differentiate $\tan x$, $\cot x$, $\sec x$ and $\operatorname{cosec} x$.

7.1 Introduction

In this chapter you will be introduced to methods for differentiating expressions such as

$y = x^3 \sin x$ which is the *product* of x^3 and $\sin x$.

You will also learn how to differentiate *quotients* such as

$$y = \frac{x^3}{\sin x}.$$

> You may think that if
>
> $y = x^3 \sin x$ then $\dfrac{dy}{dx} = 3x^2 \cos x$
>
> and if $y = \dfrac{x^3}{\sin x}$ then
>
> $\dfrac{dy}{dx} = \dfrac{3x^2}{\cos x}$.
>
> In other words, just differentiate each part of the product or quotient separately. Be warned! This approach **does not lead to the correct answer.**

7.2 Differentiation using the product rule

Consider the product

$y = u \times v,$

where u and v are each functions of x.

Making a small change δx in x produces a small change in each of the expressions u, v and y.

> This is because u, v and y are all functions of x and, therefore, their value depends on x.

Let the small changes in u, v and y be δu, δv and δy, respectively.

Since

$y = u \times v$

making the small change in x gives

$$y + \delta y = (u + \delta u)(v + \delta v)$$
$$\Rightarrow y + \delta y = uv + u\delta v + v\delta u + \delta u \delta v$$
$$\Rightarrow \delta y = uv + u\delta v + v\delta u + \delta u \delta v - y$$
$$\Rightarrow \delta y = u\delta v + v\delta u + \delta u \delta v$$

> By multiplying out the brackets.

> $uv - y = 0$ since $y = uv$.

Dividing through by δx gives

$$\frac{\delta y}{\delta x} = u\frac{\delta v}{\delta x} + v\frac{\delta u}{\delta x} + \delta u\frac{\delta v}{\delta x}$$

Now as $\delta x \to 0$ you have

$$\frac{\delta y}{\delta x} \to \frac{dy}{dx}, \quad \frac{\delta u}{\delta x} \to \frac{du}{dx}, \quad \frac{\delta v}{\delta x} \to \frac{dv}{dx} \quad \text{and } \delta u \to 0$$

giving

$$\frac{dy}{dx} = u\frac{dv}{dx} + v\frac{du}{dx} + 0 \times \frac{dv}{dx} = u\frac{dv}{dx} + v\frac{du}{dx}.$$

Thus,

> To differentiate the product $y = uv$ you can use the result:
>
> $$\frac{dy}{dx} = u\frac{dv}{dx} + v\frac{du}{dx}$$

This result is known as the **product rule**.

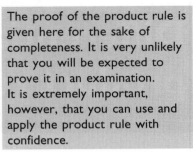

The proof of the product rule is given here for the sake of completeness. It is very unlikely that you will be expected to prove it in an examination. It is extremely important, however, that you can use and apply the product rule with confidence.

This rule is sometimes written using the 'dash' notation for derivatives, namely
$$y' = uv' + u'v.$$

Worked example 7.1

Differentiate $y = x^3 \sin x$ with respect to x.

Solution

You can write $u = x^3 \Rightarrow \dfrac{du}{dx} = 3x^2$

and $v = \sin x \Rightarrow \dfrac{dv}{dx} = \cos x.$

The product rule gives

$$\frac{dy}{dx} = u\frac{dv}{dx} + v\frac{du}{dx}$$

$$= x^3 \cos x + \sin x (3x^2)$$

Leave the first alone.   Differentiate the second.   Leave the second alone.   Differentiate the first.

$$= x^3 \cos x + 3x^2 \sin x$$

$$\Rightarrow \frac{dy}{dx} = x^2(x \cos x + 3 \sin x)$$

Worked example 7.2

Find the derivative of $y = x^4 \cos x$.

Solution

Writing $u = x^4 \Rightarrow \dfrac{du}{dx} = 4x^3$

and $v = \cos x \Rightarrow \dfrac{dv}{dx} = -\sin x$,

the product rule gives

$$\frac{dy}{dx} = u\frac{dv}{dx} + v\frac{du}{dx}$$

$$= x^4(-\sin x) + \cos x(4x^3) = -x^4 \sin x + 4x^3 \cos x$$

$$\Rightarrow \frac{dy}{dx} = x^3(4\cos x - x\sin x).$$

Worked example 7.3

Find the gradient of the curve $y = \sqrt{x}\ln x$ at the point $P(1,0)$.

Solution

$u = x^{\frac{1}{2}} \Rightarrow \dfrac{du}{dx} = \dfrac{1}{2\sqrt{x}}$

and $v = \ln x \Rightarrow \dfrac{dv}{dx} = \dfrac{1}{x}$

The product rule gives

$$\frac{dy}{dx} = u\frac{dv}{dx} + v\frac{du}{dx}$$

$$= x^{\frac{1}{2}}\left(\frac{1}{x}\right) + \ln x\left(\frac{1}{2\sqrt{x}}\right) = \frac{1}{\sqrt{x}} + \frac{1}{2\sqrt{x}}\ln x$$

$$\Rightarrow \frac{dy}{dx} = \frac{1}{\sqrt{x}}\left(1 + \tfrac{1}{2}\ln x\right)$$

At P, $\dfrac{dy}{dx} = \dfrac{1}{\sqrt{1}}\left(1 + \tfrac{1}{2}\ln 1\right) = 1(1+0) = 1$

So the gradient at P is equal to 1.

Worked example 7.4

Find the equation of the tangent to the curve $y = x^2 e^{3x}$ at the point $N(2, 4e^6)$.

Solution

$u = x^2 \Rightarrow \dfrac{du}{dx} = 2x$

and $v = e^{3x} \Rightarrow \dfrac{dv}{dx} = 3e^{3x}$

> Notice that the chain rule has been used to differentiate e^{3x}.

The product rule gives

$$\frac{dy}{dx} = u\frac{dy}{dx} + v\frac{du}{dx}$$

$$= x^2(3e^{3x}) + e^{3x}(2x) = 3x^2e^{3x} + 2xe^{3x}$$

$$\Rightarrow \frac{dy}{dx} = xe^{3x}(3x + 2)$$

At N, $\dfrac{dy}{dx} = 2e^6(6 + 2) = 16e^6$

The tangent at N has equation

$$y - 4e^6 = 16e^6(x - 2)$$
$$\Rightarrow y - 4e^6 = 16e^6x - 32e^6$$
$$\Rightarrow y + 28e^6 = 16e^6x$$

Worked example 7.5

A curve has equation $y = xe^{2x}$.

(a) Find the coordinates of the turning point of the curve.

(b) Find $\dfrac{d^2y}{dx^2}$ and hence determine the nature of the turning point.

Solution

(a) $u = x \Rightarrow \dfrac{du}{dx} = 1$

and $v = e^{2x} \Rightarrow \dfrac{dv}{dx} = 2e^{2x}$

The product rules gives

$$\frac{dy}{dx} = u\frac{dv}{dx} + v\frac{du}{dx}$$

$$= x(2e^{2x}) + e^{2x}(1) = 2xe^{2x} + e^{2x}$$

$$\Rightarrow \frac{dy}{dx} = e^{2x}(2x + 1)$$

At turning points the gradient is zero.

$$e^{2x}(2x + 1) = 0$$
$$\Rightarrow e^{2x} = 0 \text{ or } 2x + 1 = 0$$

But $e^{2x} = 0$ has no solutions, so $x = -\dfrac{1}{2}$.

$$x = -\frac{1}{2} \Rightarrow y = \left(-\frac{1}{2}\right)e^{-1} = -\frac{1}{2e}$$

Hence, the curve has a single turning point at $\left(-\dfrac{1}{2}, -\dfrac{1}{2e}\right)$.

(b) You already found that $\dfrac{dy}{dx} = 2xe^{2x} + e^{2x}$.

Notice that, in order to differentiate the first term, you have to use the product rule again.

$$\frac{d^2y}{dx^2} = 2x(2e^{2x}) + e^{2x}(2) + 2e^{2x}$$

> Using the product rule.

$$= 4xe^{2x} + 2e^{2x} + 2e^{2x} = 4xe^{2x} + 4e^{2x}$$
$$= 4e^{2x}(x + 1)$$

At the point $\left(-\dfrac{1}{2}, -\dfrac{1}{2e}\right)$, $\dfrac{d^2y}{dx^2} = 4e^{-1}\left(-\dfrac{1}{2} + 1\right) = \dfrac{2}{e} > 0.$

Since $\dfrac{d^2y}{dx^2}$ is positive, $\left(-\dfrac{1}{2}, -\dfrac{1}{2e}\right)$ is a minimum point.

EXERCISE 7A

1 Use the product rule to differentiate the following with respect to x:

(a) $y = x \sin x$,   (b) $y = x^3 \cos x$,

(c) $y = 4x \ln x$,   (d) $y = \sqrt{x} \sin x$,

(e) $y = 5x^3 e^x$,   (f) $y = \sin x \cos x$,

(g) $y = e^x \ln x$,   (h) $y = e^x \sin x$,

(i) $y = 2\sqrt{x}(\ln x)$,   (j) $y = 3x^5 e^x$.

2 Differentiate the following expressions:

(a) $y = x^3 e^{2x}$,   (b) $y = (6 - 3x)(2x - 1)^5$,

(c) $y = e^x \sin 4x$,   (d) $y = \sin 3x \cos 2x$,

(e) $y = \sqrt{x + 1} \ln x$,   (f) $y = 6x^2 \ln 5x$,

(g) $y = e^{3x} \cos 2x$,   (h) $y = 4x^3 \sqrt{2x - 1}$,

(i) $y = 4x \ln(3x + 2)$,   (j) $y = e^{5x} \sin x + 6x^2$.

> Look out for the use of the chain rule also.

3 Find the gradient of the following curves at the specified point:

(a) $y = 3x^2 e^x$ at the point $(1, 3e)$,

(b) $y = x \sin x$ at the point where $x = \dfrac{\pi}{6}$,

(c) $y = \sqrt{x} \ln x$ at the point where $x = 1$.

4 Find the equation of the tangent to the curve $y = xe^{3x}$ at the point $P(3, 3e^9)$.

5 A curve has equation $y = x \ln x$.

    (a) Find the coordinates of the turning point of the curve, leaving your answer in terms of e.

    (b) Find $\dfrac{d^2y}{dx^2}$ and hence determine whether the turning point is a maximum or a minimum.

6 A curve is defined for $x \geqslant -2$ by the equation
$$y = (x^2 + 3)\sqrt{(x + 2)}.$$

    (a) Show that $\dfrac{dy}{dx} = 0$ when $x = -1$ and find the x-coordinate of the other stationary point.

    (b) Find the value of $\dfrac{d^2y}{dx^2}$ when $x = -1$. Hence determine whether the turning point when $x = -1$ is a maximum or minimum point.   [A]

7 The diagram below shows a sketch of the curve defined for $x > 0$ by the equation $y = x^2 \ln x$.

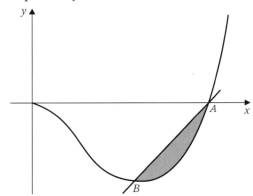

The curve crosses the x-axis at A and has a local minimum at B.

    (a) State the coordinates of A and calculate the gradient of the curve at A.

    (b) Determine the coordinates of B and determine the value of $\dfrac{d^2y}{dx^2}$ at B.   [A]

7.3 Differentiation using the quotient rule

Suppose you wish to differentiate a quotient of the form
$$y = \frac{u}{v},$$
where u and v are functions of x.

A small change, δx, in x will produce small changes in the values of u, v and y.

Let these small changes in u, v and y be δu, δv and δy, respectively.

Now $y + \delta y = \dfrac{u + \delta u}{v + \delta v}$

$\Rightarrow \delta y = \dfrac{u + \delta u}{v + \delta v} - y = \dfrac{u + \delta u}{v + \delta v} - \dfrac{u}{v}$

$\Rightarrow \delta y = \dfrac{v(u + \delta u) - u(v + \delta v)}{v(v + \delta v)}$

> By putting the fractions over a common denominator.

$\Rightarrow \delta y = \dfrac{uv + v\delta u - uv - u\delta v}{v(v + \delta v)}$

$\Rightarrow \delta y = \dfrac{v\delta u - u\delta v}{v(v + \delta v)}$

Now dividing both sides by δx gives

$\dfrac{\delta y}{\delta x} = \dfrac{v\dfrac{\delta u}{\delta x} - u\dfrac{\delta v}{\delta x}}{v(v + \delta v)}$

> As with the product rule, the proof is included here for completeness.
> You do not need to remember the proof but **you must learn this result** and feel confident when applying it.

7

and taking the limit as $\delta x \to 0$ gives

$\dfrac{dy}{dx} = \dfrac{v\dfrac{du}{dx} - u\dfrac{dv}{dx}}{v^2}$

Thus,

> To differentiate a quotient $y = \dfrac{u}{v}$
>
> you can use the result:
>
> $\dfrac{dy}{dx} = \dfrac{v\dfrac{du}{dx} - u\dfrac{dv}{dx}}{v^2}.$

> **Note:** Unlike the product rule the order in which the terms appear in the numerator is vital.

This result is known as the **quotient rule**.

> This may also be written as
>
> $y' = \dfrac{vu' - uv'}{v^2}.$

Worked example 7.6

Differentiate $y = \dfrac{\sin x}{x^2}$ with respect to x.

Solution

You can write $u = \sin x \Rightarrow \dfrac{du}{dx} = \cos x$

and $v = x^2 \Rightarrow \dfrac{dv}{dx} = 2x$

The quotient rule gives

$$\frac{dy}{dx} = \frac{v\dfrac{du}{dx} - u\dfrac{dv}{dx}}{v^2}$$

$$= \frac{x^2(\cos x) - \sin x(2x)}{(x^2)^2} = \frac{x^2\cos x - 2x\sin x}{x^4}$$

$$\Rightarrow \frac{dy}{dx} = \frac{x(x\cos x - 2\sin x)}{x^4} = \frac{x\cos x - 2\sin x}{x^3}$$

Worked example 7.7

Find the gradient of the curve with equation $y = \dfrac{\ln 2x}{x^3}$ at the point P where $x = 5$.

Solution

$u = \ln 2x \Rightarrow \dfrac{du}{dx} = \dfrac{2}{2x} = \dfrac{1}{x}$

and $v = x^3 \Rightarrow \dfrac{dv}{dx} = 3x^2$

> Notice the use of the chain rule. Or write
> $\ln 2x = \ln 2 + \ln x$.

The quotient rule gives

$$\frac{dy}{dx} = \frac{v\dfrac{du}{dx} - u\dfrac{dv}{dx}}{v^2}$$

$$= \frac{x^3\left(\dfrac{1}{x}\right) - \ln 2x(3x^2)}{(x^3)^2} = \frac{x^2 - 3x^2\ln 2x}{x^6}$$

$$\Rightarrow \frac{dy}{dx} = \frac{x^2(1 - 3\ln 2x)}{x^6} = \frac{1 - 3\ln 2x}{x^4}$$

at P, $\dfrac{dy}{dx} = \dfrac{1 - 3\ln 10}{625}$.

Worked example 7.8

A curve has equation $y = \dfrac{(2 - 3x)}{(2x - 1)^2}$, $\left(x \neq \dfrac{1}{2}\right)$.

Find the coordinates of the stationary point on the curve.

Solution

$u = 2 - 3x \Rightarrow \dfrac{\mathrm{d}u}{\mathrm{d}x} = -3$

and $v = (2x - 1)^2 \Rightarrow \dfrac{\mathrm{d}v}{\mathrm{d}x} = 4(2x - 1)$

The quotient rule gives

$$\frac{\mathrm{d}y}{\mathrm{d}x} = \frac{(2x - 1)^2(-3) - 4(2 - 3x)(2x - 1)}{(2x - 1)^4}$$

$$= \frac{-3(2x - 1) - 4(2 - 3x)}{(2x - 1)^3}$$

$$= \frac{-6x + 3 - 8 + 12x}{(2x - 1)^3}$$

$$\Rightarrow \frac{\mathrm{d}y}{\mathrm{d}x} = \frac{6x - 5}{(2x - 1)^3}$$

At stationary points the gradient is zero

$$\frac{6x - 5}{(2x - 1)^3} = 0$$

$$\Rightarrow 6x - 5 = 0 \Rightarrow x = \frac{5}{6}$$

When $x = \dfrac{5}{6}$, $y = \dfrac{\left(2 - \frac{15}{6}\right)}{\left(\frac{10}{6} - 1\right)^2} = \dfrac{-\frac{1}{2}}{\frac{4}{9}} = -\dfrac{9}{8}$

$\Rightarrow$ the curve has one stationary point at $\left(\dfrac{5}{6}, \ -\dfrac{9}{8}\right)$.

> It is important to realise that there is a common factor of $(2x - 1)$ in the numerator, that cancels one of the $(2x - 1)$ terms in the denominator.

> If you had not cancelled the factor $(2x - 1)$, you would have obtained a quadratic in the numerator and been led to the conclusion
> $(2x - 1)(6x - 5) = 0$, suggesting incorrectly that there was also a turning point when $x = \frac{1}{2}$.
> This is a very common error that some students make when using the quotient rule.

7

Worked examination question 7.1

The diagram shows a sketch of the curve with equation

$y = \dfrac{\ln x}{x} \ (x > 0).$

(a) State the coordinates of A, where the curve crosses the x-axis.

(b) Calculate, in terms of e, the coordinates of the maximum point B.

(c) Calculate, in terms of e, the value of $\dfrac{\mathrm{d}^2 y}{\mathrm{d}x^2}$ at B. [A]

Solution

(a) The curve crosses the x-axis where $y = 0$,

$$\Rightarrow \frac{\ln x}{x} = 0 \Rightarrow \ln x = 0$$

$$\Rightarrow x = 1$$

So A has coordinates $(1, 0)$.

(b) $\dfrac{dy}{dx} = \dfrac{x\left(\dfrac{1}{x}\right) - \ln x}{x^2} = \dfrac{1 - \ln x}{x^2}$

At a turning point the gradient is zero

$$\frac{1 - \ln x}{x^2} = 0 \Rightarrow 1 - \ln x = 0$$

$$\Rightarrow \ln x = 1$$
$$\Rightarrow x = e$$

When $x = e$, $y = \dfrac{1}{e}$

So B has coordinates $\left(e, \dfrac{1}{e}\right)$.

(c) Using the quotient rule again gives

$$\frac{d^2y}{dx^2} = \frac{x^2\left(-\dfrac{1}{x}\right) - 2x(1 - \ln x)}{x^4} = \frac{2\ln x - 3}{x^3}$$

> Cancelling the factor x in numerator and denominator.

At B, $\dfrac{d^2y}{dx^2} = \dfrac{2\ln e - 3}{e^3} = -\dfrac{1}{e^3}$.

EXERCISE 7B

1 Differentiate the following with respect to x:

(a) $y = \dfrac{\cos x}{x}$,

(b) $y = \dfrac{e^x}{x^2}$,

(c) $y = \dfrac{\sin x}{\sqrt{x}}$,

(d) $y = \dfrac{\ln x}{x}$,

(e) $y = \dfrac{4x^2}{e^x}$,

(f) $y = \dfrac{5\ln x}{x^3}$,

(g) $y = \dfrac{e^x}{3x^2}$,

(h) $y = \dfrac{\sin x}{e^x}$,

(i) $y = \dfrac{\sin x}{\cos x}$,

(j) $y = \dfrac{\cos x}{\sin x}$.

2 Find $\dfrac{dy}{dx}$ for each of the following expressions:

(a) $y = \dfrac{\sin 2x}{x^3}$,

(b) $y = \dfrac{e^{-x}}{\sin x}$,

(c) $y = \dfrac{4x^5}{e^{3x}}$,

(d) $y = \dfrac{(1 - 3x)}{(2x + 3)^2}$,

(e) $y = \dfrac{\ln 5x}{x}$,

(f) $y = \dfrac{x^3}{\cos 3x}$,

(g) $y = \dfrac{4 \sin 2x}{2x^3}$,

(h) $y = \dfrac{2e^{3x}}{x}$,

(i) $y = \dfrac{7 \ln 3x}{x^2}$,

(j) $y = \dfrac{e^{2-x}}{\sin 3x}$.

3 By writing $y = \dfrac{u}{v}$ in the form $y = uv^{-1}$, use the product rule to establish the quotient rule.

4 A curve is defined by the equation

$$y = \frac{x + 2}{(x - 1)^2}, x \neq 1.$$

(a) Find the equation of the tangent to the curve at the point where $x = 0$.

(b) Find the coordinates of the point where this tangent crosses the curve again. [A]

5 The volume, $V \text{ cm}^3$, in a container when the depth is x cm is given by

$$V = \frac{x^{\frac{1}{4}}}{(x + 2)^{\frac{1}{2}}}, x > 0.$$

(a) Find $\dfrac{dV}{dx}$ and determine the value of x for which $\dfrac{dV}{dx} = 0$.

(b) Calculate the rate of change of volume when the depth is 1 cm and increasing at a rate of 0.01 cm s^{-1}, giving your answer in $\text{cm}^3 \text{ s}^{-1}$ to three significant figures. [A]

7

6 The diagram shows the curve with equation

$$y = \frac{\ln x}{x^2} \text{ for } x > 0.$$

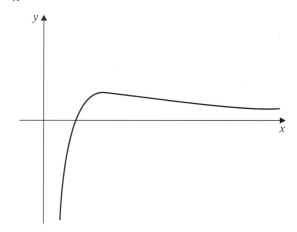

(a) State the x-coordinate of the point where the curve crosses the x-axis.

(b) Show that $\dfrac{dy}{dx} = \dfrac{1 - 2\ln x}{x^3}$.

(c) Find the coordinates of the maximum point of the curve and calculate the value of $\dfrac{d^2y}{dx^2}$ there.   [A]

7.4 Derivatives of other trigonometric functions

The derivatives of other trigonometric functions such as $\tan x$ and $\sec x$ can be found by using the derivatives of $\sin x$ and $\cos x$, together with the quotient rule.

Derivative of tan x

Suppose that you want to differentiate $y = \tan x$.
This can be rewritten as a quotient,

$$y = \frac{\sin x}{\cos x}$$

Using the quotient rule, gives

$$\frac{dy}{dx} = \frac{\cos x(\cos x) - \sin x\,(-\sin x)}{\cos^2 x} = \frac{\cos^2 x + \sin^2 x}{\cos^2 x}$$

but $\cos^2 x + \sin^2 x \equiv 1$

$$\Rightarrow \frac{dy}{dx} = \frac{1}{\cos^2 x} = \sec^2 x$$

$$\Rightarrow \qquad \frac{d}{dx}(\tan x) = \sec^2 x$$

Derivative of cot x

Suppose that you want to differentiate $y = \cot x$.
This can be rewritten as a quotient,

$$y = \frac{\cos x}{\sin x}$$

The quotient rule gives

$$\frac{dy}{dx} = \frac{\sin x(-\sin x) - \cos x(\cos x)}{\sin^2 x} = \frac{-(\sin^2 x + \cos^2 x)}{\sin^2 x}$$

but $\sin^2 x + \cos^2 x \equiv 1$

$$\Rightarrow \frac{dy}{dx} = -\frac{1}{\sin^2 x} = -\operatorname{cosec}^2 x$$

$$\Rightarrow \qquad \frac{d}{dx}(\cot x) = -\operatorname{cosec}^2 x$$

Derivative of sec x

In order to differentiate $y = \sec x$, you can rewrite it in the form
$y = \frac{1}{\cos x}$.

The quotient rule gives

$$\frac{dy}{dx} = \frac{\cos x(0) - 1(-\sin x)}{\cos^2 x} = \frac{\sin x}{\cos^2 x}$$

$$= \frac{1}{\cos x} \times \frac{\sin x}{\cos x} = \sec x \tan x$$

You can also prove this result by writing $\sec x$ in the form $(\cos x)^{-1}$ and using the chain rule with $u = \cos x$ and $y = u^{-1}$.

$$\Rightarrow \qquad \frac{d}{dx}(\sec x) = \sec x \tan x$$

Derivative of cosec x

To differentiate $y = \operatorname{cosec} x$, you can rewrite it in the form
$y = \frac{1}{\sin x}$.

The quotient rule then gives

$$\frac{dy}{dx} = \frac{\sin x(0) - 1(\cos x)}{\sin^2 x} = \frac{-\cos x}{\sin^2 x}$$

$$= -\frac{1}{\sin x} \times \frac{\cos x}{\sin x} = -\text{cosec}\, x \cot x$$

> These standard results derived in this section will be given in the formulae booklet for use in the examination.

$\Rightarrow$

$$\frac{d}{dx}(\text{cosec}\, x) = -\text{cosec}\, x \cot x$$

Worked example 7.9

Differentiate the following expressions with respect to x.

(a) $y = \tan(3x - 4)$, **(b)** $y = \sin x \sec 2x$.

Solution

(a) The chain rule gives

$$\frac{dy}{dx} = \sec^2(3x - 4) \times 3 = 3\sec^2(3x - 4)$$

> The derivative of $\tan u$ is $\sec^2 u$.

(b) The product rule gives

$$\frac{dy}{dx} = \sin x(2\sec 2x \tan 2x) + \sec 2x(\cos x)$$

$$= \sec 2x(2\sin x \tan 2x + \cos x)$$

> The derivative of $\sec u$ is $\sec u \tan u$.

Worked example 7.10

Differentiate the following expressions with respect to x:

(a) $y = \ln(\cot x)$, **(b)** $y = \dfrac{\text{cosec}\, 3x}{\sin x}$.

Solution

(a) The chain rule gives

$$\frac{dy}{dx} = \frac{1}{\cot x} \times (-\text{cosec}^2 x)$$

$$= \frac{dy}{dx} = -\frac{\sin x}{\cos x} \times \frac{1}{\sin^2 x} = -\frac{1}{\sin x \cos x}$$

(b) The quotient rule gives

$$\frac{dy}{dx} = \frac{\sin x(-3\,\text{cosec}\, 3x \cot 3x) - \text{cosec}\, 3x(\cos x)}{\sin^2 x}$$

$$= \frac{-\text{cosec}\, 3x(3\sin x \cot 3x + \cos x)}{\sin^2 x}$$

> Notice the use of the chain rule in differentiating $\text{cosec}\, 3x$.

EXERCISE 7C

1 Differentiate the following with respect to x:

(a) $y = 5x^3 + \tan 4x$,

(b) $y = \sec(6x - 3)$,

(c) $y = \cot(1 - x)$,

(d) $y = 5\operatorname{cosec} 3x$.

2 Differentiate the following expressions with respect to the appropriate variable:

(a) $y = 3t^4 \sec t$,

(b) $y = \dfrac{\cot x}{x^3}$,

(c) $y = \ln(\sec t)$,

(d) $y = \sin x + x^2 \tan x$.

3 A curve has equation $y = \tan 3x$. Find the equation of the tangent to the curve at the point P on the curve where $x = \dfrac{\pi}{4}$.

4 Show that the gradient of the curve with equation $y = \sec x \tan x$ can be written in the form

$$\sec x(2\sec^2 x - 1).$$

5 A curve is given by the equation $y = \mathrm{e}^{-x} \sec 2x$. Find an expression for the gradient of the curve.

6 By writing $y = \sec x$ as $y = (\cos x)^{-1}$, use the chain rule to establish the result $\dfrac{\mathrm{d}}{\mathrm{d}x}(\sec x) = \sec x \tan x$.

7 By writing $y = \operatorname{cosec} x$ as $y = (\sin x)^{-1}$, use the chain rule to establish the result $\dfrac{\mathrm{d}}{\mathrm{d}x}(\operatorname{cosec} x) = -\operatorname{cosec} x \cot x$.

7

The key to success in differentiation is to appreciate which of the various techniques need to be used.

The following exercise contains questions on basic differentiation, the chain rule, the product rule and the quotient rule. It is left to you to decide which technique, or combination of techniques, is most appropriate.

MIXED EXERCISE

1 Differentiate the following expressions with respect to x:

(a) $y = (x - 3)(x + 2)$,

(b) $y = 5x^3 - 2x + \mathrm{e}^{2x}$,

(c) $y = \dfrac{4x^3 - 2}{x}$,

(d) $y = x(x - 2)(x + 5)$,

(e) $y = \mathrm{e}^{-x} \sin x$,

(f) $y = 3\tan 5x$,

(g) $y = \dfrac{2\ln x}{x^3}$,

(h) $y = 4\cot(2 - 3x)$.

2 Find the gradients of the following curves at the specified points:

    (a) $y = 5 \sin 2\theta$ at the point where $\theta = \dfrac{\pi}{6}$,

    (b) $y = e^{2x+7}$ at the point where $x = -3$,

    (c) $y = \sqrt{x}(x + 1)$ at the point where $x = 9$.

3 Find the equation of the tangent to the curve with equation $y = \sqrt{x}e^x$ at the point where $x = 4$.

4 Find the equation of the tangent to the curve $y = 2 \tan 2\theta$ at the point where $\theta = \dfrac{\pi}{8}$.

5 A curve has equation $y = x^2 e^{-x}$.

    (a) Find the coordinates of its stationary points.

    (b) Find the value of $\dfrac{d^2 y}{dx^2}$ at each of the stationary points and hence determine their nature.

6 A curve is defined for $x > 0$ by the equation

$$y = (10 - x) \ln 2x.$$

Find the gradient of the curve when $x = 1$, leaving your answer in terms of $\ln 2$.

7 The radius, r cm, of a circular ink spot, t s after it first appears, is given by

$$r = \frac{1 + 4t}{2 + t}.$$

Calculate:

    (a) the time taken for the radius to double its initial size,

    (b) the rate of increase of the radius in cm s^{-1} when $t = 3$,

    (c) the value to which r tends as t tends to infinity.   [A]

8 The curve with equation $y = (x + 2)e^{-x}$ is sketched below.

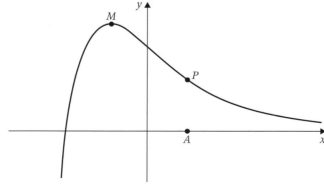

The maximum point M and the point P lie on the curve and A lies on the x-axis. The points A and P each have x-coordinate equal to 3.

(a) Find the value of $\dfrac{dy}{dx}$ at the point P, leaving your answer in terms of e.

(b) Determine the equation of the tangent to the curve at P and find the x-coordinate of the point B where this tangent crosses the x-axis.

(c) Calculate the coordinates of the maximum point M. [A]

9 The curve with equation $y = (x^2 - 4x + 1)e^{-x}$ is sketched below.

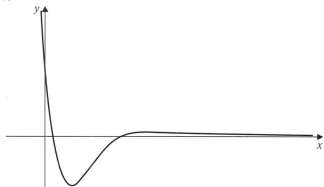

(a) Determine the exact surd values of x where the curve crosses the x-axis.

(b) Calculate the exact values of the coordinates of the turning points of the curve. [A]

10 The function f is defined by

$$f(x) = \frac{\sin^2 x}{1 + \cos^2 x}.$$

(a) Show that $f'(x) = \dfrac{2 \sin 2x}{(1 + \cos^2 x)^2}$.

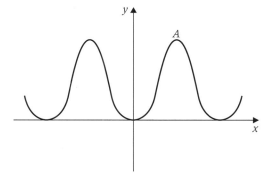

The diagram shows a sketch of the graph of $y = f(x)$.

(b) Find the coordinates of the stationary point A and hence state the range of f.

(c) Sketch the graph of $y = \dfrac{\cos^2 x}{1 + \sin^2 x}$. [A]

Key point summary

1 To differentiate a product $y = u \times v$, you can use the   *p114*
product rule:

$$\frac{dy}{dx} = u\frac{dv}{dx} + v\frac{du}{dx}$$

2 To differentiate a quotient $y = \dfrac{u}{v}$, you can use the   *p119*

quotient rule:

$$\frac{dy}{dx} = \frac{v\dfrac{du}{dx} - u\dfrac{dv}{dx}}{v^2}$$

3 $\dfrac{d}{dx}(\tan x) = \sec^2 x$ *p125*

$\dfrac{d}{dx}(\cot x) = -\text{cosec}^2 x$ *p125*

$\dfrac{d}{dx}(\sec x) = \sec x \tan x$ *p125*

$\dfrac{d}{dx}(\text{cosec}\, x) = -\text{cosec}\, x \cot x$ *p126*

Test yourself | What to review

1 Differentiate the following with respect to x: *Section 7.2*
 (a) $y = x^2(x+1)^5$,   **(b)** $y = x \sin x$,
 (c) $y = e^{-2x}\cos x$,   **(d)** $y = x^2 \ln(3x-1)$.

2 Find $\dfrac{dy}{dx}$ for each of the following expressions: *Section 7.3*

 (a) $y = \dfrac{x^2}{x+1}$,   **(b)** $y = \dfrac{x}{\cos x}$,

 (c) $y = \dfrac{\sin 3x}{x}$ **(d)** $y = \dfrac{\cos(1-2x)}{e^x}$

3 Differentiate each of the following with respect to x: *Section 7.4*
 (a) $y = 5\tan 2x$,   **(b)** $y = 2\sec(1-4x)$,
 (c) $y = 7\cot 5x$,   **(d)** $y = \text{cosec}(x^2+3)$.

1 (a) $5x^2(x+1)^4 + 2x(x+1)^5$;

(b) $x\cos x + \sin x$;

(c) $-e^{-2x}(\sin x + 2\cos x)$;

(d) $\dfrac{3x^2}{3x-1} + 2x\ln(3x-1)$.

2 (a) $\dfrac{2x(x+1) - x^2}{(x+1)^2} = \dfrac{x(2+x)}{(x+1)^2}$;

(b) $\dfrac{\cos x + x\sin x}{\cos^2 x}$;

(c) $\dfrac{3x\cos 3x - \sin 3x}{x^2}$;

(d) $\dfrac{2\sin(1-2x) - \cos(1-2x)}{e^x}$

3 (a) $10\sec^2 2x$;

(b) $-8\sec(1-4x)\tan(1-4x)$;

(c) $-35\,\mathrm{cosec}^2 5x$;

(d) $-2x\,\mathrm{cosec}\,(x^2+3)\cot(x^2+3)$.

CHAPTER 8

Logarithms and exponential growth and decay

Learning objectives

After studying this chapter you should be able to:

- solve equations of the form $a^x = b$ using logarithms
- understand what is meant by exponential growth and decay
- realise that $\dfrac{dx}{dt} = kx$ has solution $x = Ae^{kt}$
- solve problems involving growth and decay.

8.1 Equations of the form $a^x = b$

It is sometimes possible to find an exact solution to an equation of the form $a^x = b$.
For instance, the equation $2^x = 512$ has solution $x = 9$.

However, more often equations of this type do not have exact solutions and they need to be solved using logarithms. Your calculator can find logarithms to base 10 and natural logarithms, to base e, and as the next worked example shows, either of these bases can be used.

Worked example 8.1

Solve each of the following equations, giving your answers to three significant figures:

(a) $2^x = 500$,   **(b)** $7^y = 13.75$.

Solution

(a) $2^x = 500$
Taking natural logarithms of both sides gives

$$\ln(2^x) = \ln 500$$

$$\Rightarrow x \ln 2 = \ln 500$$

$$\Rightarrow x = \frac{\ln 500}{\ln 2} = 8.965\,784\ldots$$

Therefore $x = 8.97$ (to three significant figures).

> Recall that $\ln(a^x) = x \ln a$.

> Since $2^x = 512$ has the solution $x = 9$, you would expect the answer to $2^x = 500$ to be a little less than 9.

> The solution to the equation $a^x = b$ is $x = \dfrac{\ln b}{\ln a}$, where logarithms are taken to base e.

(b) $7^y = 13.75$

You could take logarithms to base 10 of both sides

$$\lg(7^y) = \lg 13.75$$

$$\Rightarrow y \lg 7 = \lg 13.75$$

$$\Rightarrow y = \frac{\lg 13.75}{\lg 7} = 1.346\,947\,5\ldots$$

Therefore $y = 1.35$ (to three significant figures).

> A common mistake is to enter $\lg\left(\dfrac{13.75}{7}\right)$ into a calculator instead of the correct expression.

> The solution to the equation $a^x = b$ is $x = \dfrac{\lg b}{\lg a}$, where logarithms are taken to base 10.

8.2 More complicated equations

Sometimes the exponent is more complicated than simply x or y and so care needs to be taken with the use of brackets.

Worked example 8.2

Solve the following equations, giving answers to four significant figures:

(a) $3^{2x-5} = 79$,　　**(b)** $5^{3-4x} = 7^{x+2}$.

Solution

(a) $3^{2x-5} = 79$ can be solved by taking logarithms to base 10.

$$\lg(3^{2x-5}) = \lg 79$$

$$\Rightarrow (2x - 5)\lg 3 = \lg 79$$

> Provided you are consistent, you can take natural logarithms of both sides and obtain the same answer. Why not try it and see?

Notice the need for brackets here.

$$\text{Hence, } (2x - 5) = \frac{\lg 79}{\lg 3}$$

$$= 3.977\,242\,8\ldots$$

$$\Rightarrow 2x = 8.977\,242\,8\ldots$$

$$\Rightarrow \ x = 4.488\,621\,4\ldots$$

Therefore $x = 4.489$ (to four significant figures).

(b) $5^{3-4x} = 7^{x+2}$

This time there are exponents on both sides of the equation, but the method of solution, namely taking logarithms, is exactly the same. Taking natural logarithms of both sides,

$$\ln{(5^{3-4x})} = \ln{(7^{x+2})}$$

Again, notice the need for brackets.

$$\Rightarrow (3 - 4x)\ln 5 = (x + 2)\ln 7$$

$$\Rightarrow (3 - 4x) = (x + 2)\frac{\ln 7}{\ln 5} = (x + 2) \times 1.209\,06\ldots$$

$$\Rightarrow 3 - (2 \times 1.209\,06\ldots) = 4x + (x \times 1.209\,06\ldots)$$

$$\Rightarrow 0.581\,876\ldots = 5.209\,06\ldots x$$

$$\Rightarrow x = 0.111\,7 \text{ (to four significant figures).}$$

EXERCISE 8A

1 Find the exact solutions to each of the following equations:

(a) $2^x = 64$,   (b) $3^x = 2187$,

(c) $2^x = 0.125$,   (d) $5^x = 3125$.

2 Find the solutions to each of the following, giving your answers to three significant figures. *You may find the answers to question 1 helpful in confirming your results.*

(a) $2^x = 62$,   (b) $3^x = 2200$,

(c) $2^x = 0.13$,   (d) $5^x = 3110$.

3 Solve each of the following, giving your answers to three significant figures.

(a) $7^x = 0.46$,   (b) $4^x = 200$,

(c) $3^x = 19$,   (d) $12^x = 58.9$.

4 Given that $3^{2x+5} = 17$, show that $x = \dfrac{1}{2}\left(\dfrac{\ln 17}{\ln 3} - 5\right)$.

5 Solve the following equations, leaving your answers in terms of natural logarithms:

(a) $2^{x+4} = 6$,   (b) $3^{2x-1} = 17$,

(c) $2^{1-4x} = 5$,   (d) $5^{3x+4} = 31$.

6 Solve each of the following, giving your answers to three significant figures:

(a) $3^{2x-5} = 7$,   (b) $5^{7x-1} = 12$,

(c) $2^{5x-2} = 19$,   (d) $7^{3-2x} = 19$.

7 Solve each of the following, giving your answers to four significant figures:

(a) $9^{x-7} = 17.5$, (b) $3^{4x-5} = 0.123$,

(c) $13^{x-5} = 1.345$, (d) $17^{5-4x} = 19.436$

(e) $8^{6x-7} = 67.23$, (f) $6^{7x-4} = 23.89$.

8 Solve each of the following, giving your answers to three significant figures:

(a) $3^x = 7^{x+1}$, (b) $5^{x-1} = 4^{1-3x}$,

(c) $2^{x-2} = 9^{3-5x}$, (d) $7^{1-2x} = 4^{x+3}$

(e) $7^{x+1} = 5^{1+3x}$, (f) $3^{2x-3} = 11^{2-3x}$.

9 Given that $2^{3x-5} = 3^{3-7x}$, show that $x = \dfrac{3k+5}{7k+3}$, where $k = \dfrac{\ln 3}{\ln 2}$.

10 State the condition that must be satisfied by b for the equation $2^x = b$ to have a solution.

8.3 Exponential growth

The graph of $N = 5000 \times 2^t$ is shown below for $t \ldots 0$.

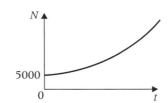

The graph increases very rapidly and demonstrates what is known as exponential growth. The graph might represent the growth of a certain strain of bacteria in a container which initially numbers 5000 and t might represent the time in hours measured from the instant an experiment begins.

Suppose you wished to find the value of t when $N = 8000$.

You could write $8000 = 5000 \times 2^t$.

Then, $2^t = \dfrac{8}{5} = 1.6$,

and by taking natural logarithms

$$t = \frac{\ln 1.6}{\ln 2} \approx 0.678\,071\,9 \ldots$$

So the time taken is approximately 0.678 hours or 41 minutes (to the nearest minute).

> The formula $x = a \times b^{kt}$, where a, b and k are positive
> constants, indicates that x is growing exponentially.

8.4 Exponential decay

Suppose the mass, M, measured in grams, of a block of ice
when it is melting is given by the formula $M = 250 \times 3^{-2t}$,
where t is the time in hours measured from a particular instant.
The graph is shown below.

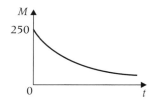

This is an example of exponential decay, where eventually M
would reduce to the value zero.

How long would it take for the block of ice to reduce to half its
original size?

Writing $125 = 250 \times 3^{-2t}$ gives $3^{-2t} = \dfrac{1}{2}$.

Taking natural logarithms, $-2t \ln 3 = \ln 0.5$.

Therefore, $2t = -\dfrac{\ln 0.5}{\ln 3} \approx 0.6309\dots$.

So that t is approximately 0.315 and hence the time taken is
about 0.315 hours or 19 minutes, to the nearest minute.

> The formula $x = a \times b^{-kt}$, where a, b and k are positive
> constants, indicates that x is decaying exponentially.

Worked example 8.3

A radioactive substance decays so that its mass, m grams, after
time t years from a given instant is given by $m = m_0 e^{-\frac{t}{50}}$.

(a) Find the percentage change in mass after 2 years.
(b) Find the time taken for the mass to reduce to a quarter of
its original size.

Solution

(a) When $t = 2$, $m = m_0 e^{-\frac{1}{25}} = m_0 \times 0.960\,789\dots$.
The mass is now 96% of its original value so the percentage
change is a decrease of 4%.

(b) When $m = \dfrac{1}{4}m_0$, the equation becomes $\dfrac{1}{4}m_0 = m_o e^{-\frac{t}{50}}$.

Hence, $\dfrac{1}{4} = e^{-\frac{t}{50}}$ and taking natural logarithms gives

$$-\dfrac{t}{50} = \ln\dfrac{1}{4} \approx -1.386\,29\dots.$$

So that $t = 50 \times 1.386\,29\dots \approx 69.3147\dots.$
Which means it will take approximately 69 years to reduce
to a quarter of its original size.

EXERCISE 8B

1 Given that $N = 300 \times 2^t$, sketch the graph of N against t for
$t \geqslant 0$. Find the value of t when:

(a) $N = 500$,   (b) $x = 1000$,   (c) $N = 1800$.

2 Given that $x = 500 \times 3^{2t}$, state the value of x when $t = 0$. Find
the value of t when:

(a) $x = 1500$,   (b) $x = 4000$,   (c) $x = 10^{10}$.

3 Given that $W = 70 \times 5^{-t}$, sketch the graph of W against t for
$t \geqslant 0$. Find the value of t when:

(a) $W = 70$,   (b) $W = 14$,   (c) $W = 0.001$.

4 The temperature $T°C$ of liquid in a container m minutes after
a particular instant is given by $T = 20 + 60 \times 3^{-m/5}$.

(a) State the initial temperature.

(b) Calculate the temperature after 5 minutes.

(c) Find the time taken for the temperature to fall to $25°C$.

5 The amount of money, £P, in a bank account at time t months
after the account is opened is given by $P = 500 \times 1.002^t$.

(a) Find the initial amount of money in the account.

(b) Find the amount of money, to the nearest penny, in the
account after one year.

(c) Determine the length of time, in complete months, when
there first will be £600 in the account.

(d) Comment on whether the formula is likely to be valid
when t is not a positive integer.

6 The population, P million, for England and Wales from 1841
to 1901 can be modelled by the equation $P = 15.9 \times 1.012^t$,
where t is the number of years after 1 January 1841.

(a) Use the model to estimate:
    (i) the population on 1 January 1861,

> **(ii)** the year when the population first reached 26 million.
>
> **(b)** Find P when $t = 160$. Discuss what this predicts and comment on whether this is likely to be accurate.

8.5 Rate of change

When $x = a \times b^{kt}$ it is not easy to find an expression for $\dfrac{dx}{dt}$.

However, it was shown in P2 chapter 7 that any expression of the form $a \times b^{kt}$ can be changed into the form $a \times e^{ct}$, where $c = k \ln b$, and this expression can be easily differentiated with respect to t.

Worked example 8.4

Given that $x = 10e^{5t}$, show that $\dfrac{dx}{dt} = kx$, stating the value of k.

Solution

$$x = 10e^{5t} \Rightarrow \frac{dx}{dt} = 5 \times 10e^{5t} = 5x.$$

Therefore, $\dfrac{dx}{dt} = kx$, where $k = 5$.

This example illustrates an important aspect of exponential growth, namely that the rate of increase of x is actually proportional to x.

> In general, $x = Ae^{kt} \Rightarrow \dfrac{dx}{dt} = kx$.

Worked example 8.5

(a) Given that $N = Ae^{kt}$, where A and k are constants, show that $\dfrac{dN}{dt} = kN$.

(b) The number of bacteria, N, in a colony is such that the rate of increase of N is proportional to N. The time, t, is measured in hours from the instant that $N = 2$ million. When $t = 3$, $N = 5$ million. Find the value of t when $N = 8$ million. [A]

Solution

(a) Differentiating $N = Ae^{kt}$ with respect to t gives

$$\frac{dN}{dt} = k \times Ae^{kt}.$$

Therefore, $\dfrac{dN}{dt} = kN$.

(b) The statement 'the rate of increase of N is proportional to N', is interpreted mathematically as $\dfrac{dN}{dt} = kN$.

This means that you need to use the result from **(a)** and therefore $N = Ae^{kt}$.

When $t = 0$, $N = 2$ million $\Rightarrow A = 2 \times 10^6$.

When $t = 3$, $N = 5$ million $\Rightarrow 5 \times 10^6 = 2 \times 10^6 \times e^{3k}$

$\Rightarrow e^{3k} = 2.5 \Rightarrow 3k = \ln 2.5 \Rightarrow k = 0.3054 \ldots$

So when $N = 8$ million, you have $8 \times 10^6 = 2 \times 10^6 \times e^{kt}$

$\Rightarrow e^{kt} = 4 \Rightarrow kt = \ln 4$

$\Rightarrow t \approx 4.54$ (to three significant figures).

Worked example 8.6

(a) Given that $T = Ae^{-kx}$, show that $\dfrac{dT}{dx} = -kT$, where k and A are positive constants.

(b) The rate of decrease of temperature, $T°C$, of the liquid in a container is proportional to the temperature of the liquid at any instant. Initially the temperature is $70°C$, and after 10 minutes the temperature has fallen to $50°C$. Find the temperature after a further 10 minutes.

Solution

(a) $T = Ae^{-kx} \Rightarrow \dfrac{dT}{dx} = -k \times Ae^{-kx} \Rightarrow \dfrac{dT}{dx} = -k \times T$.

(b) The statement 'the rate of decrease of temperature of the liquid in a container is proportional to the temperature of the liquid' can be interpreted as $\dfrac{dT}{dx} = -kT$.

Using **(a)** with T for temperature and x minutes for the time of cooling, the temperature T must satisfy $T = Ae^{-kx}$.

When $x = 0$, $T = 70$ or $70 = Ae^0 = A$.

When $x = 10$, $T = 50$ or $50 = Ae^{-10k} = 70e^{-10k}$.

$\Rightarrow e^{-10k} = \dfrac{5}{7} \Rightarrow e^{10k} = \dfrac{7}{5} = 1.4 \Rightarrow 10k = \ln 1.4 \approx 0.33647\ldots$

After a further 10 minutes, $x = 20$, so $T = 70e^{-20k} = 35.714\ldots$.

The temperature has fallen to about $35.7°C$.

8

EXERCISE 8C

1 Express each of the following in the form e^{kx}:

(a) 3^x,   **(b)** 2^x,   **(c)** 5^{2x},   **(d)** 4^{-x},

(e) 7^{-3x},   **(f)** $6^{\frac{x}{2}}$,   **(g)** $5^{-\frac{x}{3}}$.

2 Given that $y = 4e^{3x}$, show that $\dfrac{dy}{dx} = ky$, stating the value of the constant k. Find the value of $\dfrac{dy}{dx}$ when $x = 0$.

3 Given that $y = 5e^{-2x}$, show that $\dfrac{dy}{dx} = py$, stating the value of the constant p. Find the exact value of y when $x = \ln 3$ and hence find the corresponding value of $\dfrac{dy}{dx}$.

4 You are given that $y = Ae^{kx}$, where A and k are constants, and $y = 5$ when $x = 0$.

   (a) Find the value of A.

   (b) In addition, when $x = 2$, $y = 15$. Find the exact value of k and hence find the value of y when $x = 3$.

5 (a) Given that $P = Ae^{kt}$, where A and k are constants, show that $\dfrac{dP}{dt} = kP$.

   (b) The population, P, of insects in a colony is such that the rate of increase of P is proportional to P. The time, t, is measured in months from the instant that $P = 3000$. When $t = 5$, $P = 8000$. Find the value of t when $P = 15\,000$.

6 (a) Given that $m = m_0 e^{-kt}$, show that $\dfrac{dm}{dt} = -km$, where k and m_0 are positive constants.

   (b) The rate of decrease of mass of a ball of snow is proportional to the mass of the snow remaining at any instant. Initially the mass is 500 g and after 4 minutes the mass has fallen to 300 g. Find the mass after a further 6 minutes.

7 (a) Given that $N = N_0 e^{kt}$, show that $\dfrac{dN}{dt} = kN$, where N_0 and k are constants.

   (b) The number, N, of bacteria in a tank of water increases at a rate proportional to the number present at any instant. After timing for 3 hours, the number is 5000 and after 5 hours the number is 10 000. Find the initial number of bacteria and the time taken to reach 20 000.

8.6 General solution to the rate of change equation

Problems involved with growth and decay often involve a statement such as 'the rate of change of the quantity q is proportional to the quantity present at a given time t.'

This can be interpreted as $\dfrac{dq}{dt} = k \times q$.

In the previous section, you verified that when $q = Ae^{kt}$, it follows by differentiation that $\dfrac{dq}{dt} = k \times q$.

In this section you will prove the converse of this result.

Worked example 8.7

Given that $\dfrac{dy}{dt} = 5y$ and $y = 2$ when $t = 0$, prove that $y = 2e^{5t}$.

Solution

Since $\dfrac{dy}{dt} = 5y$, and from earlier work you know that $\dfrac{dy}{dx} = \dfrac{1}{\dfrac{dy}{dx}}$,

you can write $\dfrac{dt}{dy} = \dfrac{1}{5y}$.

It now follows that $t = \displaystyle\int \dfrac{1}{5y}\,dy = \dfrac{1}{5}\int \dfrac{1}{y}\,dy = \dfrac{1}{5}\ln y + C$, where C is a constant.

Putting $t = 0$ and $y = 2$, gives $0 = \dfrac{1}{5}\ln 2 + C$

or $C = -\dfrac{1}{5}\ln 2$.

Hence, $t = \dfrac{1}{5}\ln y - \dfrac{1}{5}\ln 2 = \dfrac{1}{5}(\ln y - \ln 2) = \dfrac{1}{5}\ln\left(\dfrac{y}{2}\right)$

$\Rightarrow 5t = \ln\left(\dfrac{y}{2}\right)$

Taking logarithms of both sides leads to $e^{5t} = \dfrac{y}{2} \Rightarrow y = 2e^{5t}$.

Worked example 8.8

Given that $\dfrac{dQ}{dx} = -4Q$ and $Q = 3$ when $x = 0$, find an expression for Q in terms of x.

Solution

$\dfrac{dQ}{dx} = -4Q \Rightarrow \dfrac{dx}{dQ} = \dfrac{-1}{4Q}$

Integrating with respect to Q gives

$x = \displaystyle\int \dfrac{-1}{4Q}\,dQ = \dfrac{-1}{4}\int \dfrac{1}{Q}\,dQ = -\dfrac{1}{4}\ln Q + C$

When $x = 0$, $Q = 3$. Therefore, $0 = -\dfrac{1}{4}\ln 3 + C$ or $C = \dfrac{1}{4}\ln 3$

8

Hence, $x = \dfrac{-1}{4}(\ln Q - \ln 3) = \dfrac{-1}{4}\ln\left(\dfrac{Q}{3}\right)$

Multiplying both sides by -4

$$-4x = \ln\left(\dfrac{Q}{3}\right)$$

Hence, $\mathrm{e}^{-4x} = \dfrac{Q}{3} \Rightarrow Q = 3\mathrm{e}^{-4x}$

Although you need to be able to derive solutions as in the previous two worked examples, it is important that you are aware of the following key result.

> The general solution of $\dfrac{\mathrm{d}x}{\mathrm{d}t} = kx$ is $x = A\mathrm{e}^{kt}$, where A is an arbitrary constant.

Worked example 8.9

Write down the general solutions of the following rate of change equations:

(a) $\dfrac{\mathrm{d}N}{\mathrm{d}t} = 4N,$ **(b)** $\dfrac{\mathrm{d}P}{\mathrm{d}t} = -3P,$ **(c)** $5\dfrac{\mathrm{d}Q}{\mathrm{d}t} = Q.$

Solution

(a) Using the result in the previous Key Point with $k = 4$ gives the general solution as

$$N = A\mathrm{e}^{4t},$$

where A is an arbitrary constant.

> Clearly any letter other than A could have been used for the arbitrary constant.

(b) The value of k is negative in this case, $k = -3$. The general solution is $P = B\mathrm{e}^{-3t}$, where B is an arbitrary constant.

(c) You need to rearrange the equation so it is of the form given in the Key Point above.

$$5\dfrac{\mathrm{d}Q}{\mathrm{d}t} = Q \Rightarrow \dfrac{\mathrm{d}Q}{\mathrm{d}t} = \dfrac{1}{5}Q$$

So $k = \dfrac{1}{5}$, and the general solution is $Q = C\mathrm{e}^{\frac{t}{5}}$, where C is an arbitrary constant.

Worked example 8.10

The yearly rate of increase of a population, P, of birds in a colony is proportional to P. On 1 July 2000 there were 300 birds and a year later there were 380 in the colony.
(a) Find an expression for P in terms of the time in years, t, measured from 1 July 2000.
(b) Predict the number of birds in the colony on 1 July 2008.

Solution

(a) $\dfrac{dP}{dt} = kP$, which has general solution $P = Ae^{kt}$.

When $t = 0$, $P = 300$. So $300 = Ae^0 = A$.
Therefore, $P = 300e^{kt}$.
Also, $P = 380$, when $t = 1 \Rightarrow 380 = 300e^k$.

Hence, $e^k = \dfrac{380}{300} = \dfrac{19}{15}$.

Since $e^{kt} = (e^k)^t$, it follows that

$$P = 300 \times \left(\frac{19}{15}\right)^t$$

> Notice that this model takes no account of the reduction of numbers in the colony as birds die or leave the colony, etc..

(b) When $t = 8$, $P = 300 \times \left(\dfrac{19}{15}\right)^8 \approx 1988$.

EXERCISE 8D

1 Given that $\dfrac{dy}{dt} = 7y$ and $y = 4$ when $t = 0$, prove that $y = 4e^{7t}$.

2 Given that $\dfrac{dx}{dt} = -3x$ and $x = 9$ when $t = 0$, prove that $x = 9e^{-3t}$.

3 Given that $\dfrac{dN}{dx} = -2N$ and $N = 8$ when $x = 0$, find an expression for N in terms of x.

4 Given that $\dfrac{dP}{dt} = 8P$ and $P = 4$ when $t = 0$, find an expression for P in terms of t.

5 Write down the general solutions of the following rate of change equations:

(a) $\dfrac{dN}{dt} = 5N$, **(b)** $\dfrac{dP}{dt} = -7P$, **(c)** $6\dfrac{dQ}{dt} = 5Q$.

6 The yearly rate of increase of the population, P, in a certain country is proportional to P. On 1 January 1995 there were 7 million and the population rose to 8 million six years later.

(a) Find an expression for P in terms of the time t measured in years from 1 January 1995.

(b) Predict the population of the country on 1 January 2010.

7 A radioactive substance decays at a rate proportional to its mass m. Initially its mass was 2×10^{-3} g and after 50 days its mass reduced to 1.5×10^{-3} g.

(a) Find an expression for m in terms of the time t, in days, from when the mass was 2×10^{-3} g.

(b) How long would it take for the mass to reach half its original size?

8 The amount of money, £Q, in a special deposit account grows at a rate proportional to the amount in that account at any moment in time. Initially £20 000 is deposited and after 8 years it grows to £26 000.

 (a) Find an expression for Q in terms of t, the time in years of the investment.

 (b) Determine how long it takes to have £30 000 in the account.

Key point summary

1 The solution to the equation $a^x = b$ is $x = \dfrac{\ln b}{\ln a}$, when   *p 133*
 logarithms are taken to base e.

2 The solution to the equation $a^x = b$ is $x = \dfrac{\lg b}{\lg a}$, when   *p 133*
 logarithms are taken to base 10.

3 The formula $x = a \times b^{kt}$, where a, b and k are positive   *p 136*
 constants, indicates that x is growing exponentially.

4 The formula $x = a \times b^{-kt}$, where a, b and k are   *p 136*
 positive constants, indicates that x is decaying
 exponentially.

5 In general, $x = Ae^{kt} \Rightarrow \dfrac{dx}{dt} = kx$.   *p 138*

6 The general solution of $\dfrac{dx}{dt} = kx$ is $x = Ae^{kt}$, where A *p 142*
 is an arbitrary constant.

Test yourself

	What to review
1 Solve the equation $6^x = 19$, giving your answer to three significant figures.	*Section 8.1*
2 Given that $5^{4x-1} = 19$, show that $x = \dfrac{1}{4}\left(\dfrac{\ln 19}{\ln 5} + 1\right)$.	*Section 8.2*
3 The population, P million, for a particular country is given by $P = 12.3 \times 1.02^t$, where t is the number of years after 1 January 1998. Use the formula to predict: (a) the population on 1 January 2005, (b) the year when the population will first reach 20 million.	*Section 8.3*

Test yourself (*continued*)	What to review

4 Given that $N = 300e^{-\frac{t}{12}}$:

   (a) show that $\dfrac{\mathrm{d}N}{\mathrm{d}t} = kN$ and state the value of k,

   (b) use the formula to find the value of t when $N = 200$.

Section 8.5

5 An experiment reveals that the number, N, of bacteria in a test tube increases at a rate proportional to the number present at any instant. Initially there are 2000 present and after 10 days the number has risen to 3000.

   (a) Find an expression for N in terms of the time, t, that has elapsed in days since the experiment began.

   (b) Calculate the time taken for the number of bacteria to increase to 5000.

Section 8.6

Test yourself **ANSWERS**

5 (a) $N = 2000e^{kt}$, where $k = \dfrac{\ln 1.5}{10} \approx 0.0405$;   **(b)** 22.6 days.

4 (a) $k = -\dfrac{1}{12}$;   **(b)** 4.87.

3 (a) 14.1 million;   **(b)** 2022.

1 1.64.

8

Volumes of revolution and further integration

Learning objectives

After studying this chapter you should be able to:

■ integrate expressions using the reverse idea of the chain rule
■ integrate trigonometric expressions
■ integrate expressions of te form $\dfrac{f'(x)}{f(x)}$
■ use partial fractions in integration
■ evaluate volumes of revolution.

9.1 Review

In this chapter you will learn how to integrate more functions to add to those you have already considered in P1 chapter 9 and P2 chapter 8.

You will recall from P1, the basic result

$$\int x^n \, dx = \frac{x^{n+1}}{n+1} + c, \quad n \neq -1,$$

c is the arbitrary constant.

and how, in P2, the missing link was established to give

$$\int \frac{1}{x} \, dx = \ln x + c.$$

The exponential function was also integrated in P2 to give

$$\int e^{kx} \, dx = \frac{1}{k} e^{kx} + c.$$

Worked example 9.1

Find $\displaystyle\int \left(10\sqrt{x^3} + \frac{1}{5x} + \frac{4}{e^{2x}} \right) dx.$

Solution

$$\int \left(10\sqrt{x^3} + \frac{1}{5x} + \frac{4}{e^{2x}}\right) dx = \int \left(10x^{\frac{3}{2}} + \frac{1}{5} \times \frac{1}{x} + 4e^{-2x}\right) dx$$

$$= \frac{10x^{\frac{5}{2}}}{\frac{5}{2}} + \frac{1}{5}\ln x + 4 \times \frac{e^{-2x}}{-2} + c$$

$$= 4\sqrt{x^5} + \frac{1}{5}\ln x - 2e^{-2x} + c$$

EXERCISE 9A

Find each of the following:

1 $\int \left(6x^2 + \frac{2}{x} + 7\right) dx.$

2 $\int (\sqrt{x} + e^{2x}) dx.$

3 $\int \left(\frac{1}{2x} - \frac{2}{e^{4x}}\right) dx.$

4 $\int \left(\frac{x^2 e^{3x} + x + 3}{x^2}\right) dx.$

5 $\int \left(e^{2x} - 1\right)^2 dx.$

6 $\int_0^1 (2x + 1)^4 \, dx.$

> Hint: Multiply out the brackets.

9.2 Integrating functions of the form $(ax + b)^n$ and $e^{cx + d}$ with respect to x

In chapter 6 you used the chain rule to differentiate many functions. Because integration is the reverse process to differentiation you can use the results of section 6.2 to evaluate many more integrals.

Worked example 9.2

Find $\int (2x + 7)^6 dx.$

Solution

Consider $\frac{d}{dx}(2x + 7)^7.$

> Increase the power by 1.

$$\frac{d}{dx}(2x + 7)^7 = 7(2x + 7)^6 \times 2$$

> Used the chain rule.

$$\Rightarrow 14(2x + 7)^6 = \frac{d}{dx}(2x + 7)^7$$

Integrating both sides with respect to x gives

$$\int 14(2x + 7)^6 dx = (2x + 7)^7 + k$$

$$14\int (2x + 7)^6 dx = (2x + 7)^7 + k$$

> Since 14 is a constant.

$$\Rightarrow \int (2x + 7)^6 dx = \frac{1}{14}(2x + 7)^7 + c.$$

> Where the constant $c = \frac{k}{14}$.

9

In general,

> For constants a, b and n, where $n \neq -1$,
>
> $$\int (ax+b)^n dx = \frac{1}{a(n+1)} (ax+b)^{n+1} + c.$$

In words, to integrate $(ax+b)^n$ with respect to x,

- increase index by 1
- divide at front by new index
- divide at front by derivative of $(ax+b)$, namely a.

Worked example 9.3

Evaluate $\displaystyle\int_{-1}^{0} \frac{1}{(4+3x)^2} dx$.

Solution

$$\int_{-1}^{0} \frac{1}{(4+3x)^2} dx = \int_{-1}^{0} (3x+4)^{-2} dx = \left[\frac{1}{(3)(-2+1)} (3x+4)^{-2+1} \right]_{-1}^{0}$$

$$\left[-\frac{1}{3} (3x+4)^{-1} \right]_{-1}^{0}$$

> new index $= -2+1$
> divide by $(-2+1)$
> divide by 3

$$= \frac{1}{-12} - \frac{1}{-3} = \frac{1}{4}$$

Worked example 9.4

Find $\displaystyle\int \frac{2}{\sqrt{4x+9}} dx$.

Solution

$$\int \frac{2}{\sqrt{4x+9}} dx = 2 \int (4x+9)^{-\frac{1}{2}} dx$$

$$= 2 \left[\frac{(4x+9)^{\frac{1}{2}}}{4(-\frac{1}{2}+1)} \right] + c$$

> $-\frac{1}{2} + 1 = \frac{1}{2}$

$$\Rightarrow \int \frac{2}{\sqrt{4x+9}} dx = \sqrt{4x+9} + c$$

Integrals of the type $\int e^{ax+b} dx$ can also be found by applying the reverse process to differentiation by the chain rule or by the alternative method illustrated by the next worked example.

Worked example 9.5

Find $\int e^{3x+5}dx$.

Solution

$\int e^{3x+5}dx = \int e^5 e^{3x}dx$

> By the law of indices.

$\qquad = e^5 \int e^{3x}dx = e^5 \left[\dfrac{1}{3}e^{3x} \right] + c$

> Since e^5 is a constant and
>
> $\int e^{kx}dx = \dfrac{1}{k}e^{kx} + c.$

$\qquad = \dfrac{1}{3}e^{3x+5} + c$

Try using the reverse chain rule approach to find the integral in the previous worked example.

> Start by considering $\dfrac{d}{dx}(e^{3x+5}).$

In general,

> For constants a and b,
>
> $\int e^{ax+b}dx = \dfrac{1}{a}e^{ax+b} + c.$

In words, to integrate the exponential function e^{ax+b} with respect to x,

- write down the exponential function
- divide at the front by the derivative of $(ax+b)$, namely a.

EXERCISE 9B

1 Find:

(a) $\int (x+2)^6 dx,$ **(b)** $\int (5x+1)^8 dx,$

(c) $\int (3-2x)^5 dx,$ **(d)** $\int 4-(1+2x)^6 dx,$

(e) $\int \sqrt{4x+1}\, dx,$ **(f)** $\int \sqrt[3]{8x-27}\, dx,$

(g) $\int \dfrac{1}{(x-1)^2}dx,$ **(h)** $\int \dfrac{1}{(2-5x)^3}\, dx,$

(i) $\int \dfrac{1}{2(5+4x)^4}\, dx,$ **(j)** $\int \sqrt{\dfrac{4}{2x-1}}\, dx,$

(k) $\int (e^{5x+6}-1)\, dx,$ **(l)** $\int \dfrac{4}{e^{3-2x}}\, dx.$

2 Evaluate:

(a) $\int_0^1 (2x+1)^4 dx,$ **(b)** $\int_{-1}^2 (1+3x)^5 dx,$

(c) $\int_1^2 \dfrac{1}{(1-2x)^2}\, dx,$ **(d)** $\int_0^1 \dfrac{1}{\sqrt[3]{7x+1}}\, dx,$

(e) $\int_{\frac{1}{2}}^2 e^{2x-1}dx,$ **(f)** $\int_0^{0.25} \dfrac{1}{2e^{4x-1}}\, dx.$

9

3 (a) Write $x^2 - 2x + 3$ in the form $(x - a)^2 + b$, where a and b are constants to be found.

(b) Hence, show that $\dfrac{x^2 - 2x + 3}{(x - 1)^2} \equiv 1 + \dfrac{2}{(x - 1)^2}$.

(c) Hence, evaluate $\displaystyle\int_2^3 \dfrac{x^2 - 2x + 3}{(x - 1)^2}\,\mathrm{d}x$.

4 Evaluate $\displaystyle\int_0^1 \dfrac{x^2 + 2x}{(x + 1)^2}\,\mathrm{d}x$.

9.3 Further integration of trigonometric functions

In sections 3.4 and 7.4 of this book you were shown the three results $\dfrac{\mathrm{d}}{\mathrm{d}x}(\sin x) = \cos x$, $\dfrac{\mathrm{d}}{\mathrm{d}x}(\cos x) = -\sin x$ and

$\dfrac{\mathrm{d}}{\mathrm{d}x}(\tan x) = \sec^2 x$, where x is in radians.

Integrating both sides of each of the three results leads to:

For x in radians,

$\displaystyle\int \cos x\,\mathrm{d}x = \sin x + c$

$\displaystyle\int \sin x\,\mathrm{d}x = -\cos x + c$

$\displaystyle\int \sec^2 x\,\mathrm{d}x = \tan x + c$.

These three integrals can be generalised by applying the reverse of the chain rule.

Worked example 9.6

Find $\displaystyle\int \cos(2x + 3)\,\mathrm{d}x$.

Solution

Consider $\dfrac{\mathrm{d}}{\mathrm{d}x}(\sin(2x + 3)) = 2\cos(2x + 3)$.

Integrating both sides with respect to x leads to

$\displaystyle\int 2\cos(2x + 3)\,\mathrm{d}x = \sin(2x + 3) + c$

$\Rightarrow \displaystyle\int \cos(2x + 3)\,\mathrm{d}x = \dfrac{1}{2}\sin(2x + 3) + c$.

In a similar way you can obtain the following general results:

> For constants a and b and x in radians,
>
> $$\int \cos (ax + b) \, dx = \frac{1}{a} \sin (ax + b) + c$$
>
> $$\int \sin (ax + b) \, dx = -\frac{1}{a} \cos (ax + b) + c$$
>
> $$\int \sec^2 (ax + b) \, dx = \frac{1}{a} \tan (ax + b) + c.$$

These integrals should be
memorised as they do not
appear in the formulae booklet.

Worked example 9.7

Show that $\displaystyle\int_0^{\frac{\pi}{6}} \sec^2 \left(3x - \frac{\pi}{6} \right) dx = \frac{4\sqrt{3}}{9}$.

Solution

$$\int_0^{\frac{\pi}{6}} \sec^2 \left(3x - \frac{\pi}{6} \right) dx = \left[\frac{1}{3} \tan \left(3x - \frac{\pi}{6} \right) \right]_0^{\frac{\pi}{6}}$$

$$= \frac{1}{3} \tan \left(\frac{\pi}{2} - \frac{\pi}{6} \right) - \frac{1}{3} \tan \left(0 - \frac{\pi}{6} \right)$$

$$= \frac{1}{3} \tan \left(\frac{\pi}{3} \right) - \frac{1}{3} \tan \left(-\frac{\pi}{6} \right)$$

$$= \frac{1}{3} \sqrt{3} - \frac{1}{3} \left(-\frac{1}{\sqrt{3}} \right)$$

$$= \frac{3 + 1}{3\sqrt{3}} = \frac{4\sqrt{3}}{9}.$$

$\tan \dfrac{\pi}{3} = \sqrt{3}.$

$\tan \left(-\dfrac{\pi}{6} \right) = -\tan \dfrac{\pi}{6} = -\dfrac{1}{\sqrt{3}}.$

The following three results, which you were shown in section
7.4, are given in the examination formulae booklet.

$$\frac{d}{dx} (\operatorname{cosec} x) = -\operatorname{cosec} x \cot x, \quad \frac{d}{dx} (\sec x) = \sec x \tan x \text{ and}$$

$$\frac{d}{dx} (\cot x) = -\operatorname{cosec}^2 x, \text{ where } x \text{ is in radians.}$$

Applying the chain rule you can obtain three more general

results, for example $\dfrac{d}{dx} (\operatorname{cosec} ax) = -a \operatorname{cosec} ax \cot ax.$

Integrating both sides of each of the three results with respect to x leads to:

For constants a and x in radians,

$$\int \operatorname{cosec} ax \cot ax \, dx = -\frac{1}{a} \operatorname{cosec} ax + c$$

$$\int \sec ax \tan ax \, dx = \frac{1}{a} \sec ax + c$$

$$\int \operatorname{cosec}^2 ax \, dx = -\frac{1}{a} \cot ax + c.$$

These integrals do **not** appear in the formulae booklet.

Worked example 9.8

Find the exact value of $\displaystyle\int_{\frac{\pi}{12}}^{\frac{\pi}{8}} \operatorname{cosec}^2 2x \, dx$.

Solution

$$\int_{\frac{\pi}{12}}^{\frac{\pi}{8}} \operatorname{cosec}^2 2x \, dx = \left[-\frac{1}{2} \cot 2x \right]_{\frac{\pi}{12}}^{\frac{\pi}{8}}$$

$$= -\frac{1}{2} \cot \frac{\pi}{4} - \left(-\frac{1}{2} \cot \frac{\pi}{6} \right) = -\frac{1}{2}(1) + \frac{1}{2}(\sqrt{3})$$

$$= \frac{\sqrt{3} - 1}{2}$$

$$\cot \frac{\pi}{6} = \frac{1}{\tan \frac{\pi}{6}} = \frac{1}{\left(\frac{1}{\sqrt{3}} \right)} = \sqrt{3}.$$

Sometimes you may have to rewrite the integrand in a more suitable form before integrating. The next example illustrates the point.

Worked example 9.9

Find $\displaystyle\int \left(\frac{2 \sin x}{\cos^2 x} \right) dx$.

Solution

$$\int \left(\frac{2 \sin x}{\cos^2 x} \right) dx = 2 \int \frac{1}{\cos x} \left(\frac{\sin x}{\cos x} \right) dx = 2 \int \sec x \tan x \, dx$$

$$\Rightarrow \int \frac{2 \sin x}{\cos^2 x} dx = 2 \sec x + c.$$

In section 3.3 you were shown the double-angle identities:

$\sin 2A = 2 \sin A \cos A$

$\cos 2A = \cos^2 A - \sin^2 A$

$\cos 2A = 2 \cos^2 A - 1$

$\cos 2A = 1 - 2 \sin^2 A$

You can use these identities to find more integrals.

> To integrate either $\sin^2 x$ or $\cos^2 x$ write each in terms of $\cos 2x$.

Worked example 9.10

Evaluate $\int_0^{\frac{5\pi}{12}} \sin^2 \theta \, d\theta$.

Solution

Using the identity $\cos 2A = 1 - 2\sin^2 A$ leads to

$$\int_0^{\frac{5\pi}{12}} \sin^2 \theta \, d\theta = \frac{1}{2} \int_0^{\frac{5\pi}{12}} (1 - \cos 2\theta) \, d\theta = \frac{1}{2} \left[\theta - \frac{1}{2} \sin 2\theta \right]_0^{\frac{5\pi}{12}}$$

$$= \frac{1}{2} \left(\frac{5\pi}{12} - \frac{1}{2} \sin \frac{5\pi}{6} \right) - \frac{1}{2} (0 - 0)$$

$$= \frac{5\pi}{24} - \frac{1}{4} \left(\frac{1}{2} \right) = \frac{5\pi - 3}{24}$$

Worked example 9.11

Find $\int \sin 3x \cos 3x \, dx$.

Solution

Using the identity $\sin 2A = 2\sin A \cos A$, with $A = 3x$, gives
$2 \sin 3x \cos 3x = \sin 6x$.
Integrating with respect to x leads to

$$\int \sin 3x \cos 3x \, dx = \frac{1}{2} \int \sin 6x \, dx = \frac{1}{2} \left[-\frac{1}{6} \cos 6x \right] + c$$

$$\int \sin 3x \cos 3x \, dx = -\frac{1}{12} \cos 6x + c$$

EXERCISE 9C

1 Evaluate:

   (a) $\int_0^{\frac{\pi}{2}} \cos x \, dx$,　　**(b)** $\int_0^{\frac{\pi}{4}} \sec^2 \theta \, d\theta$,　　**(c)** $\int_0^{\frac{\pi}{4}} \sin x \, dx$.

2 Integrate with respect to x:

   (a) $\int \cos 2x \, dx$,　　**(b)** $\int \sin 3x \, dx$,　　**(c)** $\int \sec^2 \frac{\theta}{2} \, d\theta$,

   (d) $\int 1 - \cos (2x + 4) \, dx$,　　**(e)** $\int x - \sin (4x - 1) \, dx$,

   (f) $\int \sec^2 (1 - 3\theta) \, d\theta$,　　**(g)** $\int \text{cosec}^2 4x \, dx$,

   (h) $\int \tan 3x \sec 3x \, dx$,　　**(i)** $\int \frac{\cos 2x}{\sin^2 2x} \, dx$.

3 By using the identity $1 + \tan^2 A \equiv \sec^2 A$, find $\int \tan^2 2x \, dx$.

4 Evaluate:

(a) $\int_0^{\frac{\pi}{12}} \sec^2 3\theta \, d\theta$,

(b) $\int_0^{\frac{\pi}{8}} \cos\left(4x + \frac{\pi}{4}\right) dx$,

(c) $\int_{\frac{\pi}{6}}^{\frac{\pi}{4}} 2\operatorname{cosec}^2 2\theta \, d\theta$,

(d) $\int_0^{\frac{\pi}{9}} 2 \cos 3x \sin 3x \, dx$,

(e) $\int_0^{\frac{\pi}{4}} 2 \cos^2 \theta \, d\theta$,

(f) $\int_0^{\frac{\pi}{6}} 4 \sin^2 \frac{x}{2} \, dx$,

(g) $\int_{\frac{\pi}{6}}^{\frac{\pi}{4}} (\cos \theta - \sin \theta)(\cos \theta + \sin \theta) \, d\theta$,

(h) $\int_0^{\frac{\pi}{9}} \frac{\sin 3x}{\cos^2 3x} \, dx$,

(i) $\int_0^{\frac{\pi}{4}} (\cos \theta + \sin \theta)^2 \, d\theta$,

(j) $\int_{\frac{\pi}{6}}^{\frac{\pi}{2}} \cot^2 x \, dx$.

5 Find the value of $\int_0^1 \cos^2 (2x + 1) \, dx$. Give your answer to three significant figures.

9.4 Integrals of the form $\int \dfrac{f'(x)}{f(x)} \, dx$

Here are four examples of integrals of the form $\int \dfrac{f'(x)}{f(x)} \, dx$:

$$\int \frac{5}{5x + 7} \, dx, \quad \int \frac{2x}{x^2 + 4} \, dx, \quad \int \frac{3e^x + 2}{3e^x + 2x + 1} \, dx, \quad \int \frac{2 \cos x}{5 + 2 \sin x} \, dx.$$

If you can find an expression for the general integral

$\int \dfrac{f'(x)}{f(x)} \, dx$, where $f(x)$ is any non-zero function of x, you will be able to write down the answers for the four integrals given above.

Again you can make use of the chain rule for differentiation.

Consider $\dfrac{d}{dx}[\ln f(x)]$.

$$\frac{d}{dx}[\ln f(x)] = \frac{1}{f(x)} \times f'(x)$$

Integrating both sides with respect to x leads to

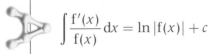

$$\int \frac{f'(x)}{f(x)} \, dx = \ln |f(x)| + c$$

> The modulus sign stresses the fact that you cannot take the natural logarithm of a negative value.

In words, the integral of a rational function, in which the numerator is the derivative of the denominator, is the natural logarithm of the modulus of the denominator.

Returning to the list of the four integrals you are now able to write down the following:

$$\int \frac{5}{5x+7} \, dx = \ln|5x+7| + c,$$

$$\int \frac{2x}{x^2+4} \, dx = \ln|x^2+4| + c,$$

$$\int \frac{3e^x+2}{3e^x+2x+1} \, dx = \ln|3e^x+2x+1| + c,$$

$$\int \frac{2\cos x}{5+2\sin x} \, dx = \ln|5+2\sin x| + c.$$

> As a first step, to integrate a rational function you check to see if the numerator is the same as the derivative of the denominator. If it is then the integral is just the natural logarithm of the modulus of the denominator.

Worked example 9.12

Find $\int \frac{x}{x^2+1} \, dx$.

Solution

Differentiating the denominator $x^2 + 1$ gives $2x$. Although this is not **exactly** the same as the numerator, x, since 2 is a constant you can write $\int \frac{x}{x^2+1} \, dx$ as $\frac{1}{2}\int \frac{2x}{x^2+1} \, dx$.

So $\int \frac{x}{x^2+1} \, dx = \frac{1}{2}\int \frac{2x}{x^2+1} \, dx = \frac{1}{2}\ln|x^2+1| + c$

$$= \frac{1}{2}\ln(x^2+1) + c$$

> **Warning**: You can only take constants outside of an integral sign. For example,
>
> $$\int \frac{1}{x^2+1} \, dx \neq \frac{1}{2x}\int \frac{2x}{x^2+1} \, dx.$$

> For real x, $x^2 + 1$ is always positive so you do not need the modulus sign.

9

Worked example 9.13

Show that the area bounded by the curve $y = \tan 2x$, the x-axis and the line $x = \frac{\pi}{6}$ is $\frac{1}{2}\ln 2$.

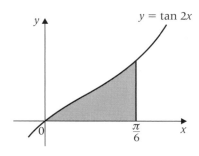

Solution

The required area is $\int_0^{\frac{\pi}{6}} \tan 2x \, dx$.

$$\int_0^{\frac{\pi}{6}} \tan 2x \, dx = \int_0^{\frac{\pi}{6}} \frac{\sin 2x}{\cos 2x} \, dx$$

$$= -\frac{1}{2} \int_0^{\frac{\pi}{6}} \frac{-2 \sin 2x}{\cos 2x} \, dx$$

$$= -\frac{1}{2} \left[\ln |\cos 2x| \right]_0^{\frac{\pi}{6}}$$

$$= -\frac{1}{2} \left(\ln \cos \frac{\pi}{3} - \ln \cos 0 \right)$$

$$= -\frac{1}{2} \left(\ln \frac{1}{2} - \ln 1 \right)$$

$$= \frac{1}{2} \left(-\ln \frac{1}{2} \right) = \frac{1}{2} \ln 2$$

$\tan \theta = \dfrac{\sin \theta}{\cos \theta}$

$f(x) = \cos 2x$
$\Rightarrow f'(x) = -2 \sin 2x$

The formulae booklet gives
$\int \tan x \, dx = \ln |\sec x| + c.$
Note:
$-\dfrac{1}{2} \ln \cos 2x = \dfrac{1}{2} \ln \sec 2x$ so
$\int \tan 2x \, dx = \dfrac{1}{2} \ln |\sec 2x| + c.$

$-\ln k = \ln \dfrac{1}{k}$

Worked example 9.13 illustrates how we can generalise integrals given in the formulae booklet to obtain

For a constant a, and x in radians,

$$\int \tan ax \, dx = \frac{1}{a} \ln |\sec ax| + c$$

$$\int \cot ax \, dx = \frac{1}{a} \ln |\sin ax| + c$$

$$\int \sec ax \, dx = \frac{1}{a} \ln |\sec ax + \tan ax| + c$$

$$\int \operatorname{cosec} ax \, dx = -\frac{1}{a} \ln |\operatorname{cosec} ax + \cot ax| + c$$

In the next exercise you will be asked to prove some of these results for particular values of a.

Worked example 9.14

Find $\int (1 + \sec 3x)^2 \, dx$.

Solution

$$\int (1 + \sec 3x)^2 \, dx = \int 1 + 2 \sec 3x + \sec^2 3x \, dx$$

$$= \int 1 \, dx + 2 \int \sec 3x \, dx + \int \sec^2 3x \, dx$$

$$= x + \frac{2}{3} \ln |\sec 3x + \tan 3x| + \frac{1}{3} \tan 3x + c$$

Worked example 9.15

Find $\int \dfrac{x + e^{2x}}{x^2 + e^{2x}} \, dx$.

Solution

Firstly differentiate $(x^2 + e^{2x})$ with respect to x to get $2x + 2e^{2x}$ which can be factorised to $2(x + e^{2x})$.

So $\int \dfrac{x + e^{2x}}{x^2 + e^{2x}} \, dx = \dfrac{1}{2} \int \dfrac{2(x + e^{2x})}{x^2 + e^{2x}} \, dx$

$$= \dfrac{1}{2} \ln (x^2 + e^{2x}) + c.$$

> Since, for real x, $x^2 + e^{2x} > 0$, you may omit the modulus sign.

EXERCISE 9D

1 Find:

(a) $\displaystyle\int \dfrac{3}{3x + 5} \, dx,$

(b) $\displaystyle\int \dfrac{6x}{3x^2 + 5} \, dx,$

(c) $\displaystyle\int \dfrac{3x^2}{x^3 + 8} \, dx,$

(d) $\displaystyle\int \dfrac{x}{2x^2 + 3} \, dx,$

(e) $\displaystyle\int \dfrac{1}{x} - \dfrac{2}{x + 3} \, dx,$

(f) $\displaystyle\int \dfrac{6x}{2x^2 + 5} \, dx,$

(g) $\displaystyle\int \dfrac{x}{(2 - x)(2 + x)} \, dx,$

(h) $\displaystyle \dfrac{e^{3x}}{4 - e^{3x}} \, dx,$

(i) $\displaystyle\int \dfrac{\cos 2x}{(\cos x + \sin x)^2} \, dx,$

(j) $\displaystyle\int (\tan x + 1)^2 \, dx,$

(k) $\displaystyle\int \dfrac{3}{x \ln x} \, dx.$

$$\left[\textbf{Hint for (k):} \ \dfrac{1}{x \ln x} = \dfrac{\frac{1}{x}}{\ln x}. \right]$$

2 Show that $\int \cot x \, dx = \ln | \sin x | + c.$

3 By writing $\sec 4x$ as $\dfrac{\sec 4x (\sec 4x + \tan 4x)}{\sec 4x + \tan 4x}$, find $\displaystyle\int \sec 4x \, dx.$

4 By writing $\operatorname{cosec} 2x$ as $\dfrac{\operatorname{cosec} 2x (\operatorname{cosec} 2x + \cot 2x)}{\operatorname{cosec} 2x + \cot 2x}$,

find $\displaystyle\int \operatorname{cosec} 2x \, dx.$

9

5 Evaluate:

(a) $\displaystyle\int_0^2 \left(\frac{1}{x+3}\right) dx,$

(b) $\displaystyle\int_1^2 \left(\frac{1}{x} + \frac{x}{x^2+1}\right) dx,$

(c) $\displaystyle\int_0^{\frac{\pi}{6}} \tan x \, dx,$

(d) $\displaystyle\int_1^2 \left(\frac{1}{4x} - \frac{x^2}{x^3+1}\right) dx,$

(e) $\displaystyle\int_0^{\frac{\pi}{2}} \left(\frac{\cos x}{3 - \sin x}\right) dx,$

(f) $\displaystyle\int_2^3 \frac{4x}{(x-1)(x+1)} \, dx,$

(g) $\displaystyle\int_0^1 \left(\frac{x+1}{x^2+2x+3}\right) dx,$

(h) $\displaystyle\int_0^1 \left(\frac{2e^x}{e^x + e^{-x}}\right) dx.$

[**Hint for (h)**: Rewrite the integrand with denominator $e^{2x}+1$.]

6 Show that the area bounded by the curve $y = \dfrac{2x(2x^2+1)}{2x^4 + 2x^2 + 5}$,

the x-axis and the line $x = 2$ is $\ln 3$.

9.5 Integration using partial fractions

In section 2.7 you studied partial fractions. In this section you will apply your knowledge of partial fractions to integration.

To solve integration problems using partial fractions, the following two integrals, where a and b are constants, are often needed:

$$\int \frac{1}{ax+b} \, dx = \frac{1}{a} \ln|ax+b| + c$$

$$\int \frac{1}{(ax+b)^2} \, dx = -\frac{1}{a(ax+b)} + c$$

You may also need to apply the laws of logarithms to obtain printed answers in examination questions.

$\ln p + \ln q = \ln(pq).$

$\ln p - \ln q = \ln\left(\dfrac{p}{q}\right).$

$\ln p^n = n \ln p.$

Worked example 9.16

Show that $\displaystyle\int_1^2 \left(\frac{2x+2}{2x+1}\right) dx = 1 + \frac{1}{2} \ln \frac{5}{3}.$

Solution

Firstly, write $\dfrac{2x+2}{2x+1}$ as a **proper fraction**.

See section 2.7.

$$\frac{2x+2}{2x+1} = \frac{2x+1+1}{2x+1} = \frac{2x+1}{2x+1} + \frac{1}{2x+1} = 1 + \frac{1}{2x+1}$$

So $\int_1^2 \left(\dfrac{2x+2}{2x+1} \right) dx = \int_1^2 1 + \dfrac{1}{2x+1} \, dx$

$$= \left[x + \dfrac{1}{2} \ln |2x+1| \right]_1^2$$

$$= \left(2 + \dfrac{1}{2} \ln 5 \right) - \left(1 + \dfrac{1}{2} \ln 3 \right)$$

$$= 1 + \dfrac{1}{2} (\ln 5 - \ln 3)$$

$$= 1 + \dfrac{1}{2} \ln \dfrac{5}{3}.$$

$\displaystyle \int \left(\dfrac{1}{2x+1} \right) dx = \dfrac{1}{2} \int \left(\dfrac{2}{2x+1} \right) dx.$

Worked example 9.17

By writing $\dfrac{x+4}{(x+1)(x-2)}$ in partial fractions, find the value of

$\displaystyle \int_3^4 \dfrac{x+4}{(x+1)(x-2)} \, dx$, leaving your answer in the form

$p \ln 4 - q \ln 5$, where p and q are integers to be found.

Solution

$\dfrac{x+4}{(x+1)(x-2)} \equiv \dfrac{A}{x+1} + \dfrac{B}{x-2}$, where A and B are constants.

Applying the cover-up rule gives $A = \dfrac{-1+4}{-1-2} = -1$

See Worked example 2.13.

$$\text{and } B = \dfrac{2+4}{2+1} = 2$$

$\displaystyle \int_3^4 \dfrac{x+4}{(x+1)(x-2)} \, dx = \int_3^4 \dfrac{-1}{x+1} + \dfrac{2}{x-2} \, dx$

$$= \left[-\ln |x+1| + 2 \ln |x-2| \right]_3^4$$

$$= (-\ln 5 + 2 \ln 2) - (-\ln 4 + 2 \ln 1)$$

$$= -\ln 5 + \ln 2^2 + \ln 4 - 0$$

$$= 2 \ln 4 - \ln 5$$

Worked examination question 9.1

(a) Express $\dfrac{2x}{(3+x)^2}$ in the form $\dfrac{A}{3+x} + \dfrac{B}{(3+x)^2}$, where A
and B are constants to be determined.

(b) Show that $\displaystyle \int_0^3 \dfrac{2x}{(3+x)^2} \, dx = p + \ln q$, where p and q are
integers to be determined. [A]

Solution

(a) $\dfrac{2x}{(3+x)^2} = \dfrac{A}{3+x} + \dfrac{B}{(3+x)^2} = \dfrac{A(3+x)+B}{(3+x)^2}$

$\Rightarrow 2x = A(3+x) + B$

Comparing coefficients of x gives $2 = A$.

Put $x = -3$ gives $-6 = B$.

$\dfrac{2x}{(3+x)^2} = \dfrac{2}{3+x} - \dfrac{6}{(3+x)^2}$

> Check: Put $x = 0$,
> $0 = 3A + B$ (?)
> $0 = 6 - 6$ is true.

(b) $\displaystyle\int_0^3 \dfrac{2x}{(3+x)^2}\,dx = \int_0^3 \dfrac{2}{3+x}\,dx - \int_0^3 \dfrac{6}{(3+x)^2}\,dx,$

$\qquad\qquad = \left[2\ln|3+x| - \dfrac{6(3+x)^{-1}}{-1} \right]_0^3$

$\qquad\qquad = \left[2\ln|3+x| + \dfrac{6}{3+x} \right]_0^3$

$\qquad\qquad = 2\ln 6 + 1 - (2\ln 3 + 2)$

$\qquad\qquad = -1 + 2\ln\dfrac{6}{3}$

$\qquad\qquad = -1 + 2\ln 2$

$\displaystyle\int_0^3 \dfrac{2x}{(3+x)^2}\,dx = -1 + \ln 4, \ (p = -1, q = 4)$

EXERCISE 9E

1 Find:

(a) $\displaystyle\int_0^1 \left(\dfrac{x+2}{x+1} \right) dx,$

(b) $\displaystyle\int_{\frac{1}{2}}^1 \left(\dfrac{2x-3}{2x+1} \right) dx,$

(c) $\displaystyle\int_1^2 \left(\dfrac{x^2+2x}{x+1} \right) dx.$

2 Find:

(a) $\displaystyle\int_1^2 \left(\dfrac{2}{x(x+1)} \right) dx,$ **(b)** $\displaystyle\int_2^3 \dfrac{4}{(x-1)(x+1)}\,dx,$

(c) $\displaystyle\int_3^4 \dfrac{1}{(x-1)(x-2)}\,dx,$ **(d)** $\displaystyle\int_2^3 \dfrac{5}{(2x-3)(x+1)}\,dx,$

(e) $\displaystyle\int_1^2 \dfrac{18}{x^2(x+3)}\,dx,$ **(f)** $\displaystyle\int_2^3 \dfrac{1}{(x-1)(x+1)^2}\,dx.$

3 (a) Express $\dfrac{2 - 5x^2}{(2 - x)(1 + x)^2}$ in terms of three partial fractions.

(b) Hence show that $\displaystyle\int_0^1 \dfrac{2 - 5x^2}{(2 - x)(1 + x)^2}\,dx = \ln 2 - \dfrac{1}{2}$.

4 (a) Find $\displaystyle\int \dfrac{x + 1}{x(2x + 1)}\,dx$.   **(b)** Find $\displaystyle\int \dfrac{x(2x + 1)}{x + 1}\,dx$.

5 (a) Express $\dfrac{2x^2 + 3x + 12}{(2x - 1)(x + 3)}$ in the form $A + \dfrac{B}{2x - 1} + \dfrac{C}{x + 3}$, where A, B and C are constants to be determined.

(b) Hence find $\displaystyle\int_1^5 \dfrac{2x^2 + 3x + 12}{(2x - 1)(x + 3)}\,dx$, giving your answer in the form $p + q\ln 2 + r\ln 3$, where p, q and r are integers to be found.

6 A curve C has equation $y = \dfrac{2x - 1}{(x - 2)(5 - x)}$.

(a) Express $\dfrac{2x - 1}{(x - 2)(5 - x)}$ in partial fractions.

(b) Find the area bounded by the curve C, the x-axis and the lines $x = 3$ and $x = 4$.

9.6 Volumes of revolution about horizontal and vertical axes

In P1, chapter 9, you were shown that the area of the region, R, bounded by the curve $y = f(x)$, the x-axis and the lines $x = a$ and $x = b$ is given by $\int_b^a f(x)\,dx$. In this section you will be shown how to find the volume of the solid which is formed by rotating the same region through 2π radians about the x-axis. Using this work you will be able to prove some of the formulae that you used in GCSE but were not able to prove.

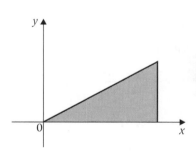

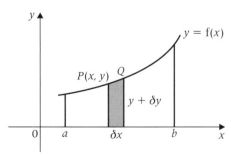

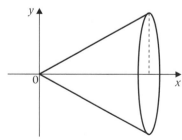

Rotating the region R through 2π radians about the x-axis gives a solid.

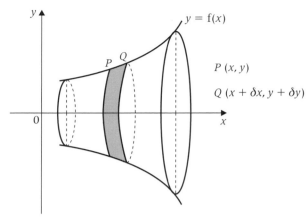

Consider the volume, δV, formed by rotating the small element, shown shaded above, and compare its volume with the volume of the two cylindrical disks

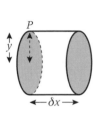

Volume $= \pi y^2 \, \delta x$

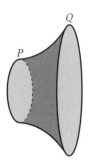

Volume $= \delta V$

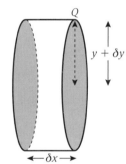

Volume $= \pi \, (y + \delta y)^2 \, \delta x$

$$\pi y^2 \delta x < \delta V < \pi (y + \delta y)^2 \delta x$$

or dividing throughout by δx

$$\pi y^2 < \frac{\delta V}{\delta x} < \pi (y + \delta y)^2$$

Compare with the work in P1 section 9.4.

As $\delta x \to 0$, $\delta y \to 0$ and $\dfrac{\delta V}{\delta x} \to \dfrac{\mathrm{d}V}{\mathrm{d}x}$

Hence, $\dfrac{\mathrm{d}V}{\mathrm{d}x} = \pi y^2$.

So, integrating both sides with respect to x, between the limits $x = a$ and $x = b$ covers the volume for the complete solid.

> When the region bounded by the curve $y = f(x)$, the x-axis and the lines $x = a$ and $x = b$ is rotated through 2π radians about the x-axis, the volume, V, of the solid generated is called the volume of revolution and is given by
>
> $$V = \int_a^b \pi y^2 \, \mathrm{d}x = \int_a^b \pi [f(x)]^2 \, \mathrm{d}x.$$

Worked example 9.18

By rotating the region bounded by the line $y = \dfrac{r}{h}x$, the x-axis

and the line $x = h$ through 2π radians about the x-axis, show

that the volume of a cone of height h and radius r is $\dfrac{1}{3}\pi r^2 h$.

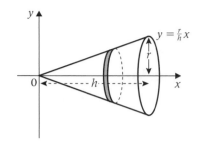

Solution

Volume of the cone = Volume of revolution of the line $y = \dfrac{r}{h}x$,

$$= \int_0^h \pi y^2 \, dx = \int_0^h \pi \left[\frac{r^2}{h^2} x^2 \right] dx = \frac{\pi r^2}{h^2} \int_0^h x^2 dx$$

$$= \frac{\pi r^2}{h^2} \left[\frac{x^3}{3} \right]_0^h = \frac{\pi r^2 h^3}{3h^2}$$

The cylindrical element has radius y and height δx.

Volume of the cone $= \dfrac{1}{3}\pi r^2 h$.

Worked example 9.19

The region bounded by the curve $y = x\sqrt{x^2 + 5}$, the x-axis and
the line $x = 2$ is rotated through 2π radians about the x-axis.
Find the volume of the solid generated.

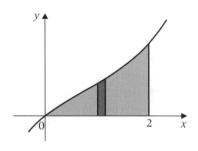

Solution

Volume $= \int_0^2 \pi y^2 dx = \pi \int_0^2 [x\sqrt{x^2+5}]^2 dx = \pi \int_0^2 x^2(x^2+5)dx$

$$= \pi \int_0^2 (x^4 + 5x^2)dx = \pi \left[\frac{x^5}{5} + \frac{5x^3}{3} \right]_0^2 = \pi \left[\left(\frac{32}{5} + \frac{40}{3} \right) - 0 \right]$$

Required volume $= \dfrac{296}{15}\pi$.

The cylindrical element has radius y and height δx.

To find the volume of a solid generated by rotating a
region bounded by a curve $y = f(x)$, vertical lines $x = a$
and $x = b$ and a horizontal line L, through 2π radians
about L:

- consider a small cylindrical element with axis of
  symmetry L
- find the radius, PA, of the element (the height of the
  element will be δx)
- use $V = \int_a^b \pi (PA)^2 \, dx$, rewriting PA in terms of x before
  integrating.

If the equation of line L is $y = k$,
then $PA = |f(x) - k|$
$\Rightarrow PA^2 = [f(x) - k]^2$.

Worked example 9.20

The region enclosed by the curve $y = x^2 - 4$, the y-axis, the line $x = 2$ and the line $y = 1$ is rotated through 2π radians about the line $y = 1$ to form a solid S. Find the volume of S.

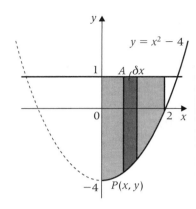

Solution

The small cylindrical element has radius $PA = |y - 1|$.

$$\text{Volume of } S = \int_0^2 \pi(x^2 - 4 - 1)^2 dx$$

$$\pi \int_0^2 (x^2 - 5)^2 \, dx$$

$$= \pi \int_0^2 (x^4 - 10x^2 + 25) \, dx$$

$$= \pi \left[\frac{x^5}{5} - \frac{10x^3}{3} + 25x \right]_0^2$$

$$= \pi \left[\left(\frac{32}{5} - \frac{80}{3} + 50 \right) - (0) \right]$$

$$\text{Volume of } S = 29\frac{11}{15}\pi.$$

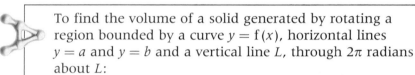

> To find the volume of a solid generated by rotating a region bounded by a curve $y = f(x)$, horizontal lines $y = a$ and $y = b$ and a vertical line L, through 2π radians about L:
> - consider a small cylindrical element with axis of symmetry L
> - find the radius, PA, of the element (the height of the element will be δy)
> - use $V = \int_a^b \pi(PA)^2 \, dy$, rewriting PA in terms of y before integrating.

If the equation of line L is $x = k$, then $PA = |x - k|$
$\Rightarrow PA^2 = (x - k)^2$.

Worked example 9.21

The region bounded by the curve $y = x^3$, the y-axis and the line $y = 8$ is rotated through 2π radians about the y-axis. Find the volume of the solid generated.

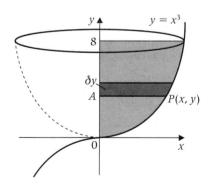

Solution

The small cylindrical element has radius $PA = |x - 0|$

$$y = x^3 \Rightarrow x = y^{\frac{1}{3}} \Rightarrow x^2 = y^{\frac{2}{3}}$$

$$\text{Volume of solid} = \int_0^8 \pi x^2 dy = \pi \int_0^8 y^{\frac{2}{3}} \, dy$$

$$= \pi \left[\frac{3}{5} y^{\frac{5}{3}} \right]_0^8$$

$$= \pi \left[\left(\frac{3}{5} \times 2^5 \right) - (0) \right]$$

$$\text{Volume of solid} = \frac{96}{5}\pi.$$

EXERCISE 9F

1 Find the volumes of the solids formed by rotating, through 2π radians about the x-axis, the following regions:

    (a) bounded by the curve $y = 2x + 1$, the x-axis and the lines $x = 0$ and $x = 2$,

    (b) bounded by the curve $y = x^2 + 1$, the coordinate axes and the line $x = 1$,

    (c) bounded by the curve $y = \sin x$, the x-axis and the lines $x = \dfrac{\pi}{4}$ and $x = \dfrac{\pi}{2}$,

    (d) bounded by the curve $y = \dfrac{2}{x}$, the x-axis and the lines $x = 2$ and $x = 4$,

    (e) bounded by the curve $y = \dfrac{3}{\sqrt{x}}$, the x-axis and the lines $x = 1$ and $x = 9$.

2 (a) Show that the curve $y = (2x - 1)^2$ only meets the x-axis at the point $\left(\dfrac{1}{2}, 0 \right)$.

    (b) The region bounded by the curve $y = (2x - 1)^2$ and the coordinate axes is rotated through 2π radians about the x-axis. Find the volume of the solid generated.

3 The region bounded by the curve $y = e^x$, the coordinate axes and the line $x = 1$ is rotated through 2π radians about the x-axis. Find the volume of the solid generated.

4 The region bounded by the curve $y = x^5$, the y-axis and the lines $y = 1$ and $y = 32$ is rotated through 2π radians about the y-axis. Find the volume of the solid generated.

5 (a) Write down the equation of the circle with centre $(0, 0)$ and radius r.

    (b) By rotating the region bounded by the coordinate axes and the part of the circle in the first quadrant about the x-axis, show that the volume of a hemisphere is $\dfrac{2}{3}\pi r^3$.

6 The region enclosed by the curve $y = x^2 - 9$, the y-axis, the line $x = 3$ and the line $y = 1$ is rotated through 2π radians about the line $y = 1$ to form a solid S. Find the volume of S.

7 The region enclosed by the curve $y = x^2 - 9$, the negative y-axis and the positive x-axis, is rotated through 2π radians about the line $y = 1$ to form a solid T. Find the volume of T.
[**Hint**: Use your answer to question 6.]

9

8 The points $P(3, 2)$ and $Q(0, 1)$ lie on the curve $y^2 = x + 1$.

(a) Calculate the volume of the solid generated when the region bounded by the lines $y = 0$, $x = 0$, $x = 3$ and the arc PQ of the curve is rotated completely about the x-axis. Give your answer as a multiple of π.

(b) S is the region bounded by the lines $y = 1$, $x = 3$ and the arc PQ of the curve. Show that when S is rotated completely about the x-axis the volume of the solid generated is $\dfrac{9\pi}{2}$.

(c) When S is rotated completely about the line $x = 3$ show that the volume of the solid generated is $\pi \int_1^2 (4 - y^2)^2 \, dy$ and calculate this volume in terms of π. [A]

MIXED EXERCISE

1 The equation of a curve C is given by $y = \dfrac{\cos x}{2 - \sin x}$, $0 \leqslant x \leqslant \pi$.

Find the exact area of the region bounded by the curve C, the x- and y-axes and the line $x = \dfrac{\pi}{6}$. Express your answer in its simplest form. [A]

2 (a) The expression $\dfrac{5x^2 - 2x + 2}{(x + 1)(x^2 - x + 1)}$ can be written in the

form $\dfrac{A}{x + 1} + \dfrac{Bx + C}{x^2 - x + 1}$, where A, B and C are

constants. Determine the value of A, and show that $B = 2$ and $C = -1$.

(b) Hence, given that $x^3 + 1 = (x + 1)(x^2 - x + 1)$, show

that $\displaystyle\int_1^2 \dfrac{5x^2 - 2x + 2}{x^3 + 1} \, dx = \ln \dfrac{81}{8}$. [A]

3 Evaluate $\displaystyle\int_0^{\frac{\pi}{8}} (\sec 2x - \cos 2x) \, dx$.

4 Show that $\displaystyle\int_2^3 \dfrac{2x - 3}{(2x - 1)(x - 1)} \, dx = \ln \dfrac{25}{18}$.

5 Show that $\displaystyle\int_{-\frac{\pi}{4}}^{\frac{\pi}{2}} (\sin 2x + 2\cos^2 x) \, dx = 1 + \dfrac{3}{4}\pi$.

6 The region bounded by the curve $y = \sec\left(2x - \dfrac{\pi}{4}\right)$, the x-axis

and the lines $x = 0$ and $x = \dfrac{\pi}{4}$ is rotated through 2π radians

about the x-axis. Find the volume of the solid generated.

Key point summary

1 For constants a, b and n, where $n \neq -1$, $\qquad$ *p 148*

$$\int (ax + b)^n \, dx = \frac{1}{a(n + 1)} (ax + b)^{n+1} + c.$$

2 For constants a and b, $\qquad$ *p 149*

$$\int e^{ax+b} \, dx = \frac{1}{a} e^{ax+b} + c.$$

3 For x in radians, $\qquad$ *p 150*

$\int \cos x \, dx = \sin x + c$

$\int \sin x \, dx = -\cos x + c$

$\int \sec^2 x \, dx = \tan x + c.$

4 For constants a and b and x in radians, $\qquad$ *p 151*

$$\int \cos (ax + b) \, dx = \frac{1}{a} \sin (ax + b) + c$$

$$\int \sin (ax + b) \, dx = -\frac{1}{a} \cos (ax + b) + c$$

$$\int \sec^2 (ax + b) \, dx = \frac{1}{a} \tan (ax + b) + c.$$

5 For constants a and x in radians, $\qquad$ *p 152*

$$\int \operatorname{cosec} ax \cot ax \, dx = -\frac{1}{a} \operatorname{cosec} ax + c$$

$$\int \sec ax \tan ax \, dx = \frac{1}{a} \sec ax + c$$

$$\int \operatorname{cosec}^2 ax \, dx = -\frac{1}{a} \cot ax + c.$$

6 To integrate either $\sin^2 x$ or $\cos^2 x$ write each in terms $\qquad$ *p 153*
of $\cos 2x$.

7 $\displaystyle \int \frac{f'(x)}{f(x)} \, dx = \ln |f(x)| + c$ $\qquad$ *p 154*

8 For a constant a, and x in radians, $\qquad$ *p 156*

$$\int \tan ax \, dx = \frac{1}{a} \ln |\sec ax| + c$$

$$\int \cot ax \, dx = \frac{1}{a} \ln |\sin ax| + c$$

$$\int \sec ax \, dx = \frac{1}{a} \ln |\sec ax + \tan ax| + c$$

$$\int \operatorname{cosec} ax \, dx = -\frac{1}{a} \ln |\operatorname{cosec} ax + \cot ax| + c.$$

9

9 To solve integration problems using partial fractions, the following two integrals, where a and b are constants, are often needed:

$$\int \frac{1}{ax+b}\,dx = \frac{1}{a}\ln|ax+b| + c$$

$$\int \frac{1}{(ax+b)^2}\,dx = -\frac{1}{a(ax+b)} + c.$$

p158

10 When the region bounded by the curve $y = f(x)$, the x-axis and the lines $x = a$ and $x = b$ is rotated through 2π radians about the x-axis, the volume, V, of the solid generated is called the volume of revolution and is given by

$$V = \int_a^b \pi y^2\,dx = \int_a^b \pi[f(x)]^2\,dx.$$

p162

11 To find the volume of a solid generated by rotating a region bounded by a curve $y = f(x)$, vertical lines $x = a$ and $x = b$ and a horizontal line L, through 2π radians about L:
- consider a small cylindrical element with axis of symmetry L
- find the radius, PA, of the element (the height of the element will be δx)
- use $V = \int_a^b \pi(PA)^2\,dx$, rewriting PA in terms of x before integrating.

p163

12 To find the volume of a solid generated by rotating a region bounded by a curve $y = f(x)$, horizontal lines $y = a$ and $y = b$ and a vertical line L, through 2π radians about L:
- consider a small cylindrical element with axis of symmetry L
- find the radius, PA, of the element (the height of the element will be δy)
- use $V = \int_a^b \pi(PA)^2\,dy$, rewriting PA in terms of y before integrating.

p164

Test yourself	**What to review**
1 Find $\displaystyle\int \left(\frac{x}{4}+3\right)^7 + e^{4x-3} + \frac{6}{\sqrt{9x+1}}\,dx.$	*Sections 9.1 and 9.2*
2 (a) Evaluate $\displaystyle\int_0^{\frac{\pi}{4}} \tan^2\left(2x - \frac{\pi}{4}\right) + 2\sin^2 x\,dx.$ **(b)** Find $\int (\sec 2x + \tan 2x)^2\,dx.$	*Section 9.3*

Test yourself (*continued*)

What to review

3 Find $\displaystyle\int \frac{2e^x}{e^x + 1} + \cot 5x + \frac{x(x-1)}{2x^3 - 3x^2 + 7}\, dx.$

Section 9.4

---

4 (a) Express $\dfrac{9x^2}{(1+x)(2-x)^2}$ in the form

Section 9.5

$\dfrac{A}{1+x} + \dfrac{B}{2-x} + \dfrac{C}{(2-x)^2}.$

(b) Hence show that $\displaystyle\int_0^1 \frac{9x^2}{(1+x)(2-x)^2}\, dx = 6 - 7\ln 2.$

---

5 The region bounded by the curve $y = x + \dfrac{1}{x}$, the x-axis and

Section 9.6

the lines $x = 1$ and $x = 3$ is rotated through 2π radians about the x-axis. Find the volume of the solid generated.

Test yourself ANSWERS

1 $\dfrac{1}{2}\left(\dfrac{x}{4} + 3\right)^2 + \dfrac{1}{4}e^{4x-3} + \dfrac{4}{3}\sqrt{9x+1} + c.$

2 (a) $\dfrac{1}{2};$ **(b)** $\tan 2x - x + \sec 2x + c.$

3 $2\ln(e^x + 1) + \dfrac{1}{5}\ln|\sin 5x| + \dfrac{1}{6}\ln|2x^3 - 3x^2 + 7| + c.$

4 (a) $A = 1,\ B = -8,\ C = 12.$

5 $13\dfrac{1}{3}\pi.$

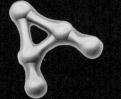

CHAPTER 10

Sequences and numerical methods

Learning objectives

After studying this chapter you should be able to:

- understand the principle of iteration
- realise that some non-convergent sequences are oscillating
- find the period of periodic sequences
- use numerical methods such as bisection, decimal search and linear interpolation to find solutions of equations
- appreciate the need for convergence in iterations
- use the Newton–Raphson Iterative Method
- understand how cobweb and staircase diagrams demonstrate convergence or divergence for equations of the form $x = g(x)$.

10.1 Introduction

Suppose you wish to find the square root of 17 but do not have a square root function on your calculator.

This problem is essentially the same as saying, what would be the length of the side of a square with area 17 square units?

This side would be
17/4 = 4.25 units

Guess 4 units for this side | Area 17 square units

Thinking geometrically, if you guess that one side of a rectangle has length 4 units and the area is known to be 17 square units, then the other side must have length $17/4 = 4.25$ units.

Since you are hoping to produce a square, a better guess for the side of the square is the average of these two lengths, namely

$$\frac{1}{2}(4 + 4.25) = 4.125 \text{ units.}$$

Repeating the process, if one side has length 4.125 units then the other side is $17/4.125 = 4.1212\ldots$ units. Therefore a better guess for the side of the square is

$$\frac{1}{2}(4.25 + 4.1212\ldots) = 4.123\,106\,06\ldots \text{ units.}$$

This is an example of an **iterative method** where the previous answer is fed into a formula to produce the next result.

If you have a graphics calculator with an ANS key, this procedure can be speeded up considerably.

Try typing in 4 followed by $\boxed{\text{EXE}}$ (on a Casio calculator) or $\boxed{\text{ENTER}}$ (on a Texas or Sharp calculator).

Then type in 0.5 (ANS + 17 ÷ ANS) followed by $\boxed{\text{EXE}}$ or $\boxed{\text{ENTER}}$ and you will see the value 4.125.

Now keep pressing the $\boxed{\text{EXE}}$ or $\boxed{\text{ENTER}}$ key and you will get the sequence

    4.123 106 061 . . .
    4.123 105 626 . . .
    4.123 105 626 . . .

> You can check this is correct by pressing $\sqrt{17}$ on your calculator.

We say that the sequence **converges** to the value 4.1231, to four decimal places.

In general the square root of any positive number N can be found by this method using 0.5(ANS + N ÷ ANS) after inputting your first guess.

> Try it with a few values and you will see that your first guess does not even have to be close to the value of the square root of N. You should see that after a few key presses the values converge to $\sqrt{N}$.

10.2 Recurrence relations

A sequence can be generated by a simple recurrence relation of the form $x_{n+1} = f(x_n)$.

For example, when $x_1 = 2$ and $x_{n+1} = x_n^2 - 1$, you can find

$$x_2 = 2^2 - 1 = 3$$

$x_3 = 8$, $x_4 = 63$, $x_5 = 3968$, etc.

A recurrence relation, or iterative formula, to find the square root of N (discussed in the previous section) would be

$$x_{n+1} = \frac{1}{2}\left(x_n + \frac{N}{x_n}\right)$$ with a suitable starting value x_1.

Worked example 10.1

A sequence is defined by $x_{n+1} = \dfrac{x_n - 3}{1 + 2x_n}$, $x_1 = 2$.

Find the values of x_2, x_3 and x_4.

10

Solution

You can find x_2 by using $x_2 = \dfrac{x_1 - 3}{1 + 2x_1} = -\dfrac{1}{5}$.

Then $x_3 = \dfrac{x_2 - 3}{1 + 2x_2} = \dfrac{\dfrac{-1}{5} - 3}{1 + \dfrac{-2}{5}} = \dfrac{\dfrac{-16}{5}}{\dfrac{3}{5}} = \dfrac{-16}{3} = -5\dfrac{1}{3}$.

Finally, $x_4 = \dfrac{x_3 - 3}{1 + 2x_3} = \dfrac{\dfrac{-16}{3} - 3}{1 + \dfrac{-32}{3}} = \dfrac{\dfrac{-25}{3}}{\dfrac{-29}{3}} = \dfrac{25}{29}$.

> You could have obtained decimal equivalents from your calculator using 4 ENTER
> (ANS − 3) ÷ (1 + 2 ANS)
> ENTER

10.3 Convergent and divergent sequences

A sequence may be defined inductively by a recurrence relation such as in the previous worked example, or by a defining formula such as $u_n = \dfrac{1 + 3n}{n + 2}$.

In this case, you need to substitute $n = 1, 2, \ldots$ to obtain

$$u_1 = \frac{1 + (3 \times 1)}{1 + 2} = \frac{4}{3}, \ u_2 = \frac{1 + (3 \times 2)}{2 + 2} = \frac{7}{4}, \text{ etc.}$$

As n gets larger, $u_{100} = \dfrac{1 + (3 \times 100)}{100 + 2} = \dfrac{301}{102} \approx 2.951$

and $u_{1000} = \dfrac{1 + (3 \times 1000)}{1000 + 2} = \dfrac{3001}{1002} \approx 2.995$

> An intuitive idea of whether a sequence converges or diverges is all that is required for the P4 examination.

so that the values are getting closer and closer to 3.
This sequence is said to **converge** on to the value 3.

Worked example 10.2

For each of the following sequences, find x_2, x_3 and x_4, and state whether the sequence is convergent or divergent.

(a) $x_n = \dfrac{1 + n^3}{2n - 1}$,

(b) $x_{n+1} = 1 + 2x_n$, $x_1 = 5$,

(c) $x_{n+1} = \dfrac{5x_n + 1}{1 + 2x_n}$, $x_1 = 2$.

Solution

(a) Substituting $n = 2$ gives $x_2 = \dfrac{1 + 2^3}{(2 \times 2) - 1} = \dfrac{9}{3} = 3$.

Substituting $n = 3$ gives $x_3 = \dfrac{1 + 3^3}{(2 \times 3) - 1} = \dfrac{28}{5} = 5.6$.

Substituting $n = 4$ gives $x_4 = \dfrac{1 + 4^3}{(2 \times 3) - 1} = \dfrac{65}{7} = 9.2857\ldots$.

The numbers are getting larger and this is not surprising since the numerator involves n^3, whereas the denominator is only a linear term.

Putting $n = 100$ gives $x_{100} = \dfrac{1 + 100^3}{(2 \times 100) - 1} = \dfrac{100\,000\,1}{199} \approx 5025$.

The sequence diverges to ∞.

(b) $x_{n+1} = 1 + 2x_n$ and $x_1 = 5$, so $x_2 = 1 + 2x_1 = 1 + 10 = 11$.

Similarly, $x_3 = 1 + 2x_2 = 1 + 22 = 23$ and $x_4 = 1 + 2x_3 = 1 + 46 = 47$.

The values will continue to increase and so, once again, the sequence diverges to ∞.

(c) Since $x_{n+1} = \dfrac{5x_n + 1}{1 + 2x_n}$ and $x_1 = 2$, you can find

$$x_2 = \frac{5x_1 + 1}{1 + 2x_1} = \frac{10 + 1}{1 + 4} = \frac{11}{5} = 2.2.$$

Similarly, $x_3 = \dfrac{5x_2 + 1}{1 + 2x_2} = \dfrac{11 + 1}{1 + 4.4} = \dfrac{12}{5.4} = 2.2222\ldots$ and

also $x_4 = \dfrac{5x_3 + 1}{1 + 2x_3} = \dfrac{12.111\ldots}{5.444\ldots} = 2.224\ldots$.

It is difficult to see from just a few values, but this sequence is converging to a limit.

If you use the ANS key on a graphics calculator with

2 $\boxed{\text{EXE}}$

$(5\,\text{ANS} + 1) \div (1 + 2\,\text{ANS})$

$\boxed{\text{EXE}}$

$\boxed{\text{EXE}}$, etc., you find it quickly settles down to the value $2.224\,744\,871\ldots$.

10

EXERCISE 10A

1 A sequence is defined by $x_{n+1} = \dfrac{x_n + 5}{1 - 3x_n}$, $x_1 = 0$. Find the values of x_2, x_3 and x_4.

2 A sequence is defined by $u_{n+1} = \dfrac{u_n^2 + 1}{3 + u_n}$, $u_1 = 2$.

Find the values of u_2, u_3 and u_4.

3 Use the iterative formula $x_{n+1} = \dfrac{1}{2}\left(x_n + \dfrac{N}{x_n}\right)$ with $x_1 = 3$ to find x_2, x_3 and x_4, giving your answers to six significant figures, in the cases where:

(a) $N = 10$, **(b)** $N = 13$.

Verify that these successive values are getting closer to:

(a) $\sqrt{10}$, **(b)** $\sqrt{13}$.

4 An iterative formula to find the cube root of the number V is given by $x_{n+1} = \dfrac{1}{3}\left(2x_n + \dfrac{V}{x_n^2}\right)$.

> Can you justify this formula by thinking of a cube, making a guess at the length of two equal sides and a suitable averaging technique to obtain the next approximation?

(a) With $V = 30$ and $x_1 = 3$, find the values of x_2, x_3 and x_4, giving your answers to six significant figures.

(b) With $V = 100$ and $x_1 = 5$, find the values of x_2, x_3 and x_4, giving your answers to six significant figures.

5 The iteration $x_{n+1} = x_n(2 - Nx_n)$ can be used to find the reciprocal of N without needing to use division.

(a) Use $N = 7$ and $x_1 = 0.1$ to find three iterations and verify that the values are approaching $1/7$.

(b) Use $N = 53$ and $x_1 = 0.02$ to find three iterations and verify that the values are approaching $1/53$.

6 For each of the following sequences, find the values of x_2, x_3 and x_4, and ascertain whether the sequence converges or diverges.

(a) $x_{n+1} = 4 + 5x_n$, $x_1 = -1$.

(b) $x_{n+1} = 4 + 5x_n$, $x_1 = -2$.

(c) $x_{n+1} = 3 - \frac{1}{2}x_n$, $x_1 = -2$.

(d) $x_{n+1} = \dfrac{7x_n - 1}{3 + 2x_n}$, $x_1 = 1.7$.

7 For each of the following sequences, find the first four terms and state whether the sequence converges or diverges.

(a) $x_n = \dfrac{2 + n^4}{2n - 1}$, **(b)** $y_n = \dfrac{1 + 3n}{1 + 2n}$, **(c)** $z_n = \dfrac{5 + n^2}{n^2 + 1}$.

8 Find the first six terms of the sequence defined by
$t_n = \sqrt{(n^2 + n)} - n$ giving your answers to four significant figures. Can you discover what limit the sequence tends to as n tends to infinity?

> You may find it interesting to set up the values on a spreadsheet.

9 (a) Show that $\dfrac{5 + 7n}{3 + 2n}$ can be written in the form $\dfrac{\dfrac{5}{n} + 7}{\dfrac{3}{n} + 2}$.

(b) Using the fact that $\dfrac{k}{n} \to 0$ as $n \to \infty$ for all constants k,

show that the sequence defined by $u_n = \dfrac{5 + 7n}{3 + 2n}$

converges with limit 3.5.

10 Using the method of the previous question, find the limits of the following convergent sequences.

(a) $u_n = \dfrac{8 + 5n}{7 + 10n}$,

(b) $u_n = \dfrac{2 - 8n}{5 + 2n}$,

(c) $u_n = \dfrac{4 - 3n}{2n - 5}$,

(d) $u_n = \dfrac{1 + 3n^2}{2 + n^2}$.

10.4 Oscillating sequences

The sequence with nth term $t_n = 1 + \dfrac{3}{n}$ is convergent and clearly has limit 1 as $n \to \infty$.

Some divergent sequences such as $u_n = n^2 + 3$ tend to $+\infty$, whereas others such as $v_n = 5 - 2n$ tend to $-\infty$.

> A non-convergent sequence which does not diverge to $+\infty$ or to $-\infty$ is said to be **oscillating**.

An oscillating sequence may oscillate finitely such as the sequence with nth term $x_n = (-2)^n$, where the terms are $-2, 2, -2, 2, \dots$.

However, the sequence given by $y_n = n^3 \cos (n\pi)$ oscillates infinitely.

The first few terms are

$\cos \pi, 8 \cos 2\pi, 27 \cos 3\pi, 64 \cos 4\pi, \dots$

or $-1, 8, -27, 64, -125, \dots$.

The sequences $\{x_n\}$ and $\{y_n\}$ are both examples of oscillating sequences.

10

Worked example 10.3

The nth terms of various sequences are given below.
For each sequence, determine whether it converges, and if it is convergent, find its limit.
For any non-convergent sequence, indicate whether it diverges to $+\infty$, diverges to $-\infty$, or oscillates.

(a) $3 - \dfrac{7}{n}$, **(b)** $\dfrac{3+n}{4}$, **(c)** $n^2 \sin\left(\dfrac{n\pi}{3}\right)$,

(d) $2 + (-1)^n$ **(e)** $5 - n^2$, **(f)** $4 + \left(-\tfrac{1}{3}\right)^n$,

(g) $7 - 3^n$, **(h)** $\cos(3n)$.

Solution

(a) Since $\dfrac{7}{n} \to 0$ as $n \to \infty$, the sequence converges and has limit 3.

(b) Since n increases without limit, adding 3 then dividing by 4 will mean that the nth term is still very large as $n \to \infty$. The sequence diverges to $+\infty$.

(c) Listing a few terms gives $\sin\left(\dfrac{\pi}{3}\right)$, $4\sin\left(\dfrac{2\pi}{3}\right)$, $9\sin\left(\dfrac{3\pi}{3}\right)$,
$\ldots$ or $\dfrac{\sqrt{3}}{2}$, $2\sqrt{3}$, 0, $-8\sqrt{3}$, $\ldots$ which shows that in magnitude most of the terms are getting bigger (with the occasional zero) and yet there will be some positive terms and some negative terms.
The sequence is **not** convergent.
Neither does it diverge to $+\infty$ or to $-\infty$.
Hence, the sequence is oscillating.

(d) This sequence can be written in the form $1, 3, 1, 3, 1, 3, \ldots$ which is clearly oscillating.

(e) The first few terms are $4, 1, -4, -11, -20, -31, -42, \ldots$. Even though the first two terms are positive, all the other terms are negative and growing larger in magnitude. The sequence diverges to $-\infty$.

(f) As $n \to \infty$, the expression $\left(-\tfrac{1}{3}\right)^n$ gets smaller and smaller in magnitude and tends to zero. The sequence therefore converges with limit 4.

(g) Since $3^n \to \infty$ as $n \to \infty$, it means that $-3^n \to -\infty$ and so $7 - 3^n \to -\infty$ as $n \to \infty$.
The sequence diverges to $-\infty$.

(h) The values of the sequence $\cos(3n)$ would need to be evaluated on your calculator, remembering to use the radians setting.

The numbers will appear random, but some will be positive and some negative.

However, all the values will lie between $+1$ and -1.

The sequence does not converge.

It is an oscillating sequence.

10.5 Periodic sequences

Some oscillating sequences are said to be periodic.

For instance, the sequence $3, 5, 7, 4, 2, 3, 5, 7, 4, 2, 3, 5, 7, 4, 2, 3, 5, \ldots$ is periodic with period 5.

The sequence $3, -3, 3, -3, 3, -3, \ldots$ is periodic with period 2.

Certain sequences defined inductively by a recurrence relation may be periodic.

Worked example 10.4

A sequence is defined by $u_{n+1} = \dfrac{u_n - 3}{u_n - 2}$, $u_1 = 3$.

(a) Find u_2, u_3, u_4, u_5.

(b) Explain why the sequence is periodic and state its period.

Solution

(a) $u_2 = 0$, $u_3 = 1.5$, $u_4 = 3$, $u_5 = 0$.

(b) The pattern starts to repeat and because the sequence is defined inductively, the sequence must be

$$3, 0, 1.5, 3, 0, 1.5, 3, 0, 1.5, 3, 0, 1.5, \ldots$$

and therefore it is periodic.

The period is 3 because there are 3 numbers in the repeating pattern.

The sequence

$$a_1, a_2, a_3, a_4, \ldots, a_n, a_1, a_2, a_3, a_4, \ldots, a_n, a_1, a_2, a_3, \ldots$$

is said to be periodic with period n since there are n terms in the cycle of repeated values.

EXERCISE 10B

1 The nth terms of various sequences are given below. For each sequence, determine whether it converges, and if it does, find its limit. If a sequence is not convergent, state whether it diverges to $+\infty$, diverges to $-\infty$, or oscillates.

(a) $\dfrac{3 - 2n}{4 + n}$,

(b) $n^3 \tan\left(\dfrac{n\pi}{4}\right)$,

(c) $5 - \left(\dfrac{3}{4}\right)^n$,

(d) $2n - 8$,

(e) $7 + \left(-\dfrac{2}{3}\right)^n$,

(f) $12 - 2^n$,

(g) $\sin(4n)$, **(h)** $7 + (-5)^n$ **(i)** $\dfrac{4 - n^2}{5 + n^2}$,

(j) $n^2(-1)^n$, **(k)** $\dfrac{\cos(\pi n)}{n^3}$ **(l)** $\dfrac{5 - n^3}{n}$.

2 The oscillating sequence
$$\{u_n\} = \{5, 1, 7, 3, \quad 5, 1, 7, 3, \quad 5, 1, 7, 3, \ldots\}$$
is said to be periodic with period 4.
State the period of each of the following periodic sequences:

(a) $3, 0, 4, 1, 5, \quad 3, 0, 4, 1, 5, \quad 3, 0, 4, 1, 5, \quad 3, 0, \ldots$.

(b) $5, -4, 7, 1, \quad 5, -4, 7, 1, \quad 5, -4, 7, 1, \quad 5, -4, \ldots$.

3 Write down the first six terms of each of the following periodic sequences and state the period in each case.

(a) $u_n = \sin\left(\dfrac{2n\pi}{3}\right)$,

(b) $u_{n+1} = 1 - u_n^2$, and $u_1 = 1$,

(c) $u_{n+1} = 4u_n(1 - u_n)$, and $u_1 = 0.75$,

(d) $u_1 = 0$, $u_{n+1} = \dfrac{4u_n - 13}{2u_n + 6}$.

4 A sequence is defined by $u_{n+1} = \dfrac{1}{1 - u_n}$, $u_1 = 2$.

(a) Find u_2, u_3, u_4, u_5.

(b) Explain why the sequence is periodic and state its period.

5 Show that the following sequences are periodic and state the period in each case.

(a) $u_{n+1} = 1 - u_n$, $u_1 = \frac{1}{4}$.

(b) $u_{n+1} = \dfrac{u_n + 4}{u_n - 1}$, $u_1 = 2$.

6 A sequence is defined by $u_1 = 0$, $u_{n+1} = \dfrac{6u_n + 2}{4 - 13u_n}$.

(a) Find u_2, u_3, u_4, u_5 and u_6.

(b) Hence, explain why the sequence is periodic and state its period. [A]

7 Prove that the sequence $u_1 = a$, $u_{n+1} = b - u_n$ has period 2 when $b \neq 2a$.
State the period when $b = 2a$.

10.6 Roots of equations

It was shown in P1 chapter 10 that equations do not always have exact solutions and that it is sometimes necessary to use numerical methods to find approximations to the roots. This is reviewed in the following worked example.

Worked example 10.5

Prove that the real root of the equation $x^3 - 3x + 4 = 0$ is -2.196 correct to three decimal places.

Solution

Your graphics calculator would show that the graph of $y = x^3 - 3x + 4$ is continuous and that it crosses the x-axis once only.

Let $f(x) = x^3 - 3x + 4$.

In order to prove that the root is -2.196 correct to three decimal places, it is necessary to show that the root lies between -2.1955 and -2.1965.

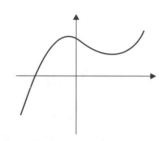

Can you see why?

$f(-2.1955) = 0.003\,706\,4\ldots$ and $f(-2.1965) = -0.007\,760\,8\ldots$.

The change of sign shows that the root lies between -2.1955 and -2.1965. Hence, the root is equal to -2.196 correct to three decimal places.

10.7 The bisection method

A systematic way to make use of this change of sign technique is the bisection method. As the name suggests, this involves repeated bisection of the interval in which the root is known to lie.

Worked example 10.6

(a) Prove that the equation $x^4 + x^3 = 1$ has a root between 0.78 and 0.82.

(b) Use the bisection method to find an interval of width 0.01 in which the root lies.

Solution

(a) Let $f(x) = x^4 + x^3 - 1$.
$$f(0.78) = 0.78^4 + 0.78^3 - 1 = -0.155\ldots$$
$$f(0.82) = 0.82^4 + 0.82^3 - 1 = 0.003\,49\ldots$$

Since the graph of $y = f(x)$ is continuous, the change of sign implies that at least one root lies in the interval $0.78 < x < 0.82$.

(b) Bisecting the interval means you **must** next try $f(0.80)$, even though you expect the root to lie fairly close to 0.82.
$$f(0.80) = 0.80^4 + 0.80^3 - 1 = -0.0784\ldots$$

Change of sign means that root lies in the interval $0.80 < x < 0.82$.

10

Again, bisecting the interval your next evaluation must be $f(0.81)$.

$$f(0.81) = 0.81^4 + 0.81^3 - 1 = -0.038\,09\ldots$$

Hence, at least one root lies in the interval $0.81 < x < 0.82$.

This is now an interval of width 0.01 and so there is no need to find the root to any greater precision.

10.8 Decimal search

Although the bisection method is an easy algorithm to follow, the process of bisecting the interval may lead to an answer such as 'the root lies between 0.818 75 and 0.820 00'.

Since we work with a decimal and not a binary system, this kind of answer is not very user-friendly.

An improvement is called **decimal search**. This involves finding a root correct to one decimal place, then to two decimal places, etc.

This technique involves lots of calculations and is quite tedious.

Worked example 10.7

Show that the equation $e^{-x} = x$ has a root between 0.56 and 0.57 and find this root correct to two decimal places.

Solution

Let $f(x) = e^{-x} - x$.

Since $f(0.56) = 0.0112\ldots$ and $f(0.57) = -0.004\,47\ldots$ and the graph of $y = f(x)$ is continuous, then the equation $f(x) = 0$ has a root between 0.56 and 0.57

Because the value of $f(0.57)$ is nearer to zero than $f(0.56)$, it suggests that the root is nearer to 0.57 than 0.56.

A sensible next guess might be 0.567 or 0.568.
$f(0.567) = 0.000\,245\,6\ldots$ whereas $f(0.568) = -0.001\,34\ldots$
Hence, the root is likely to be 0.567 to three decimal places.

In order to verify this, you need to calculate $f(0.5675)$ which equals $-0.000\,558\,9\ldots$ and because $f(0.567)$ is positive, the root must lie between 0.567 and 0.5675.

Therefore, the root is 0.567 correct to three decimal places.

The process of decimal search can be speeded up by the method of linear interpolation.

10.9 Linear interpolation

When a root of $f(x) = 0$ is known to lie between two particular values $x = a$ and $x = b$, the graph of $y = f(x)$ must cross the x-axis at some value between a and b.

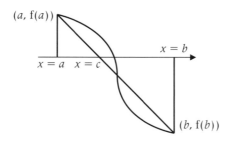

The method approximates the curve by a straight line joining the two points and uses the value of $x = c$, where the straight line crosses the x-axis as the next approximation.

The straight line through the points has equation

$$\frac{y - f(a)}{x - a} = \frac{f(b) - f(a)}{b - a}$$

When $y = 0$, $x = c$, therefore, $c - a = -f(a)\dfrac{b - a}{f(b) - f(a)}$.

Hence,

$$c = a - f(a)\frac{b - a}{f(b) - f(a)}$$

$$= \frac{a[f(b) - f(a)] - f(a)[b - a]}{f(b) - f(a)}$$

$$= \frac{af(b) - bf(a)}{f(b) - f(a)}$$

Although you can learn this formula off by heart it is often easy to derive it from first principles using the equation of a straight line or even similar triangles.

Worked example 10.8

Show that the equation $x^3 - 4x - 10 = 0$ has root between 2 and 3. Use linear interpolation to obtain a two significant figure approximation to this root.

Solution

Writing $f(x) = x^3 - 4x - 10$ gives $f(2) = -10$ and $f(3) = 5$.
Using the formula above gives

$$c = \frac{(5 \times 2) - (-10 \times 3)}{5 - (-10)} = \frac{40}{15} \approx 2.7$$

Alternatively, the straight line through $(2, -10)$ and $(3, 5)$ has gradient 15 and hence equation $y = 15x - 40$.

Hence, when $y = 0$, $x = \dfrac{40}{15} = \dfrac{8}{3} \approx 2.7$.

10

A simple diagram and using similar triangles is just as effective.

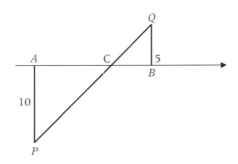

Since $AC:CB = 10:5 = 2:1$, the point C is $\frac{2}{3}$ the way along AB. But A is $(2,0)$ and B is $(3,0)$, so the x-coordinate of C is $2 + \frac{2}{3} = 2\frac{2}{3}$.

(The actual value of the root is 2.7608… and this value could easily be obtained by repeating the linear interpolation process.)

10.10 The Newton–Raphson iterative formula

The previously mentioned techniques for finding roots of equations are quite slow and fairly tedious.

An iterative formula that uses calculus techniques was produced by Isaac Newton and modified by Raphson and is known as the Newton–Raphson Method.

It is used to find approximate solutions of the equation $f(x) = 0$.

The method is based on the following diagram, making use of the tangent drawn to the curve with equation $y = f(x)$.

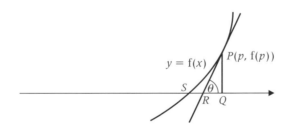

The point P lies on the curve with equation $y = f(x)$ and the tangent to the curve at P cuts the x-axis at R. Then, in general, if the point Q is a first approximation to the point S, where the curve crosses the x-axis, a better approximation is that the curve crosses the x-axis at R.

Let the x-coordinate of P be p.
So the y-coordinate of P is $f(p)$. Hence, $PQ = f(p)$.

The gradient of the curve at P is given by $f'(p)$.
But the gradient of the tangent is also $\tan\theta$ and from the diagram

$$\tan\theta = \frac{PQ}{QR}. \text{ Hence, } f'(p) = \frac{PQ}{QR} = \frac{f(p)}{QR}.$$

Rearranging gives $QR = \dfrac{f(p)}{f'(p)}$.

So, if the x-coordinate of Q is p, then the x-coordinate of R is

$$p - \frac{f(p)}{f'(p)}.$$

This is, in effect, the Newton–Raphson formula, namely that if p is an approximation to a root of $f(x) = 0$, then usually a better approximation to the root is $p - \dfrac{f(p)}{f'(p)}$.

This can be expressed as an iterative formula where successive approximations are x_n and x_{n+1}.

> The Newton–Raphson iterative formula for solving
>
> $f(x) = 0$ is $x_{n+1} = x_n - \dfrac{f(x_n)}{f'(x_n)}$.

This formula is given in the booklet for use in the examination under the heading *Numerical Solution of Equations.*

Worked example 10.9

Show, by sketching two graphs on the same axes that the equation $x + e^x = 0$ has a single root.

Use the Newton–Raphson method with first approximation $x_1 = -0.6$ to find further approximations x_2 and x_3, giving your answers to five decimal places.

Solution

Drawing the graphs of $y = e^x$ and $y = -x$ on the same axes, they are seen to cross exactly once and so the equation $x + e^x = 0$ has a single root.

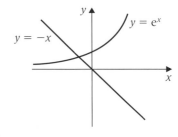

Now let $f(x) = x + e^x$.

Differentiating gives $f'(x) = 1 + e^x$.

Since the Newton–Raphson formula is $x_{n+1} = x_n - \dfrac{f(x_n)}{f'(x_n)}$

and $x_1 = -0.6$, you have $x_2 = x_1 - \dfrac{f(x_1)}{f'(x_1)} = -0.6 - \dfrac{f(-0.6)}{f'(-0.6)}$.

Again you could use the ANS key on your graphics calculator effectively. Input -0.6 then $\boxed{\text{EXE}}$ followed by $\text{ANS} - (\text{ANS} + e^{\wedge}\text{ANS}) \div (1 + e^{\wedge}\text{ANS})$ then $\boxed{\text{EXE}}$.

$f(-0.6) = -0.6 + e^{-0.6} = -0.051\,188\ldots$
$f'(-0.6) = 1 + e^{-0.6} = 1.548\,811\,6\ldots$

Hence, $x_2 = -0.566\,95$ to five decimal places.

In order to find x_3 you need to use

$$x_3 = x_2 - \frac{f(x_2)}{f'(x_2)} = -0.566\,95 - \frac{f(-0.566\,95)}{f'(-0.566\,95)}$$

which gives $-0.567\,14$ to five decimal places.

This value is in fact correct to five decimal places as you would see if you tried further iterations.

The iterations take place as shown in the diagram.

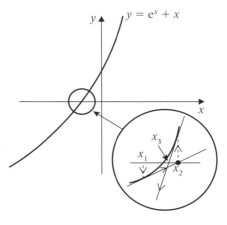

10

EXERCISE 10C

1 Show that the equation $x^3 - 3x + 7 = 0$ has a root between -2.2 and -2.6.

   (a) Use the bisection method to find an interval of width 0.1 in which the root lies.

   (b) Use decimal search to obtain the value of the root correct to two decimal places.

2 Sketch the graphs of $y = 2^x$ and $y = 2 - x$ on the same axes. Explain why the equation $2^x + x - 2 = 0$ has exactly one real root α.

   (a) Show that α lies between 0.3 and 0.7.

   (b) Use the bisection method, showing your working clearly, to find an interval of width 0.1 which contains α.   [A]

3 Use the Newton–Raphson method, with the given value of x_1 in order to find the next approximation, x_2, to a root of the given equations, giving your answers to three significant figures:

   (a) $x^3 - 5x + 11 = 0$, $x_1 = -3$,

   (b) $x^4 - 5x^3 + 6 = 0$, $x_1 = 1$,

   (c) $x^5 - 2x^3 - 17 = 0$, $x_1 = 2$,

   (d) $2x + \tan 2x = 0$, $x_1 = 1$.

4 Two students are attempting to use Newton–Raphson's method to solve the equation $x^3 - 3x + 4 = 0$. Student A decides to use $x_1 = -1$ and student B uses $x_1 = -3$ as a first approximation. Explain why one of the students will be successful in finding the value of the root and yet the other will not.

5 The equation $4x^3 - 5x^2 + 2 = 0$ has a single root α. Use the Newton–Raphson iterative method with first approximation $x_1 = -0.5$ to find the next two successive approximations for α, giving your answers to five decimal places.

6 (a) Prove that the equation $x^3 - 5x + 7 = 0$ has a root α between -3 and -2.

   (b) The Newton–Raphson method is to be used to find an approximation for α. Use $x_1 = -3$ as a first approximation to find the value of x_2, giving your answer correct to three decimal places.   [A]

7 The curve with equation $y = e^x - x^2$ crosses the x-axis at the single point $(\alpha, 0)$. An approximation to α can be found using an iterative method. Use the Newton–Raphson iterative formula with $x_1 = -1$ to find the values of x_2 and x_3, giving your answers to four significant figures.

8 A curve has equation $y = x^2 + 5 + \dfrac{2}{x}$ and it crosses the x-axis at the single point $(\alpha, 0)$.

   (a) Show that α lies between -0.4 and -0.3.

   (b) Use linear interpolation once to find a further approximation, giving your answer to two decimal places.

   (c) Use Newton–Raphson's iterative method with first approximation $x_1 = -0.4$ to find the values of x_2 and x_3, giving your answers to five decimal places.

9 The equation $x^5 - 5x + 6 = 0$ has a single root α.

   (a) Show that α lies between -1 and -2.

   (b) Use the bisection method to find an interval of width 0.25 in which the root lies.

   (c) Use linear interpolation once to find an approximation to the value of α, giving your answer to one decimal place.

   (d) Use decimal search to find the value of α, giving your answer to two decimal places.

   (e) Use Newton–Raphson's iterative method with first approximation $x_1 = -2$ to find further approximations x_2 and x_3, giving your answers to two decimal places.

10 Prove that the equation $\sqrt{(x+1)} - \sqrt{x} = 0.2$ has a root between 4 and 6. Use the bisection method to find an interval of width 0.125 in which the root lies. Refine your answer by decimal search to find the value of the root to two decimal places.

11 (a) Sketch the graphs of $y = x$ and $y = 3\sin x$ to determine the number of roots of the equation $x - 3\sin x = 0$.

> Remember to have the radian setting on your calculator.

   (b) The positive root of the equation $x - 3\sin x = 0$ is required.

      (i) Verify that it lies between 2 and 3.

      (ii) Use linear interpolation once with values of $x = 2$ and $x = 3$ to estimate the value of this root, giving your answer to two decimal places.

      (iii) Use Newton–Raphson's method with first approximation $x_1 = 2$ to find further approximations x_2 and x_3, giving your answers to four decimal places.

12 A positive solution to the equation $x \ln x = x + 2$ is to be found using the Newton–Raphson method.
Using an initial value of $x = 5$, carry out sufficient iterations to obtain the value of the root correct to three decimal places. Prove that your solution has the required accuracy.

Explain by means of a diagram how the Newton–Raphson method converges to the root.

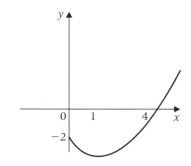

10

Indicate whether or not convergence takes place with initial values of **(a)** 2, **(b)** 1, **(c)** 0.5, explaining your answers carefully by using a copy of the sketch of the graph of $y = x \ln x - 2 - x$.

10.11 Cobweb and staircase diagrams

It is sometimes possible to rearrange an equation into the form $x = g(x)$ and then an iterative formula of the form $x_{n+1} = g(x_n)$ can be used to try to find a solution to the equation. This all depends on whether the iteration converges and you can draw diagrams to ascertain whether this is the case.

Consider the iterative formula $x_{n+1} = \frac{1}{2}x_n + 1$.

You can draw the graphs of $y = x$ and $y = \frac{1}{2}x + 1$ on the same axes.

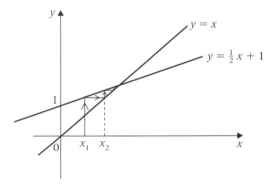

On your calculator, try 0.5 EXE followed by 0.5 ANS + 1 EXE and you will see convergence to the value **2**.

Suppose $x_1 = \frac{1}{2}$. The next value is $x_2 = \frac{1}{2}x_1 + 1 = \frac{5}{4}$. A vertical line can be drawn to $y = \frac{1}{2}x + 1$ to obtain the y-value equivalent to x_2. In order to get the next x-value as x_2 you draw a horizontal line to meet $y = x$ and then a vertical line to $y = \frac{1}{2}x + 1$ again and the process is repeated.

A diagram of the form shown is produced which converges to the point of intersection and this is known as **staircase convergence**.

Because it looks like a staircase.

Suppose the limit exists and let it be L. Then as $n \to \infty$, $x_n \to L$ and $x_{n+1} \to L$.

So $L = \frac{1}{2}L + 1 \Rightarrow \frac{1}{2}L = 1 \Rightarrow L = 2$.

The iteration converges to the value 2, which is the x-coordinate of the point of intersection of the two graphs.

Try using the diagram with $x_1 = 3$ and you should see that convergence takes place with a staircase coming downwards to the limit this time. Remember to draw the vertical line to meet $y = \frac{1}{2}x + 1$ **first** then the horizontal line to $y = x$, etc.

Another situation occurs with the following recurrence relation $x_{n+1} = 2 - \frac{1}{3}x_n$ with $x_1 = \frac{1}{2}$.

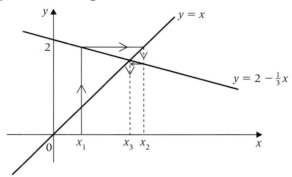

This diagram is known as a **cobweb diagram** and for this iteration there is convergence. Again, try different values of x_1 and you will see it still converges. This will not always be the case, however.

The limit L can be found as in the previous example.

$x_n \to L$ and $x_{n+1} \to L$.

So $L = 2 - \frac{1}{3}L \Rightarrow \frac{4}{3}L = 2 \Rightarrow L = 1.5$.

The limit of the sequence is 1.5.

Convergence does not always take place as you can see below.

Suppose $x_{n+1} = 5 - 3x_n$ with $x_1 = 1$.

The terms of the sequence are $1, 2, -1, 8, -19, \ldots$ and the cobweb diagram below shows the spiralling outwards with clearly no convergence, whatever the starting value of x_1.

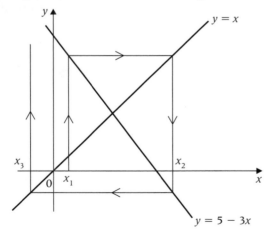

Worked example 10.10

Show that the equation $x^3 - 5x + 7 = 0$ can be rearranged to form the following iterative formulae:

(a) $x_{n+1} = \frac{1}{5}(x_n^3 + 7),$ **(b)** $x_{n+1} = \sqrt[3]{(5x_n - 7)}.$

Using $x_1 = -2$ in each case, find the values of x_2 and x_3. Show on separate diagrams whether or not convergence takes place.

Solution

(a) $x^3 - 5x + 7 = 0 \Rightarrow 5x = x^3 + 7 \Rightarrow x = \frac{1}{5}(x^3 + 7)$

Hence, an iterative formula is $x_{n+1} = \frac{1}{5}(x_n^3 + 7)$.

$x_1 = -2 \Rightarrow x_2 = 0.2(-8 + 7) = -0.2$

$\Rightarrow x_3 = 0.2(-0.008 + 7) = 1.3984$

The graphs of $y = x$ and $y = \frac{1}{5}(x^3 + 7)$ are drawn and the diagram below shows that the iteration is **not** convergent.

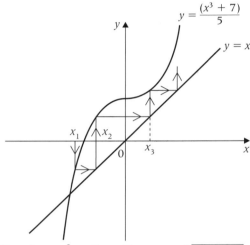

(b) $x^3 - 5x + 7 = 0 \Rightarrow x^3 = 5x - 7 \Rightarrow x = \sqrt[3]{(5x - 7)}$

Hence, an iterative formula is $x_{n+1} = \sqrt[3]{(5x_n - 7)}$.

$x_1 = -2 \Rightarrow x_2 = \sqrt[3]{-17} = -\sqrt[3]{17} = -2.571\,28\ldots$

$\Rightarrow x_3 = \sqrt[3]{-19.856\ldots} = -\sqrt[3]{19.856\ldots} = -2.7079\ldots$

The graphs of $y = x$ and $y = \sqrt[3]{(5x - 7)}$ are drawn and the diagram below shows that the iteration is convergent.

Note: Many calculators cannot find cube roots of negative numbers and so you have to input a positive number and deal with the minus sign yourself.

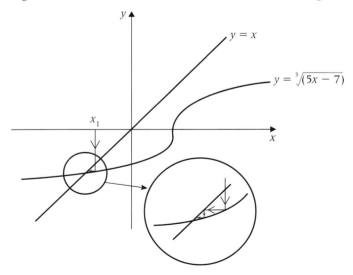

An iteration of the form $x_{n+1} = g(x_n)$ converges when the gradient of $y = g(x)$ at the point of intersection with the line $y = x$ satisfies the condition $|g'(x)| < 1$, provided a suitable value for x_1 is chosen.

Worked example 10.11

A sequence is defined by $x_{n+1} = \sqrt{(28 - 3x_n)}$, $x_1 = 3$.

(a) Find the values of x_2, x_3 and x_4.

(b) Given that the sequence has limit L:

  (i) show that L must satisfy the equation
  $$L^2 + 3L - 28 = 0,$$

  (ii) find the limit of the sequence.

(c) Draw an appropriate diagram to show how convergence takes place.

Solution

(a) $x_2 = 4.358\,898\,9\ldots$, $x_3 = 3.863\,069\ldots$, $x_4 = 4.051\,02\ldots$

(b) **(i)** Since the limit exists and it equals L. Then as $n \to \infty$,
$x_n \to L$ and $x_{n+1} \to L$.

So, $L = \sqrt{(28 - 3L)} \Rightarrow L^2 = 28 - 3L \Rightarrow L^2 + 3L - 28 = 0$.

(ii) $L^2 + 3L - 28 = 0 \Rightarrow (L + 7)(L - 4) = 0 \Rightarrow L = -7, L = 4$
But since all the terms of the sequence are positive, the value of L must be positive. You can reject the negative root.
Hence $L = 4$.
The limit of the sequence is 4.

(c) The diagram below shows how convergence takes place.

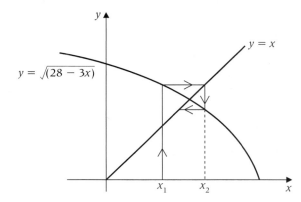

EXERCISE 10D

1 Draw diagrams to illustrate whether convergence takes place for each of the following recurrence relations with $x_1 = 0$.

(a) $x_{n+1} = \frac{1}{2}x_n - 2$,   (b) $x_{n+1} = 2x_n + 1$,

(c) $x_{n+1} = 3 - \frac{1}{4}x_n$,   (d) $x_{n+1} = 4 - 2x_n$,

(e) $x_{n+1} = 5 + \frac{3}{4}x_n$.

2 Using the results from question 1 and any further sketches you may need, determine the condition on the constant k for the iterative formula $x_{n+1} = kx_n + c$ to be convergent.

3 The equation $x = \sin 2x$, where x is in radians, has a single positive root β.

(a) Use the iterative formula $x_{n+1} = \sin 2x_n$ with $x_1 = 1$ to find x_2 and x_3, giving your answers to four decimal places.

(b) On a copy of the diagram below, indicate whether the sequence of iterations starting with $x_1 = 1$ (indicated by the mark on the x-axis) converges to β or diverges.

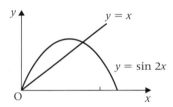

4 Show that the equation $\theta = 1 + \sin\theta$ has a root between 1.8 and 2.0 and use the bisection method to find an interval of width 0.05 in which this root lies.
Draw a diagram to show whether the iteration $\theta_{n+1} = 1 + \sin\theta_n$ converges to this root with $\theta_1 = 1.9$ and find the values of $\theta_2, \theta_3, \theta_4$ and θ_5, to four decimal places.

5 (a) The equation $x^5 - 3x + 7 = 0$ has a single root α. Use the Newton–Raphson method with first approximation -2 to find the next three successive approximations for α, giving your answers to three decimal places.

(b) Rearrange the equation $x^5 - 3x + 7 = 0$ in different ways and form two iterative equations of the form $x_{n+1} = g(x_n)$. By means of appropriate sketches of cobweb or staircase diagrams, determine whether the iteration converges to α in each case.

6 The graph of $y = x^3 - 4x^2 + x + 6$ intersects the line with equation $y = 10 + x$ at the point where $x = \alpha$. Show that α satisfies the equation $x = 4 + \dfrac{4}{x^2}$ and that α lies between 4 and 5.

Use the iterative formula $x_{n+1} = 4 + \dfrac{4}{x_n^2}$ with $x_1 = 4$ to find x_5, giving your answer to four significant figures.
Draw a diagram to show how these iterations converge to α.

7 Sketch the curve with equation $y = e^x$ and on the same axes draw an appropriate straight line to show that the equation $e^x + x - 3 = 0$ has exactly one root α.

(a) Prove that α lies between 0.7 and 0.8.

(b) Using 0.8 as a first approximation to α, use the Newton–Raphson method once to obtain a second approximation to α, giving your answer to three decimal places.

(c) Show that the equation $e^x + x - 3 = 0$ can be rearranged in the form $x = \ln [f(x)]$. Use an iteration of the form $x_{n+1} = g(x_n)$ based on this rearrangement with $x_1 = 0.8$ to find the values of x_2, x_3 and x_4, giving your answers to three decimal places. Draw a diagram to show how convergence takes place. [A]

8 (a) Sketch the graph of $y = 3^x - 5$ and an appropriate straight line to show that the equation $x = 3^x - 5$ has two real roots.

(b) Explain by means of an appropriate cobweb or staircase diagram how the iteration $x_{n+1} = 3^{x_n} - 5$ behaves for all possible values of x_1.

(c) By means of an appropriate value of x_1, determine one of the roots correct to three decimal places.

(d) Determine a possible rearrangement of the formula which would enable you to converge to the other root with an appropriate starting value.

9 Find a cubic equation whose single root can be found using the iterative formula $x_{n+1} = 3 + \dfrac{2}{x_n^2}$.

Using any non-zero value for x, evaluate the iterations until they agree to five decimal places. Hence, find the value of the root to four decimal places.
Show on a diagram how convergence takes place.

10 A sequence is defined by $x_{n+1} = \sqrt{(2x_n + 3)}$, $x_1 = 2$.

    (a) Find the values of x_2, x_3 and x_4.

    (b) Explain why all the values of x_n are positive.

    (c) Given that the limit of the sequence is L:

        (i) show that L must satisfy the equation
$$L^2 - 2L - 3 = 0,$$

        (ii) find the limit of the sequence.

    (d) Draw an appropriate diagram to show how convergence takes place.

11 A sequence is defined by $x_{n+1} = \dfrac{1}{5}(x_n{}^2 + 6)$, $x_1 = 2.5$.

    (a) Find the values of x_2, x_3 and x_4.

    (b) Show that if $x_n < 3$ then $x_{n+1} < 3$.

    (c) Given that the limit of the sequence is L:

        (i) show that L must satisfy the equation
$$L^2 - 5L + 6 = 0,$$

        (ii) find the limit of the sequence.

    (d) Draw an appropriate diagram to show how convergence takes place.

12 A sequence is defined by $x_{n+1} = -\sqrt{(3x_n + 10)}$, $x_1 = -1$.

    (a) Find the values of x_2, x_3 and x_4.

    (b) Explain why all the values of x_n are negative.

    (c) Given that the limit of the sequence is L:

        (i) show that L must satisfy the equation
$$L^2 - 3L - 10 = 0,$$

        (ii) find the limit of the sequence.

    (d) Draw an appropriate diagram to show how convergence takes place.

Key point summary

1 A non-convergent sequence which does not diverge to $+\infty$ or to $-\infty$ is said to be **oscillating**.   *p 175*

2 The sequence   *p 177*
$$a_1, a_2, a_3, a_4, \ldots, a_n, a_1, a_2, a_3, a_4, \ldots, a_n, a_1, a_2, a_3, \ldots$$
is said to be periodic with period n since there are n terms in the cycle of repeated values.

3 Approximate values of roots of equations can be found using the bisection method, decimal search, linear interpolation or Newton–Raphson's method.   *p 179*
    p 180
    p 181
    p 182

4 The Newton–Raphson iterative formula for solving   *p 183*
$f(x) = 0$ is $x_{n+1} = x_n - \dfrac{f(x_n)}{f'(x_n)}$.

5 Cobweb and/or staircase diagrams can be drawn to   *p 186*
illustrate whether convergence takes place or not for
iterations of the form $x_{n+1} = g(x_n)$.

6 An iteration of the form $x_{n+1} = g(x_n)$ converges   *p 189*
when the gradient of $y = g(x)$ at the point of
intersection with the line $y = x$ satisfies the condition
$|g'(x)| < 1$, provided a suitable value for x_1 is
chosen.

Test yourself	**What to review**

1 A sequence is defined by $u_{n+1} = \dfrac{2 - u_n^2}{3 + u_n}$, $u_1 = 0$. Find the   *Section 10.2*
values of u_2 and u_3.

2 For each of the following sequences, find the values of x_2, x_3 *Section 10.3*
and x_4 and state whether the sequence is convergent or not:

   (a) $x_{n+1} = 3 - 4x_n$, $x_1 = 2$.

   (b) $x_{n+1} = \dfrac{x_n - 3}{1 - 2x_n}$, $x_1 = -1$.

3 A sequence is defined by $u_{n+1} = \dfrac{u_n + 5}{u_n - 1}$, $u_1 = 3$.   *Section 10.5*

   (a) Find u_2, u_3, u_4, and u_5.

   (b) Explain why the sequence is periodic and state its
period.

4 Show that the equation $x^3 - 7x^2 - 1 = 0$ has a root between   *Section 10.7*
6.8 and 7.2. Use the bisection method to find an interval of
width 0.1 in which the root lies.

5 The equation $\ln x - 3 + x = 0$ has a single root. Use the   *Section 10.10*
Newton–Raphson method to find an approximation to the
root, using $x_1 = 2$ to find the values of x_2 and x_3, giving your
answers to three decimal places.

6 The iterative formula $x_{n+1} = \frac{1}{4}\cos x_n$ is to be used with $x_1 = 0$.   *Section 10.11*
Find the values of x_2, x_3 and x_4 to four significant figures, and
draw a diagram to show whether the sequence converges or
diverges.

10

Test yourself   ANSWERS

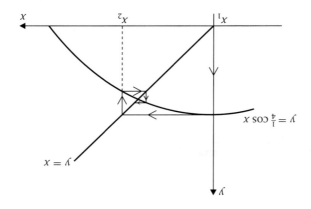

$y = \frac{1}{4}\cos x$

1 $\frac{2}{3}; \frac{14}{33}.$

2 **(a)** $-5, 23, -89,$ not convergent;
(b) $-1.33, -1.18, -1.243,$ convergent.

3 **(a)** $4, 3, 4, 3;$ **(b)** pattern repeats, period is 2.

4 $(7.0, 7.1).$

5 $2.205, 2.208.$

6 $0.2500, 0.2422, 0.2427,$

Exam style practice paper

Time allowed 1 hour 15 minutes

Answer **all** questions

1 The polynomial p(x) is given by $p(x) = x^3 - 3x - 1$.
   (a) Find the value of the remainder when p(x) is divided by $(2x + 1)$. (*2 marks*)
   (b) The equation $p(x) = 0$ has a positive solution which can be found approximately by using the iteration

   $$x_{n+1} = \sqrt{3 + \frac{1}{x_n}}.$$

   Starting with $x_1 = 2$, use this iteration four times to determine this positive solution of $p(x) = 0$ correct to three decimal places. (*3 marks*)

2 (a) Given that $y = \dfrac{\sin x}{x}$, find $\dfrac{dy}{dx}$. (*2 marks*)

   (b) When x increases by a small amount from π to $\pi + \alpha$, the change in $\dfrac{\sin x}{x}$ is approximately equal to $k\alpha$. Find k in terms of π. (*2 marks*)

3 For a positive integer n, when $\left(1 - \dfrac{3x}{2}\right)^n$ is expanded in ascending powers of x, the coefficient of x is -12.
   (a) Find the value of n. (*2 marks*)
   (b) Find, as an integer, the coefficient of x^3. (*2 marks*)
   (c) Write down the coefficient of x^3 in the expansion in ascending powers of x, of

   $$\left(1 - \frac{3x}{2}\right)^n + \left(1 + \frac{3x}{2}\right)^n.$$ (*1 mark*)

4 Solve the equation $3\cos 2x - \sin x = 1$, giving all solutions in degrees to the nearest $0.1°$, in the interval $0° \leqslant x \leqslant 360°$. (*6 marks*)

5 (a) Determine the coordinates of the centre and the radius of the circle with equation
   $$x^2 + y^2 - 4x + 8y + 16 = 0.$$ (*3 marks*)

(b) Show that the y-axis is a tangent to this circle and find the equation of the other tangent that passes through the origin. *(4 marks)*

(c) Find the tangent of the acute angle between these two tangents. *(2 marks)*

6 (a) Show that $\displaystyle\int_0^{\frac{\pi}{8}} \tan^2 2x \, dx = \frac{1}{8}(4 - \pi)$ *(3 marks)*

(b) The equation of a curve C is given by $y = 1 + \tan 2x$. The region enclosed by the coordinate axes, the curve C and the line $x = \dfrac{\pi}{8}$ is rotated through $360°$ about the x-axis. Find the volume generated, giving your answer in the form $\dfrac{\pi}{2}(a + \ln b)$, where a and b are positive integers to be determined. *(6 marks)*

7 It is given that $f(x) = \dfrac{6x^2 + 5x - 4}{(x + 4)(x + 1)^2}$.

(a) Express $f(x)$ in the form $\dfrac{A}{x + 4} + \dfrac{B}{x + 1} + \dfrac{C}{(x + 1)^2}$. *(4 marks)*

(b) Differentiate $f(x)$ to find the value of $f'\left(\dfrac{1}{2}\right)$. *(6 marks)*

(c) The curve $y = \dfrac{6x^2 + 5x - 4}{(x + 4)(x + 1)^2}$ crosses the positive x-axis at the point P.

Show that the equation of the tangent to the curve at P is

$$81y = 88x - 44.$$ *(3 marks)*

8 In a model to estimate the increase in population of a small island it is assumed that the population, x, at time t years after 1 January 2000, is a continuous variable which satisfies the differential equation

$$\frac{dx}{dt} = kx, \text{ where } k \text{ is a positive constant.}$$

(a) Given that the population was 60 000 on 1 January 2000, show that $x = 60\,000\,e^{kt}$. *(3 marks)*

(b) The population on the island was 61 000 on 1 January 2001. Calculate the value of k, giving your answer to four significant figures. *(3 marks)*

(c) Calculate an estimate of the population of the island on 1 January 2010, giving your answer to three significant figures. *(3 marks)*

Answers

1 Factorials and binomial expansions

EXERCISE 1A

1 (a) 6; **(b)** 720; **(c)** 40 320; **(d)** 576; **(e)** 1.

2 (a) 20; **(b)** 210; **(c)** 14;
(d) 19; **(e)** 336; **(f)** 24.

3 (a) 140; **(b)** 2520; **(c)** 1980; **(d)** 36 720; **(e)** 285.

4 (a) 10; **(b)** 35; **(c)** 1; **(d)** 1; **(e)** 28;
(f) 28; **(g)** 36; **(h)** 25; **(i)** 1; **(j)** 286;
(k) 680; **(l)** 100; **(m)** 3160.

5 15 504. **6** 27 405.

EXERCISE 1B

1

```
                                    1
                               1         1
                          1         2         1
                     1         3         3         1
                1         4         6         4         1
           1         5        10        10         5         1
      1         6        15        20        15         6         1
 1         7        21        35        35        21         7         1
1    8        28        56        70        56        28         8    1
1    9    36        84       126       126        84       36     9    1
```

2 1   16   120   560   1820
      1   17   136   680   2380

3 1   21   210   1330   5985
      1   22   231   1540   7315

4 (a) $a^3 + 3a^2b + 3ab^2 + b^3$;
  (b) $c^5 + 5c^4d + 10c^3d^2 + 10c^2d^3 + 5cd^4 + d^5$;
  (c) $x^7 + 7x^6y + 21x^5y^2 + 35x^4y^3 + 35x^3y^4 + 21x^2y^5 + 7xy^6 + y^7$;
  (d) $r^8 + 8r^7s + 28r^6s^2 + 56r^5s^3 + 70r^4s^4 + 56r^3s^5 + 28r^2s^6 + 8rs^7 + s^8$.

5 (a) $1 + 5x + 10x^2 + 10x^3 + 5x^4 + x^5$;
  (b) $1 + 6y + 12y^2 + 8y^3$;
  (c) $1 + 2x + \frac{5}{3}x^2 + \frac{20}{27}x^3 + \frac{5}{27}x^4 + \frac{2}{81}x^5 + \frac{1}{729}x^6$;
  (d) $1 + 2p + \frac{3}{2}p^2 + \frac{1}{2}p^3 + \frac{1}{16}p^4$.

6 (a) $1 - 3a + 3a^2 - a^3$;

(b) $1 - 12b + 54b^2 - 108b^3 + 81b^4$;

(c) $1 - \frac{5}{2}x + \frac{5}{2}x^2 - \frac{5}{4}x^3 + \frac{5}{16}x^4 - \frac{1}{32}x^5$;

(d) $1 - 2x + \frac{4}{3}x^2 - \frac{8}{27}x^3$.

7 (a) $243 + 405p + 270p^2 + 90p^3 + 15p^4 + p^5$;

(b) $625 + 500x + 150x^2 + 20x^3 + x^4$;

(c) $8 - 12m + 6m^2 - m^3$;

(d) $729 - 2916t + 4860t^2 - 4320t^3 + 2160t^4 - 576t^5 + 64t^6$.

8 (a) $1 - 5x + 10x^2 - 10x^3$;　　**(b)** $1 + 12x + 54x^2 + 108x^3$;

(c) $1 - 2x + \frac{5}{3}x^2 - \frac{20}{27}x^3$;　　**(d)** $1 + 2x + \frac{8}{5}x^2 + \frac{16}{25}x^3$.

9 (a) $y^5 + 10y^4 + 40y^3 + 80y^2$;

(b) $64y^6 - 192y^5 + 240y^4 - 160y^3$;

(c) $256y^4 + 768y^3 + 864y^2 + 432y$;

(d) $2187y^7 - 5103y^6 + 5103y^5 - 2835y^4$.

10 (a) $216x^3 + 24x$;

(b) $480y^4 + 2160y^2 + 486$.

11 $\binom{4}{0} \binom{4}{1} \binom{4}{2} \binom{4}{3} \binom{4}{4}$; $\binom{5}{0} \binom{5}{1} \binom{5}{2} \binom{5}{3} \binom{5}{4} \binom{5}{5}$.

EXERCISE 1C

1 (a) $1 + 11x + 55x^2 + 165x^3$;　　**(b)** $1 + 15x + 105x^2 + 455x^3$;

(c) $1 - 8x + 28x^2 - 56x^3$;　　**(d)** $1 + 14x + 84x^2 + 280x^3$;

(e) $1 - 12x + 66x^2 - 220x^3$;　　**(f)** $1 + 3x + 4x^2 + \frac{28}{9}x^3$;

(g) $1 - 5x + \frac{45}{4}x^2 - 15x^3$;

(h) $512 - 2304x + 4608x^2 - 5376x^3$.

2 (a) $x^{12} + 12x^{11} + 66x^{10} + 220x^9$;

(b) $x^{17} + 34x^{16} + 544x^{15} + 5440x^{14}$;

(c) $x^{10} - 30x^9 + 405x^8 - 3240x^7$;

(d) $128x^7 - 448x^6 + 672x^5 - 560x^4$.

3 (a) $21\,840x^4$;　　**(b)** $1224x^2$;

(c) $-18\,304x^3$;　　**(d)** $364x^{12}$;

(e) $\frac{880}{9}x^4$;　　**(f)** $247\,860x^{14}$.

4 (a) -330;　　**(b)** 1140;

(c) $-20\,127\,744$;　　**(d)** $-21\,840$;

(e) $\frac{14}{9}$;　　**(f)** -3400.

5 $1 + 4x + 7x^2 + 7x^3$.

6 $1 + 7x + 21x^2 + 35x^3$, $1.000\,070\,002\,100\,035$.

7 $1 - 33x + 49x^2 - 4455x^3$, -5445.

8 (a) $h^4 + 10h^3 + 40h^2 + 80h + 80$;

(b) 80.

9 (a) $5 + 176x + 2826x^2 + 27\,324x^3$;

(b) $2 - 5x + 3x^2 + 5x^3$.

2 Division of polynomials and the remainder theorem

EXERCISE 2A

1 $\dfrac{2x}{x+4}$.

2 $\dfrac{x+3}{3(x+2)}$.

3 $\dfrac{5+x}{4-9x}$.

4 $\dfrac{-(5+4x)}{2x+5}$.

5 $\dfrac{4x-9}{2x-9}$.

6 $x+2$.

7 $\dfrac{3(x-1)}{(x+1)(2x-5)}$.

EXERCISE 2B

1 $\dfrac{x+6}{2x}$.

2 $\dfrac{1}{x+3}$.

3 $\dfrac{3}{x-1}$.

4 $\dfrac{x-1}{x(2x-3)}$.

5 $\dfrac{-(x+2)}{6}$

6 $\dfrac{x-1}{(x+2)(2x+3)}$.

EXERCISE 2C

1 **(a)** $\dfrac{4}{(x-2)(x+2)}$;

(b) $\dfrac{11-4x}{(x-2)(x+2)}$;

(c) $\dfrac{7x+18}{(x+3)(x+2)}$;

(d) $\dfrac{2(x-1)}{(x-3)(x+2)}$;

(e) $\dfrac{2}{x-1}$;

(f) $\dfrac{2}{6-x}$;

(g) $\dfrac{2}{x(x-3)}$;

(h) $\dfrac{3-x}{x(x-1)(x+1)}$.

EXERCISE 2D

1 **(a)** $1+\dfrac{4}{(x+2)}$;

(b) $x-1+\dfrac{1}{x+1}$;

(c) $4x^2-x-3-\dfrac{4}{x-1}$;

(d) $2x^2+11x+18+\dfrac{41}{x-2}$;

(e) $x^2-\dfrac{5x}{3}+\dfrac{11}{9}-\dfrac{20}{9(3x+1)}$;

(f) $3x^2+\dfrac{5x}{2}-\dfrac{9}{4}+\dfrac{3}{4(2x-1)}$;

(g) $x^2-\dfrac{4x}{5}+\dfrac{23}{25}-\dfrac{71}{25(5x+2)}$;

(h) $x^2+\dfrac{3}{5}+\dfrac{1}{5(5x-2)}$;

(i) $2x^2-\dfrac{3x}{2}-\dfrac{11}{4}+\dfrac{15}{4(2x+1)}$;

(j) $3x^2+2x+\dfrac{4}{3}+\dfrac{5}{3(3x-2)}$.

2 **(a)** **(i)** $2x-1$,

(ii) -2;

(b) **(i)** $3x^2-\dfrac{3x}{2}-\dfrac{1}{4}$,

(ii) $7\frac{1}{4}$;

(c) **(i)** $x^3-\frac{1}{2}x^2+\frac{1}{4}x-\frac{1}{8}$,

(ii) $-\frac{7}{8}$;

(d) **(i)** $x^2+\dfrac{7x}{2}-\dfrac{7}{4}$,

(ii) $-7\frac{1}{4}$.

3 $k=9,\ x^2-2x-3$.

EXERCISE 2E

1 (a) 7;   (b) 43;   (c) $-2\frac{5}{8}$;

   (d) $29\frac{7}{8}$;   (e) -5.

2 (a) $-2\frac{7}{8}$;   (b) 26;   (c) $\frac{7}{8}$;

   (d) -19;   (e) $2\frac{31}{32}$;   (f) 630.

4 $k = -19$.   5 6.   6 44.

7 $k = 2\frac{1}{2}$.

8 (a) $a = 24$, $b = 26$.

9 (a) $k = 4$;   (c) $-\frac{1}{3}$ and 2.

10 $p = -3$, $R = -1$.

11 (a) $k = 4$;   (b) -65;   (c) $2, 1 \pm \sqrt{3}$.

EXERCISE 2F

1 $A = 3$, $B = -2$.   2 $A = 13$, $B = -10$.

3 $A = \frac{1}{3}$, $B = -\frac{2}{3}$.   4 $A = -1$, $B = 1$.

5 $A = 1$, $B = -\frac{1}{2}$, $C = \frac{1}{2}$.   6 $A = -\frac{1}{3}$, $B = \frac{1}{3}$, $C = \frac{4}{3}$.

7 $\dfrac{6}{x + 2} - \dfrac{3}{x + 1}$.   8 $\dfrac{4}{x + 1} - \dfrac{1}{x - 1}$.

9 $\dfrac{1}{x} - \dfrac{2}{(x + 1)^2}$.   10 $\dfrac{8}{7(x + 2)} + \dfrac{13x - 12}{7(x^2 + 3)}$.

11 $-1 + \dfrac{1}{2 + x} + \dfrac{1}{2 - x}$.   12 $\dfrac{6}{x + 1} - \dfrac{3}{(x + 1)^2} - \dfrac{6}{x + 2}$.

13 $\dfrac{1}{x + 2} - \dfrac{2}{x^2 + 1}$.   14 $\dfrac{1}{2(x + 3)} - \dfrac{2}{x + 2} + \dfrac{3}{2(x + 1)}$.

3 Additional formulae in trigonometry

EXERCISE 3A

1 (a) $\dfrac{\pi}{3}$;   (b) 0;   (c) $\dfrac{2\pi}{3}$;

   (d) $\dfrac{2\pi}{3}$;   (e) $\dfrac{\pi}{6}$;   (f) $\dfrac{5\pi}{6}$.

2 (a) $\dfrac{\pi}{6}$;   (b) -1;   (c) $-\dfrac{\pi}{4}$;

   (d) $\sqrt{3}$;   (e) $2\sqrt{2}$;   (f) $\dfrac{1}{\sqrt{5}}$.

3 (a) $-\dfrac{\pi}{4}$;   (b) $\dfrac{5\pi}{4}$.

4 1.

5 0.

6 3.

EXERCISE 3B

4 (a) $\sin 60°$;   **(b)** $\sin 20°$;   **(c)** $\sin 80°$;   **(d)** $\sin 20°$.

8 $\tan y = \dfrac{1-k}{1+k}$.   **9** $1.84, 5.49$.   **10** $0, \frac{1}{2}, x = 75°, y = 15°$.

12 $\dfrac{4\pi}{3}, \dfrac{5\pi}{3}$.   **13** translation $\begin{bmatrix} \frac{\pi}{3} \\ 0 \end{bmatrix}$.   **14** translation $\begin{bmatrix} \frac{\pi}{3} \\ 0 \end{bmatrix}$.

EXERCISE 3C

3 $0°, 75.5°, 180°, 284.5°$.

4 $\dfrac{\pi}{2}, \dfrac{3\pi}{2}, 0.167, 2.97$.

5 $\dfrac{\pi}{3}, \pi, \dfrac{5\pi}{3}$.

9 $\dfrac{\pi}{6}, \dfrac{5\pi}{6}$.

10 $0, \dfrac{\pi}{6}, \dfrac{5\pi}{6}, \pi, \dfrac{7\pi}{6}, \dfrac{11\pi}{6}, 2\pi$.

11 $22.5°, 112.5°, 202.5°, 292.5°$.

12 $0°, 60°, 120°, 180°, 240°, 300°$.

13 $\dfrac{2\tan x}{3\tan^2 x - 1}$.   **14** $\sqrt{2} - 1$.   **15** $\pm \dfrac{2\pi}{3}$.

17 (b) $120°$.

18 (b) $\dfrac{\pi}{12}, \dfrac{5\pi}{12}, \dfrac{3\pi}{4}$.

19 $0, \dfrac{\pi}{3}, \pi, \dfrac{5\pi}{3}, 2\pi$.

EXERCISE 3D

1 (a) $3\sin x$;   **(b)** $2 + 3\cos x$;

   (c) $4\cos x + 3\sin x$;   **(d)** $\dfrac{1}{2}\cos x + \dfrac{2}{x^3}$.

2 (a) 11;   **(b)** 5;   **(c)** -4;   **(d)** 7.

4 $\left(\dfrac{5\pi}{6}, 2 \right), \left(\dfrac{11\pi}{6}, -2 \right)$.

5 $\left(-\dfrac{\pi}{4}, -\sqrt{2} \right), \left(\dfrac{3\pi}{4}, \sqrt{2} \right)$.

6 $\sqrt{3}$.

7 gradients are $-\sqrt{3}$ and $\sqrt{3}$.

8 $\dfrac{7\pi}{6}$ and $\dfrac{11\pi}{6}$.

10 $\left(\dfrac{\pi}{6}, 7 - \sqrt{3} \right), \left(\dfrac{5\pi}{6}, 7 + \sqrt{3} \right)$.

4 Coordinate geometry of lines and circles

EXERCISE 4A

1 (a) $18°$;　　**(b)** $72°$;　　**(c)** $8°$;　　**(d)** $8°$;　　**(e)** $60°$.

2 $x - 2y + 3 = 0, 2x + y - 4 = 0$.

3 $2x - y + 4 = 0, x + 2y - 3 = 0$.

4 (a) $\frac{7}{24}$.

EXERCISE 4B

1 (a) 2;　　**(b)** 3;　　**(c)** $\frac{6\sqrt{13}}{13}$;　　**(d)** 1.6.

2 (a) 1.2;　　**(b)** 1.

3 $\frac{12\sqrt{17}}{17}$.　　　**5** $k = -1$ or -5.　　**6** 16.

7 $3\sqrt{2}$.　　　　**8** $\frac{4\sqrt{5}}{5}$.

9 (c) 5;　　**(d)** $2\sqrt{5}$.

EXERCISE 4C

1 (a) $(x - 2)^2 + y^2 = 4$;　　　**(b)** $(x - 2)^2 + (y - 3)^2 = 16$;
　　(c) $(x - 2)^2 + (y + 1)^2 = 9$;　　**(d)** $(x + 3)^2 + (y + 2)^2 = 9$.

2 (a) centre $(1, -2)$, radius $\sqrt{5}$;　　**(b)** centre $(3, -2)$, radius 4;
　　(c) centre $(6, -2)$, radius $5\sqrt{2}$;　　**(d)** centre $(4, -1)$, radius $\sqrt{\frac{35}{2}}$.

3 (a) $(x - 4)^2 + y^2 = 4$;　　　**(b)** $x^2 + (y - 2)^2 = 9$;
　　(c) $4(x - 4)^2 + (2y - 5)^2 = 25$;　　**(d)** $(x - 5)^2 + (y - 1)^2 = 20$;
　　(e) $4(x - 2)^2 + (2y + 1)^2 = 89$;　　**(f)** $(2x - 1)^2 + (2y + 1)^2 = 50$.

4 (b) $(2x + 9)^2 + (2y - 3)^2 = 50$.

5 $B(-1, 4)$.　　　　**6** $A(4, -2)$.

EXERCISE 4D

1 $(5, 0), (-3, 4)$.　　　**3** $(-2, 1)$.

4 $(-1, -2)$.　　　　**6** $(2, 1), (8, -5)$.

7 (a) $m = \pm\frac{4}{3}$;　　　**(b)** $\frac{24}{5}$.

EXERCISE 4E

1 $\sqrt{21}$.　　　**2** $4\sqrt{2}$.　　　**3** $k = \pm5$.

EXERCISE 4F

1 $3y = 4x - 25$.　　　**2** $x^2 + y^2 = 100$.

3 $3x + y = 20$.　　　**4** $(x + 2)^2 + (y + 1)^2 = 25$.

5 (a) $5x + y = 33$;　　　**(b)** $2(x + 2)^2 + 2(y - 4)^2 = 117$.

6 (a) centre $(3, -4)$, radius 5;　　**(b)** $(7, -1), (7, -7)$;
　　(c) $3y + 4x = 25, 3y - 4x + 49 = 0$.

MIXED EXERCISE

1 (a) centre $(3, -2)$, radius $2\sqrt{5}$;

(b) $x = -1, x = 7$, $\cos ABC = \dfrac{2\sqrt{5}}{5}$.

2 (a) $x^2 + y^2 = 29$, $(x-7)^2 + (y-4)^2 = 26$;

(b) $5y + 2x = 29$, $y = 5x - 5$;

(c) $\frac{27}{5}$;

(d) $(2\sqrt{5}, 3)$, $(-2\sqrt{5}, 3)$, $(12, 3)$, $(2, 3)$.

3 (a) (i) 10,

(ii) $(x-2)^2 + (y-1)^2 = 100$,

(iii) $P(8, 9)$;

(c) (i) $4(x-11)^2 + (2y-1)^2 = 325$,

(ii) $17y = 6x + 105$.

4 (a) $(x+1)^2 + (y-8)^2 = 20$; **(b)** $2y + x = 5$;

(c) $R(3, 6)$; **(d)** $S(1, 2)$.

5 (a) $(x+3)^2 + (y-2)^2 = 25$; **(b)** $(0, 6)$, $(0, -2)$;

(c) $73.7°$; **(d)** $R\left(\frac{16}{3}, 2\right)$;

(e) $6\frac{2}{3}$;

6 (a) centre $(6, -3)$, radius $\sqrt{65}$;

(b) $4\sqrt{5}$.

7 (a) $r = 5$; **(c)** $(10, 11)$; $(10, -5)$.

8 (b) $x = 3 \pm \sqrt{5}$.

9 (a) $(7 + \sqrt{51}, 0)$, $(7 - \sqrt{51}, 0)$;

(b) $(0, 7 + \sqrt{51})$, $(0, 7 - \sqrt{51})$.

10 (a) $x = 4, y = 1$;

(b) Line is a tangent to the circle at the point $(4, 1)$.

5 Secant, cosecant and cotangent

EXERCISE 5A

1 (a) 2.9238; **(b)** 1.0642; **(c)** 2.7475;

(d) 2.9238; **(e)** 1; **(f)** 4.3640;

(g) $\frac{1}{3}$; **(h)** 0.4.

2 (a) -2.4030; **(b)** $1.\dot{5}523$; **(c)** 1.8305;

(d) 1.8508; **(e)** 2.6131; **(f)** 6.4142;

(g) 0.4875; **(h)** 0.1356.

3 (a) 2; **(b)** $\dfrac{2\sqrt{3}}{3}$; **(c)** $\sqrt{3}$;

(d) -1; **(e)** $\sqrt{2}$; **(f)** $\dfrac{3 + \sqrt{3}}{3}$;

(g) $\sqrt{3}$; **(h)** 0.5.

4 (a) $\sqrt{2}$; **(b)** 3;

(c) $\frac{1}{3}$; **(d)** $6 + 4\sqrt{3}$.

5 **(a)** 56.3°, 303.7°;

　　(b) 206.4°, 333.6°;

　　(c) 18.4°, 198.4°;

　　(d) 140.3°, 219.7°;

　　(e) 19.5°, 160.5°;

　　(f) 157.4°, 337.4°;

　　(g) 62.4°, 117.6°, 242.4°, 297.6°;

　　(h) 55.9°, 145.9°, 235.9°, 325.9°.

6 **(a)** $\dfrac{\pi}{3}, \dfrac{5\pi}{3}$;

　　(b) $\dfrac{7\pi}{6}, \dfrac{11\pi}{6}$;

　　(c) $\dfrac{\pi}{8}, \dfrac{5\pi}{8}, \dfrac{9\pi}{8}, \dfrac{13\pi}{8}$;

　　(d) $\dfrac{\pi}{5}, \dfrac{3\pi}{5}, \pi, \dfrac{7\pi}{5}, \dfrac{9\pi}{5}$;

　　(e) $\dfrac{\pi}{9}, \dfrac{2\pi}{9}, \dfrac{7\pi}{9}, \dfrac{8\pi}{9}, \dfrac{13\pi}{9}, \dfrac{14\pi}{9}$;

　　(f) $\dfrac{5\pi}{12}, \dfrac{11\pi}{12}, \dfrac{17\pi}{12}, \dfrac{23\pi}{12}$;

　　(g) $0, \dfrac{2\pi}{3}, \dfrac{4\pi}{3}, 2\pi$;

　　(h) $\dfrac{\pi}{9}, \dfrac{4\pi}{9}, \dfrac{7\pi}{9}, \dfrac{10\pi}{9}, \dfrac{13\pi}{9}, \dfrac{16\pi}{9}$.

EXERCISE 5B

1 **(a)** horizontal stretch, scale factor $\frac{1}{4}$;

　　(b) $\dfrac{\pi}{2}$.

2 **(a)** horizontal stretch, scale factor 4;

　　(b) 4π.

3

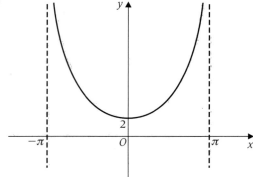

4 (a)

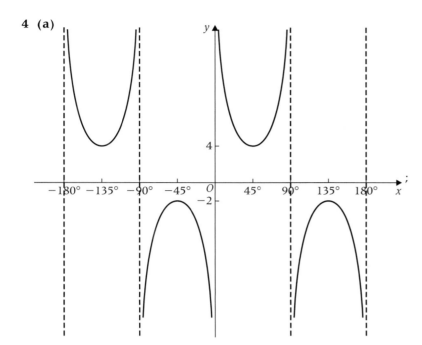

(b) Translation $\begin{pmatrix} \frac{\pi}{2} \\ 0 \end{pmatrix}$, horizontal stretch scale factor $\frac{1}{2}$, vertical stretch

scale factor 3, translation $\begin{pmatrix} 0 \\ 1 \end{pmatrix}$.

EXERCISE 5C

4 $\pm\sqrt{2}$.

5 $\pm\dfrac{1}{\sqrt{3}}$.

9 $x^2 = 16y^2 + 1$.

10 $(x - 2)^2 = \dfrac{1 + 16y^2}{16y^2}$.

11 $63.4°, 135°, 243.4°, 315°$.

12 $45°, 146.3°, 225°, 326.3°$.

13 $45°, 63.4°, 225°, 243.4°$.

14 $0°, \pm 120°$.

15 $19.5°, 160.5°, 194.5°, 345.5°$.

16 $108°, 252°$.

17 $\dfrac{\pi}{6}, \dfrac{5\pi}{6}, \dfrac{7\pi}{6}, \dfrac{11\pi}{6}$.

18 $0, \dfrac{\pi}{3}, \dfrac{5\pi}{3}$.

19 $3.318, 6.107$.

20 $-2.588, -1.017, 0.554, 2.124, -\dfrac{5\pi}{8}, -\dfrac{\pi}{8}, \dfrac{3\pi}{8}, \dfrac{7\pi}{8}$.

EXERCISE 5D

6 (b) $\dfrac{\pi}{6}, \dfrac{\pi}{3}$.

7 $\dfrac{\pi}{4}, \dfrac{3\pi}{4}, \dfrac{5\pi}{4}, \dfrac{7\pi}{4}, \dfrac{\pi}{2}, \dfrac{3\pi}{2}$.

6 Tangents to curves and the chain rule in differentiation

EXERCISE 6A

1 $y = 10x - 12$.

2 $y + 24x + 8 = 0$.

3 $4y + 27x = 24$.

4 $2y = 7x + 4$.

6 $y = 4x - 3$.

7 $y = 6e^{-3}x + 8e^{-3} + 5$.

8 (a) $y = 7x - 2$;

(b) $y = 9x - 2 - 2\ln 2$.

9 area $= 9.8$.

10 tangent at P: $y = 6x + 6$, tangent at Q: $y = -6x + 30$, $M(2, 18)$.

11 tangent at A: $y = x + 8$, tangent at B: $y = 4x - 4$, $C(4, 12)$.

12 $N(-1, 0)$.

EXERCISE 6B

1 (a) $32(8x + 3)^3$;

(b) $-24(3 - 4x)^5$;

(c) $150(3x - 2)^9$;

(d) $-56(7 - x)^7$;

2 (a) $5e^{5x - 2}$;

(b) $18\cos(6x + 2)$;

(c) $-16\sin 8x$;

(d) $\dfrac{45}{9x + 1}$;

(e) $-\dfrac{2}{(2x + 7)^2}$.

3 (a) $\dfrac{9(2x + 1)}{3x^2 + 3x - 1}$;

(b) $\dfrac{8}{(3 - 2x)^2}$;

(c) $-\dfrac{24}{(6x + 1)^3}$;

(d) $-\dfrac{e^x}{(e^x + 4)^2}$;

(e) $2xe^{x^2}$.

4 (a) $48(4x - 1)^5$;

(b) $-(8 - 3x)^4$;

(c) $\frac{1}{2}\cos(6x + 1)$;

(d) $\dfrac{4}{x - 3}$;

(e) $-6e^{9 - 2x}$;

(f) $-3\sin(5 - 3x)$;

(g) $3e^{3x} + 12x$;

(h) $18x^2 - \dfrac{2}{x}$;

(i) $8\cos(6x - 5)$;

(j) $-3e^{4 - 3x} + 5\cos 5x$.

5 (a) 648;

(b) -8;

(c) $-4e$;

(d) -2;

(e) -74.

6 $y + 8x = 9$.

7 (a) $\dfrac{8}{(2x - 1)^3} - 1$, $\left(\frac{3}{2}, -2\right)$; stationary point;

(b) $\dfrac{d^2y}{dx^2} = -3$, $(1.5, -2)$ is a minimum point.

8 (a) $9(3x - 2)^2 - 10x$;

(b) $162x - 118$;

maximum $(0.435, -1.28)$, minimum $(1.02, -4.01)$.

9 (a) $A = 32\,000$;

(b) $k = 0.144$ (3 s.f.);

(c) £2240 per year.

10 (a) greatest depth $25\,\text{m}$, least depth $15\,\text{m}$;

(c) $k = 0.559$ (3 s.f.);

(d) $-2.51\,\text{m h}^{-1}$, minus sign $\Rightarrow$ depth is decreasing.

EXERCISE 6C

1 $10 \sin 5x \cos 5x$.

2 $-36 \cos^3 9x \sin 9x$.

3 $4 \cot 4x$.

4 $-40 \cos^4 4x \sin 4x$.

5 $6e^{2x}(e^{2x} - 5)^2$.

6 $\dfrac{3 \cos \sqrt{3x + 1}}{2\sqrt{3x + 1}}$.

7 $\dfrac{\ln x}{2x}$.

8 $\dfrac{3e^{\sqrt{6x}}}{\sqrt{6x}}$.

9 $\dfrac{-\sin(\ln 8x)}{x}$.

10 $\dfrac{-5 \sin(\sqrt{x}) \cos^4(\sqrt{x})}{2\sqrt{x}}$.

EXERCISE 6D

1 $21\pi \, \text{cm}^2 \, \text{s}^{-1}$ (≈ 65.97).

2 $25.1 \, \text{m}^2 \, \text{min}^{-1}$.

3 $0.64 \, \text{cm} \, \text{s}^{-1}$.

4 decreasing at rate of $2.4 \, \text{cm}^2 \, \text{s}^{-1}$.

5 $0.576 \, \text{cm}^3 \, \text{s}^{-1}$.

6 $0.106 \, \text{cm} \, \text{s}^{-1}$.

7 $0.0891 \, \text{cm} \, \text{min}^{-1}$.

8 $30 \, \text{cm}^3 \, \text{s}^{-1}$.

9 $-31.4 \, \text{cm}^3 \, \text{year}^{-1}$, minus sign means that the volume is decreasing.

10 (a) Area $= 18 \sin \theta \cos \theta$;

(c) $-0.9 \, \text{cm}^2 \, \text{s}^{-1}$ minus sign $\Rightarrow$ area is decreasing.

EXERCISE 6E

1 0.01.

2 (a) 1.1;　　**(b)** 0.9.

3 (a) 1.05;　　**(b)** 2.25;　　**(c)** 9.95;　　**(d)** 49.99.

4 (a) 1.02;　　**(b)** 0.98.

5 2.　　　　**6** 3.52.　　　　**7** 90.48.

7 Differentiation using the product and quotient rules

EXERCISE 7A

1 (a) $x \cos x + \sin x$;

(b) $x^2(3 \cos x - x \sin x)$;

(c) $4(\ln x + 1)$;

(d) $\sqrt{x} \cos x + \dfrac{1}{2\sqrt{x}} \sin x$;

(e) $5x^2 e^x(x + 3)$;

(f) $\cos^2 x - \sin^2 x = \cos 2x$;

(g) $e^x\left(\dfrac{1}{x} + \ln x\right)$;

(h) $e^x(\cos x + \sin x)$;

(i) $\dfrac{1}{\sqrt{x}}(2 + \ln x)$;

(j) $3x^4 e^x(x + 5)$.

2 **(a)** $x^2 e^{2x}(2x + 3)$; **(b)** $(2x - 1)^4(63 - 36x)$;

(c) $e^x(4\cos 4x + \sin 4x)$;

(d) $3\cos 3x \cos 2x - 2\sin 3x \sin 2x$;

(e) $\dfrac{\sqrt{x+1}}{x} + \dfrac{\ln x}{2\sqrt{x+1}}$; **(f)** $6x(1 + 2\ln 5x)$;

(g) $e^{3x}(3\cos 2x - 2\sin 2x)$; **(h)** $\dfrac{4x^3}{\sqrt{2x-1}} + 12x^2\sqrt{2x-1}$;

(i) $\dfrac{12}{3x+2} + 4\ln(3x + 2)$; **(j)** $e^{5x}\cos x + 5e^{5x}\sin x + 12x$.

3 **(a)** $9\mathrm{e}$; **(b)** $\dfrac{\sqrt{3}\pi + 6}{12}$; **(c)** 1.

4 $y + 27e^9 = 10e^9 x$.

5 **(a)** $\left(\dfrac{1}{\mathrm{e}}, -\dfrac{1}{\mathrm{e}}\right)$; **(b)** $\dfrac{1}{x}$, minimum point.

6 **(a)** $x = -\frac{3}{5}$; **(b)** -1, maximum point.

7 **(a)** $A(1, 0)$, 1; **(b)** $B(e^{-\frac{1}{2}}, -\frac{1}{2}e^{-1})$, 2.

EXERCISE 7B

1 **(a)** $\dfrac{-x\sin x - \cos x}{x^2}$; **(b)** $\dfrac{e^x(x-2)}{x^3}$;

(c) $\dfrac{2x\cos x - \sin x}{2\sqrt{x}x}$; **(d)** $\dfrac{1 - \ln x}{x^2}$;

(e) $\dfrac{4x(2-x)}{e^x}$; **(f)** $\dfrac{5(1 - 3\ln x)}{x^4}$;

(g) $\dfrac{e^x(x-2)}{3x^3}$; **(h)** $\dfrac{\cos x - \sin x}{e^x}$;

(i) $\sec^2 x$; **(j)** $-\mathrm{cosec}^2 x$.

2 **(a)** $\dfrac{2x\cos 2x - 3\sin 2x}{x^4}$; **(b)** $\dfrac{-e^{-x}(\sin x + \cos x)}{\sin^2 x}$;

(c) $\dfrac{4x^4(5 - 3x)}{e^{3x}}$; **(d)** $\dfrac{12x^2 - 8x - 39}{(2x+3)^4} = \dfrac{6x - 13}{(2x+3)^3}$;

(e) $\dfrac{1 - \ln 5x}{x^2}$; **(f)** $\dfrac{3x^2(\cos 3x + x\sin 3x)}{\cos^2 3x}$;

(g) $\dfrac{2(2x\cos 2x - 3\sin 2x)}{x^4}$; **(h)** $\dfrac{2e^{3x}(3x - 1)}{x^2}$;

(i) $\dfrac{7(1 - 2\ln 3x)}{x^3}$; **(j)** $\dfrac{-e^{2-x}(\sin 3x + 3\cos 3x)}{\sin^2 3x}$.

4 $y = 5x + 2$, $\left(\frac{8}{5}, 10\right)$.

5 **(a)** $\dfrac{2 - x}{4x^{\frac{3}{4}}(x + 2)^{\frac{3}{2}}}$, $x = 2$; **(b)** $0.000\,481\ \mathrm{cm^3\,s^{-1}}$.

6 **(a)** $x = 1$; **(c)** $\left(e^{\frac{1}{2}}, \dfrac{1}{2e}\right)$, $-\dfrac{2}{e^2}$.

EXERCISE 7C

1 (a) $15x^2 + 4\sec^2 4x$;

(b) $6\sec(6x-3)\tan(6x-3)$;

(c) $\csc^2(1-x)$;

(d) $-15\csc 3x\cot 3x$.

2 (a) $3t^3 \sec t(t\tan t + 4)$;

(b) $\dfrac{-x\csc^2 x - 3\cot x}{x^4}$;

(c) $\tan t$;

(d) $\cos x + x^2 \sec^2 x + 2x\tan x$.

3 $y = 6x - \frac{3}{2}\pi - 1$;

5 $e^{-x}\sec 2x(2\tan 2x - 1)$.

MIXED EXERCISE

1 (a) $2x - 1$;

(b) $15x^2 - 2 + 2e^{2x}$;

(c) $8x + \dfrac{2}{x^2}$;

(d) $3x^2 + 6x - 10$;

(e) $e^{-x}(\cos x - \sin x)$;

(f) $15\sec^2 5x$;

(g) $\dfrac{2(1 - 3\ln x)}{x^4}$;

(h) $12\csc^2(2 - 3x)$.

2 (a) 5;

(b) $2e^{-13}$;

(c) $\frac{14}{3}$.

3 $4y + 28e^4 = 9e^4 x$.

4 $y = 8x + 2 - \pi$.

5 $(0, 0)$ minimum, $(2, 4e^{-2})$ maximum.

6 $9 - \ln 2$.

7 (a) $\frac{1}{3}$ s;

(b) $\frac{7}{25}$ cm s^{-1};

(c) 4 cm.

8 (a) $-4e^{-3}$;

(b) $y + 4e^{-3}x = 17e^{-3}$; $x = 4\frac{1}{4}$;

(c) $(-1, e)$.

9 (a) $x = 2 \pm \sqrt{3}$;

(b) $(1, -2e^{-1})$, $(5, 6e^{-5})$.

10 (b) $\left(\dfrac{\pi}{2}, 1\right)$, $0 \leqslant f(x) \leqslant 1$;

(c) $y = f(x)$ translated by $\dfrac{\pi}{2}$ to the right or left.

8 Logarithms and exponential growth and decay

EXERCISE 8A

1 (a) 6;

(b) 7;

(c) -3;

(d) 5.

2 (a) 5.95;

(b) 7.01;

(c) -2.94;

(d) 5.00.

3 (a) -0.399;

(b) 3.82;

(c) 2.68;

(d) 1.64.

5 (a) $\left(\dfrac{\ln 6}{\ln 2} - 4\right)$;

(b) $\dfrac{1}{3}\left(\dfrac{\ln 17}{\ln 3} + 1\right)$;

(c) $\dfrac{1}{4}\left(1 - \dfrac{\ln 5}{\ln 2}\right)$;

(d) $\dfrac{1}{3}\left(\dfrac{\ln 31}{\ln 5} - 4\right)$.

6 (a) 3.39; **(b)** 0.363; **(c)** 1.25; **(d)** 0.743.

7 (a) 8.303; **(b)** 0.7731; **(c)** 5.116;
(d) 0.9882; **(e)** 1.504; **(f)** 0.8244.

8 (a) −2.30; **(b)** 0.519; **(c)** 0.683;
(d) −0.419; **(e)** 0.117; **(f)** 0.862.

10 $b > 0$.

EXERCISE 8B

1
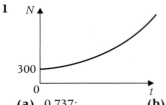

(a) 0.737; **(b)** 1.74; **(c)** 2.58.

2 500; **(a)** 0.5; **(b)** 0.946; **(c)** 7.65.

3 (a) 0; **(b)** 1;
(c) 6.93.

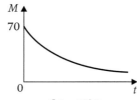

4 (a) 80°C; **(b)** 40°C; **(c)** 11.3 min.

5 (a) £500; **(b)** £512.13; **(c)** 92 months;
(d) perhaps not, since interest is usually added each month, though
some banks do add interest daily.

6 (a) (i) 20.2 million, **(ii)** 1882;
(b) 107 million in 2001. Ignores wars, changes in social behaviour,
family planning, etc.

EXERCISE 8C

1 (a) $e^{x\ln 3}$; **(b)** $e^{x\ln 2}$; **(c)** $e^{2x\ln 5}$; **(d)** $e^{-x\ln 4}$;
(e) $e^{-3x\ln 7}$; **(f)** $e^{\frac{1}{2}x\ln 6}$; **(g)** $e^{-\frac{1}{3}x\ln 5}$.

2 $k = 3$; 12.

3 $p = -2$; $y = \dfrac{5}{9}$; $\dfrac{dy}{dx} = -\dfrac{10}{9}$.

4 (a) $A = 5$; **(b)** $\dfrac{1}{2}\ln 3$, $15\sqrt{3} \approx 26.0$.

5 (b) 8.20. **6 (b)** 139 g. **7** 1768, 7 hours.

EXERCISE 8D

3 $N = 8e^{-2x}$.

4 $P = 4e^{8t}$.

5 (a) $N = Ae^{5t}$; **(b)** $P = Ae^{-7t}$;
(c) $Q = Ae^{\frac{5}{6}t}$, where A is an arbitrary constant.

6 (a) $P = 7e^{kt}$, where $k = \dfrac{1}{6}\ln\left(\dfrac{8}{7}\right)$; **(b)** 9.77 million.

7 (a) $m = 2 \times 10^{-3} \times e^{-kt}$, where $k = 0.02\ln\left(\dfrac{4}{3}\right) \approx 0.00575$;

  (b) 120 days.

8 (a) $Q = 20\,000e^{kt}$, where $k = \dfrac{1}{8}\ln(1.3) \approx 0.0328$; **(b)** 12.4 years.

9 Volumes of revolution and further integration

EXERCISE 9A

1 $2x^3 + 2\ln x + 7x + c.$ **2** $\dfrac{2}{3}\sqrt{x^3} + \dfrac{1}{2}e^{2x} + c.$

3 $\dfrac{1}{2}\ln x + \dfrac{1}{2e^{4x}} + c.$ **4** $\dfrac{1}{3}e^{3x} + \ln x - \dfrac{3}{x} + c.$

5 $\dfrac{1}{4}e^{4x} - e^{2x} + x + c.$ **6** 24.2.

EXERCISE 9B

1 (a) $\dfrac{1}{7}(x+2)^7 + c;$ **(b)** $\dfrac{1}{45}(5x+1)^9 + c;$

  (c) $-\dfrac{1}{12}(3-2x)^6 + c;$ **(d)** $4x - \dfrac{1}{14}(1+2x)^7 + c;$

  (e) $\dfrac{1}{6}\sqrt{(4x+1)^3} + c;$ **(f)** $\dfrac{3}{32}\sqrt[3]{(8x-27)^4} + c;$

  (g) $-\dfrac{1}{x-1} + c;$ **(h)** $\dfrac{1}{10(2-5x)^2} + c;$

  (i) $-\dfrac{1}{24(5+4x)^3} + c;$ **(j)** $2\sqrt{2x-1} + c;$

  (k) $\dfrac{1}{5}e^{5x+6} - x + c;$ **(l)** $2e^{2x-3} + c.$

2 (a) 24.2; **(b)** 6532.5; **(c)** $\dfrac{1}{3};$

  (d) $\dfrac{9}{14};$ **(e)** $\dfrac{e^3-1}{2};$ **(f)** $\dfrac{e-1}{8}.$

3 (a) $(x-1)^2 + 2;$ **(c)** 2. **4** $\dfrac{1}{2}.$

EXERCISE 9C

1 (a) 1; **(b)** 1; **(c)** $1 - \dfrac{\sqrt{2}}{2}.$

2 (a) $\dfrac{1}{2}\sin 2x + c;$ **(b)** $-\dfrac{1}{3}\cos 3x + c;$

  (c) $2\tan\dfrac{\theta}{2} + c;$ **(d)** $x - \dfrac{1}{2}\sin(2x+4) + c;$

  (e) $\dfrac{1}{2}x^2 + \dfrac{1}{4}\cos(4x-1) + c;$ **(f)** $-\dfrac{1}{3}\tan(1-3\theta) + c;$

(g) $-\dfrac{1}{4}\cot 4x + c$;

(h) $\dfrac{1}{3}\sec 3x + c$;

(i) $-\dfrac{1}{2}\operatorname{cosec} 2x + c$.

3 $\dfrac{1}{2}\tan 2x - x + c$.

4 (a) $\dfrac{1}{3}$;

(b) 0;

(c) $\dfrac{\sqrt{3}}{3}$;

(d) $\dfrac{1}{4}$;

(e) $\dfrac{\pi + 2}{4}$;

(f) $\dfrac{\pi - 3}{3}$;

(g) $\dfrac{2 - \sqrt{3}}{4}$;

(h) $\dfrac{1}{3}$;

(i) $\dfrac{\pi + 2}{4}$;

(j) $\dfrac{3\sqrt{3} - \pi}{3}$.

5 0.351.

EXERCISE 9D

1 (a) $\ln|3x + 5| + c$;

(b) $\ln(3x^2 + 5) + c$;

(c) $\ln|x^3 + 8| + c$;

(d) $\dfrac{1}{4}\ln(2x^2 + 3) + c$;

(e) $\ln|x| - 2\ln|x + 3| + c$;

(f) $\dfrac{3}{2}\ln(2x^2 + 5) + c$;

(g) $-\dfrac{1}{2}\ln|4 - x^2| + c$;

(h) $-\dfrac{1}{3}\ln|4 - e^{3x}| + c$;

(i) $\ln|\cos x + \sin x| + c$;

(j) $\tan x + 2\ln|\sec x| + c$;

(k) $3\ln|\ln x| + c$.

3 $\dfrac{1}{4}\ln|\sec 4x + \tan 4x| + c$.

4 $-\dfrac{1}{2}\ln|\operatorname{cosec} 2x + \cot 2x| + c$.

5 (a) $\ln\dfrac{5}{3}$;

(b) $\dfrac{1}{2}\ln 10$;

(c) $\dfrac{1}{2}\ln\dfrac{4}{3}$;

(d) $\dfrac{1}{12}(7\ln 2 - 4\ln 9)$;

(e) $\ln\dfrac{3}{2}$;

(f) $2\ln\dfrac{8}{3}$;

(g) $\dfrac{1}{2}\ln 2$;

(h) $\ln\left(\dfrac{e^2 + 1}{2}\right)$.

EXERCISE 9E

1 (a) $1 + \ln 2$;

(b) $\dfrac{1}{2} + 2\ln\dfrac{2}{3}$;

(c) $2\dfrac{1}{2} + \ln\dfrac{2}{3}$.

2 (a) $2\ln\dfrac{4}{3}$;

(b) $2\ln\dfrac{3}{2}$;

(c) $\ln\dfrac{4}{3}$;

(d) $\ln\dfrac{9}{4}$;

(e) $3 - 2\ln\dfrac{8}{5}$;

(f) $\dfrac{1}{4}\left(\ln\dfrac{3}{2} - \dfrac{1}{6}\right)$.

3 (a) $\dfrac{3}{1 + x} - \dfrac{2}{2 - x} - \dfrac{1}{(1 + x)^2}$.

4 (a) $\ln|x| - \dfrac{1}{2}\ln|2x + 1| + c;$ **(b)** $x^2 - x + \ln|x + 1| + c.$

5 (a) $A = 1,\ B = 4,\ C = -3;$ **(b)** $p = 4,\ q = -3,\ r = 4.$

6 (a) $\dfrac{1}{x - 2} + \dfrac{3}{5 - x};$ **(b)** $4\ln 2.$

EXERCISE 9F

1 (a) $\dfrac{62}{3}\pi;$ **(b)** $\dfrac{28}{15}\pi;$ **(c)** $\dfrac{\pi(\pi + 2)}{8};$

    (d) $\pi;$ **(e)** $9\pi\ln 9.$

2 (b) $\dfrac{1}{10}\pi.$

3 $\dfrac{\pi}{2}(e^2 - 1).$

4 $\dfrac{635}{7}\pi.$

5 (a) $x^2 + y^2 = r^2.$

6 $168\dfrac{3}{5}\pi.$

7 $165\dfrac{3}{5}\pi.$

8 (a) $\dfrac{15}{2}\pi;$ **(c)** $3\dfrac{8}{15}\pi.$

MIXED EXERCISE

1 $\ln\dfrac{4}{3}.$

2 (a) $A = 3.$

3 $\dfrac{1}{2}\ln(1 + \sqrt{2}) - \dfrac{\sqrt{2}}{4}.$

6 $\pi.$

10 Sequences and numerical methods

EXERCISE 10A

1 $x_2 = 5,\ x_3 = -\dfrac{5}{7},\ x_4 = \dfrac{15}{11}.$

2 $u_2 = 1,\ u_3 = \dfrac{1}{2},\ u_4 = \dfrac{5}{14}.$

3 (a) 3.166 67, 3.162 28, 3.162 28;
   (b) 3.666 67, 3.606 06, 3.605 55.

4 (a) 3.111 11, 3.107 247, 3.107 23;
   (b) 4.666 67, 4.641 73, 4.641 59.

5 (a) 0.13, 0.1417, 0.142 847 77;

(b) 0.0188, 0.018 867 68, 0.188 679 245 3.

6 (a) $-1, -1, -1$, converges;

(b) $-6, -26, -126$, diverges;

(c) 4, 1, 2.5, converges;

(d) 1.703 125, 1.704 878..., 1.705 860..., 1.444 44..., converges.

7 (a) 3, 6, 16.6, 36.857..., diverges;

(b) 1.333 33..., 1.4, 1.428 57..., converges;

(c) 3, 1.8, 1.4, 1.235, converges.

8 0.4142..., 0.4495..., 0.4641..., 0.4721..., limit is 0.5.

10 (a) 0.5; **(b)** -4; **(c)** -1.5, **(d)** 3.

EXERCISE 10B

1 (a) converges to -2; **(b)** oscillates;

(c) converges to 5; **(d)** diverges to $+\infty$;

(e) converges to 7; **(f)** diverges to $-\infty$;

(g) oscillates; **(h)** oscillates;

(i) converges to -1; **(j)** oscillates;

(k) converges to 0; **(l)** diverges to $-\infty$.

2 (a) 5; **(b)** 4.

3 (a) $\dfrac{\sqrt{3}}{2}, -\dfrac{\sqrt{3}}{2}, 0, \dfrac{\sqrt{3}}{2}, -\dfrac{\sqrt{3}}{2}, 0$; period 3;

(b) 1, 0, 1, 0, 1, 0; period 2;

(c) 0.75, 0.75, 0.75, 0.75, 0.75, 0.75, 0.75; period 1;

(d) $0, -\dfrac{13}{6}, -13, \dfrac{13}{4}, 0$; period 4.

4 $-1, \dfrac{1}{2}, 2, -1$;

(b) starts to repeat pattern, period 3.

5 (a) $\dfrac{1}{4}, \dfrac{3}{4}, \dfrac{1}{4}, \dfrac{3}{4}$, period 2; **(b)** 2, 6, 2, 6, 2, 6, period 2.

6 (a) $\dfrac{1}{2}, -2, -\dfrac{1}{3}, 0, \dfrac{1}{2}$;

(b) starts to repeat pattern, period 4.

7 when $b = 2a$ period $= 1$.

EXERCISE 10C

1 (a) $(-2.5, -2.4)$; **(b)** -2.43.

2 (b) $(0.5, 0.6)$.

3 (a) -2.95; **(b)** 1.18; **(c)** 2.02; **(d)** 1.01.

4 Student A has problems since $f'(-1) = 0$; student B gets -2.42 as next iteration and it converges to root.

5 $-0.531 25, -0.530 00$.

6 (b) -2.773.

7 $-0.7330, -0.7038.$

8 (c) $-0.387\,97, -0.388\,29.$

9 (b) $(-1.75, -1.5);$ **(c)** $-1.7;$

  (d) $-1.71;$ **(e)** $-1.82, -1.74.$

10 $(5.75, 5.875).$

11 (a) 3 roots;   **(b)** **(ii)** 2.22,   **(iii)** 2.3237, 2.2796.

12 $4.3493, 4.319\ldots,$

  (a) yes;   **(b)** no, since $f'(1) = 0,$

  (c) no, since next value obtained is negative.

EXERCISE 10D

1 (a)

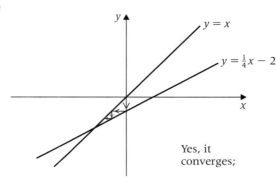

Yes, it converges;

(b)

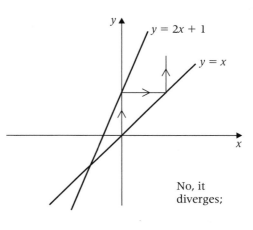

No, it diverges;

(c)

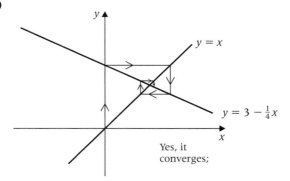

Yes, it converges;

(d)

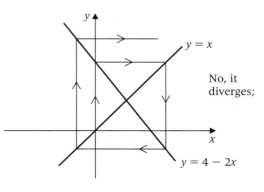

No, it diverges;

(e)

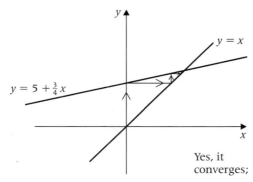

Yes, it converges;

2 $-1 < k < 1.$

3 **(a)** 0.9093, 0.9695;   **(b)** cobweb convergence.

4 (1.9, 1.95); 1.9463, 1.9303, 1.9361, 1.9340.

5 **(a)** $-1.753, -1.656, -1.642;$

    (b) $x_{n+1} = \sqrt[5]{(7 - 3x)}$, yes; $x_{n+1} = \dfrac{1}{3}(x_n{}^5 + 7)$, no; etc.;

6 4.224.

7 **(b)** 0.792;

    (c) $x = \ln(3 - x)$; 0.788, 0.794, 0.791, cobweb convergence

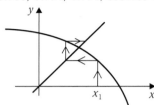

8 **(a)**

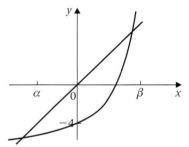

    (b) $x_1 < \alpha$ converges to α; $\alpha < x_1 < \beta$, converges to α; $x_1 > \beta$ diverges;

    (c) $-4.996;$ **(d)** $x = \dfrac{\ln(x + 5)}{\ln 3}$

9 $x^3 - 3x^2 - 2 = 0$, 3.1958, cobweb convergence.

10 **(a)** $2.6457\ldots, 2.879\ldots, 2.959\ldots;$ **(c) (ii)** 3.

11 **(a)** $2.45, 2.4005, 2.352\ldots;$ **(c) (ii)** 2.

12 **(a)** $-2.6457\ldots, -1.436\ldots, -2.3856\ldots;$

     (c) (ii) $-2.$

Exam style practice paper

1 **(a)** $\frac{3}{8};$ **(b)** 1.879.

2 **(a)** $\dfrac{x \cos x - \sin x}{x^2};$ **(b)** $-\dfrac{1}{\pi}.$

3 **(a)** 8;   **(b)** $y = -189;$ **(c)** 0.

4 $30°, 150°, 221.8°$ and $318.2°.$

5 **(a)** $(2, -4)$, radius 2;   **(b)** $4y + 3x = 0;$

    (c) $\frac{4}{3}.$

6 **(b)** $a = 1, b = 2.$

7 **(a)** $A = 8, B = -2, C = -1;$ **(b)** $\frac{88}{81}.$

8 **(b)** $k = 0.016\,53;$ **(c)** 70 800.

Index

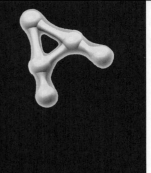